Transistor Physics

AND Circuits

Transistor Physics

AND Circuits

Robert L. Riddle

Marlin P. Ristenbatt

Staff Engineers, Haller,
Raymond & Brown, Inc.

PRENTICE-HALL, INC. | *Englewood Cliffs, N. J.*

Library of Congress Catalog Card Number: 57-14923

First printing................January, 1958
Second printing.................July, 1958
Third printing...............December, 1958
Fourth printing.................June, 1959
Fifth printing ....July, 1960
Sixth printing ....September, 1961
Seventh printing ....June, 1962
Eighth printing .... August, 1963
Ninth printing ....February, 1964

PRINTED IN THE UNITED STATES OF AMERICA

93014—C

Preface

Transistor technology has developed rapidly during recent years. The transistor can now be produced in large quantities at a fairly low cost, and the characteristics can be held within useable limits. As a direct consequence, the transistor has been taken from the laboratory and is appearing in consumer products. Numerous products employing transistors, such as radios and hearing aids, are now on the market and many more commercial devices will be appearing in the near future.

The advantages of using transistors are well known and need only cursory mention here. Chief among the advantages are the small physical size and the extreme ruggedness of the transistor. Although designed to perform many of the functions of the vacuum tube, this device requires no filament power and operates with very low bias voltages. One of the greatest boons to the ready acceptance of the transistor has been the fact that it has a life expectancy measured in years rather than hours.

Although the disadvantages of the transistor are steadily being diminished, present limitations to its use exist. The power-handling ability of the transistor is currently limited, and the temperature dependence of its characteristics sometimes make its application difficult. In the past, noise was a troublesome factor; however, the present status is that a noise level comparable to the vacuum tube noise level has been achieved. The low resistance of transistors to radiation fields from nuclear reactors is another disadvantage.

With the increased utilization of transistors it has become essential that technicians and electronics designers acquire an understanding of transistors. The main purpose of this book is to serve as a source of transistor circuit theory for these technicians and designers. We hope this book will be a direct aid to any person wishing to obtain an understanding of transistors, such as the radio amateur. The electrical engineer will find here a useful introduction to the subject.

We present the theory of transistors from the vantage point of a person having a basic high school knowledge of physics and algebra and either classroom or practical experience with electronic circuits. Emphasis is placed on illustrating the practical results of any theory. The use of mathematics for calculating the performance of transistors is limited to algebra; knowledge of the basic theory of electronic circuits will be of help but is not necessary. The equivalent circuits which depict the operation of the transistor are expressed in terms of the h parameters. These are the parameters that are being supplied by most transistor manufacturing companies, and most parameter measuring equipment on the market measure the h parameters.

Problems are included at the end of each chapter, where applicable. These problems are used to help explain important points throughout the book. A chapter on transistor experiments is given in order that practical experience with transistors may be obtained. The practical knowledge obtained from these experiments is essential for the serviceman. These experiments are purposely designed to be very general so that any available transistors may be used. This does not permit detailed direction in each experiment and therefore leaves much of the circuit design as a problem for the experimenter.

The bulk of the material in Chapters 2 and 6 is included for those who wish to review the basic physics and electrical circuitry applicable to an understanding of the rest of the book. This material may be omitted without destroying the continuity of the remainder of the book.

The material is divided into two parts, covering the physics of transistors and the circuit aspects of transistors. The section on physics includes the first five chapters. A practical approach is taken to the fundamental principles of physics in Chapter 2. The remainder of the section is devoted to the study of semiconductors and their application to transistors.

The section on the circuit aspects includes Chapters 6 through 15. In these chapters the performance calculations and some design procedures are studied both for small-signal and large-signal transistor circuits. Such topics as frequency response and feedback methods are treated thoroughly.

Although the physics of semiconductors is essential to understanding the physical action of transistors, the two parts are written in such a manner that the reader may begin with the section on circuit aspects. In addition, each chapter has been made as self-explanatory as possible in order that the book may serve usefully as a reference. Even though this requires a certain amount of repetition, it is felt that the goals of the book are best served by this technique.

A set of selected transistor characteristics is given in the Appendix, as an illustration of transistor properties and to aid in solving the problems. The Appendix also includes a short treatment of determinants and the necessary relations between the various matrices used with transistors.

With this treatment it is believed that a clear, practical approach to the subject of transistors has been achieved.

R. L. R.

M. P. R.

Contents

List of Symbols

A_e	voltage gain
A_i	amplifier current gain
α	short circuit, grounded-base current gain
A_p	power gain
β	short circuit, grounded-emitter current gain
B	bandwidth
B_C	capacitive susceptance
B_L	inductive susceptance
BW	bandwidth in cycles per second
C	capacitance
C_{0b}	grounded-base collector capacitance
C_{0e}	grounded-emitter collector capacitance
C_W	wiring capacitance
db	loss of interstage in decibels
Db	gain of transistor stages in decibels
Δ	small change in
Δ^h	determinant value of h parameters
E	electric field in volts per centimeter
E_n	rms value of transistor noise voltage squared
E_2	voltage (effective value of sine wave)
F	noise figure
$f_{\alpha 0}$	3 db cutoff point for grounded-base current gain
f_{b0}	3 db cutoff point for grounded-emitter current gain
f_H	high, half-power frequency point
f_{Hf}	upper 3 db frequency with feedback
f_L	lower, half-power frequency point

f_{Lf} lower 3 db frequency with feedback
F_0 noise figure at 1000 c for a 1-c bandwidth

G conductance
γ conductivity in mhos per centimeter

h refers to hybrid parameters in general
h_{11} or h_{ib} grounded-base input resistance
h_{12} or h_{rb} grounded-base voltage feedback ratio
h_{21} or h_{fb} grounded-base forward current ratio
h_{22} or h_{ob} grounded-base output admittance
h_{fc} grounded-collector forward current gain
h_{fe} grounded-emitter forward current gain
h_{ic} grounded-collector input resistance
h_{ie} grounded-emitter input resistance
h_{oc} grounded-collector output admittance
h_{oe} grounded-emitter output admittance
h_{re} grounded-emitter voltage feedback ratio
h_{rc} grounded-collector voltage feedback ratio
h^* parameters for series feedback
h^1 parameters for shunt feedback

I current (effective value of sine wave)
I_B base current
I_c collector current
I_{CEO} grounded emitter, cutoff current
I_{CO} grounded base, cutoff current
I_e emitter current

J current density in amperes per square centimeter

L inductance

M.A.G.   maximum available gain

P power
P_{RN} thermal noise power of R_g
P_{TN} transistor input noise power

Q d-c operating point

R resistance
R_{eq} noise equivalent resistance

R_f	feedback resistance
R_g	source resistance
R_i	input resistance
R_l	load resistance
R_o	output resistance
S	stability factor
V	voltage
V_{CB}	collector to base voltage
V_{CE}	collector to emitter voltage
V_{EB}	emitter to base voltage
X_L	inductive reactance
X_C	capacitive reactance
Y	admittance
Z	impedance
$1Z1$	magnitude of impedance

Part One

PHYSICS

I

Introduction

Before delving into the physical and circuitry aspects of transistors it is useful to deal first with the question, "What is a transistor and what does it do?" The usual answer is, "The transistor is an electronic device that performs the same functions as the vacuum tube." Taking into consideration the wide publicity afforded the vacuum tube by radio and television, this definition seems sufficient. However, it is useful to consider for a moment the basic function of both the vacuum tube and the transistor.

In a very basic sense, either of these two devices serves mainly to *amplify* electronic communication signals. Note that this definition does not restrict the devices to amplifiers as such; amplification is intrinsic to oscillators, electronic switches, function generators, and some mixers and detectors. In other words, the property of amplification is essential to each of the applications to which either transistors or vacuum tubes, excluding diodes, may be put. In this sense then, either of the two devices produces at its output, when an electric signal appears at its input, some sort of amplified signal. The output signal is usually uniquely related to the input, but this does not mean that the output is necessarily a replica of the input.

Another concept that is useful for electronic devices is that they function as continuous controls. The implication here is that an input signal causes the device to *control* a larger output signal. As in any control circuit, the fact that the output signal is larger stems from the fact that there is a source of power in the output circuit. Thus in

3

both vacuum tubes and transistors the object that allows the "enlargement" is the battery (or power supply) in the output side. The device itself acts as a converter in the sense that it converts such battery power to power that is in the form of the input signal.

In any of its many applications, then, the vacuum tube and the transistor can be thought of as acting primarily as amplifiers or as continuous controls.

Whereas the basic vacuum tube requires a plate, cathode, grid, and heater (to cause the cathode to emit electrons), the transistor appears, on the surface, to be far simpler. It consists essentially of a piece of prepared semiconductor to which three leads are attached. The fact that it appears thus so simple does not mean that it is a simple device to manufacture or apply. The preparation of the semiconductor is indeed a very difficult process, and many phenomena have to be taken into account when applying the transistor in a circuit.

Since the transistor consists essentially of a solid piece of material, it is seen that physically the transistor differs in conception from the vacuum tube. Whereas the vacuum tube requires the passage of electrons from the cathode to the plate within an evacuated bulb, all the electronic action in a transistor occurs within a solid piece of material. Although there are many differences between the two devices, as we shall see in the following chapters, the above is certainly the difference which strikes one at the beginning.

Considering this physical difference, it is clear that the transistor requires no such element as a heater. The saving in power requirements as a result of this is probably the greatest boon resulting from the use of transistors. Also, as a result of the physical construction described, the transistor is very small and extremely rugged. Another asset, not evident from the construction, is the long life expectancy of transistors.

These assets do not come without their price, however. Two of the major problems associated with transistors are the difficulty of producing units with uniform characteristics, and the temperature dependence of the characteristics. Formerly noise and low power-handling ability were also disadvantages, but these considerations have been improved considerably.

With this brief over-all look at the transistor, we will scan the history and development of this device.

Development of the Transistor and Its Early Applications

In 1948 Brattain and Bardeen of the Bell Telephone Laboratories were studying the surface properties of germanium semiconductor rectifiers. During these studies they noted that the conduction properties of a semiconductor diode could be controlled by an additional electrode attached to the semiconductor. This simple phenomenon resulted in what we now know as the *point contact transistor*. It consists essentially of a small slab of germanium (semiconductor) upon which two metal contacts are placed. In terms of the original experiment, the semiconductor and the one contact (called the collector) make up the rectifier and the additional control contact is called the *emitter*.

It was found that when an input current was inserted in the emitter contact a larger current resulted in the collector contact. This, coupled with the fact that the input impedance was much smaller than the output impedance, resulted in a revolutionary amplifying device.

Although the principle involved held great potential, this basic point contact unit had several drawbacks. Its internally generated noise was much higher than that for the vacuum tube; it reacted adversely to high humidity and temperature; and its structure was rather fragile.

The next major step in the transistor history occurred in July 1949. W. Shockley, also of the Bell Telephone Laboratories, published an analysis that predicted the possibility of a *junction transistor*. Soon thereafter experimental evidence that corroborated the theory was published and the junction transistor was brought into being. The basic difference from the previous device is that here the important action occurs wholly *within* the semiconductor instead of at the metal contacts. The emitter-collector action is achieved by providing three regions within the semiconductor; one region acts as the emitter and another as the collector. This is often described as utilizing an *area* contact instead of a point contact.

A basic operational difference between the two types is that the junction type has an emitter-to-collector current gain slightly less than unity. It still has emitter-to-collector voltage and power gain, however, because of the ratio of input to output impedance.

This junction transistor showed greater promise than its predecessor because it had better noise properties and was immediately more rugged. Also, it was deemed that the characteristics of the three-region semiconductors are more amenable to improvement than the characteristics of the point contact type. The progress that followed was devoted mostly to the junction type and consisted of attempts to improve the techniques of producing the semiconductor junctions, and also different schemes to acquire the junction action.

The first junction transistors were prepared by a process called the *grown-junction* technique, and this process resulted mainly in N-P-N junction devices. A significant development occurred in 1951 when the alloy method of producing junctions was perfected. The semi-conductors resulting from this process are largely of the P-N-P type. Present-day commercial transistors are usually made with this process.

NPN

PNP

In 1953, during attempts to raise the upper frequency limit of transistors, a research group at Philco Corporation developed a revolutionary method of producing active semiconductor devices; this resulted in the *surface-barrier transistors*. In addition to differing drastically in production technique, the surface barrier transistor also differs in physical operation from the basic junction type.

Many new types of transistors have been produced since these forerunners in the field. They include the N-P-I-N and P-N-I-P devices, a closely related type known as the *drift transistor*, the *diffused-base transistor*, and the latest, known as the *spacistor*.

Throughout the entire period of these changes in junction transistors, efforts were constantly directed toward improving the basic properties of the semiconductors themselves. A most significant development occurred when the techniques of handling silicon were perfected, permitting the fabrication of silicon junction transistors. Silicon devices will operate at higher temperatures than those made from germanium.

The technique of producing silicon semiconductor devices has not reached the same level as for germanium devices and therefore these devices are not quite so reliable as they could be. However, their ability to operate at higher temperatures overshadows this to a great extent.

Other semiconducting materials such as gallium arsenide (GaAs) and indium antimonide (InSb) have been investigated with the idea of using them in transistor production. Gallium arsenide has a better temperature characteristic than even silicon, and InSb has greater electron mobility which might allow for higher-frequency devices.

At the present time these compounds, although they have been obtained in simple crystal form, have not been pure enough to permit fabrication of useful transistor devices. However, some diodes have been made from GaAs.

The great interest in nuclear energy has created the need for electron devices that will work in high-density neutron and gamma fields. Transistors have been investigated with this in mind and it has been discovered that semiconductors are very sensitive to gamma and neutron bombardment. At the present time efforts throughout the industry are concentrating on the problem of producing transistors which are insensitive to the radiation from nuclear reactors.

Applications

From the very beginning the electronics industry was keenly in-interested in the transistor. The possibility of light weight, small size, and low power consumption devices was very intriguing. The first application of any commercial importance was in hearing aids where the size and operating expense of these devices were drastically reduced.

Other early applications were in the Bell Telephone Company's dial switching and rural carrier systems. Many companies placed miniature portable radios on the market and several automobile companies are using transistorized car radios.

The applications at present are as numerous as there are applications for amplifiers, multivibrators, oscillators, etc. In other words, transistors are being used wherever the advantages of transistors (their small size, reliability, and low power consumption) outweigh their disadvantages (temperature sensitivity, relative cost, and slightly higher noise figure than vacuum tubes).

More or less as a by-product of the interest stimulated by transistors, a whole family of semiconductor devices has come into being. These include the photodiode, phototransistor, zener diode for voltage regulation, double-base diode, and the solar and atomic batteries.

Present State

It is useful to summarize the state of the art in transistor performance and applications. Because of the greater emphasis, in the past twenty years, on research in the technical fields, it may safely be said that the transistor has advanced as far in eight years as the technology of vacuum tubes advanced in forty.

At the present time experimental transistors are being built which have a frequency response up to 1000 megacycles. Other transistors are available having a power dissipation of up to hundreds of watts. At present commercial transistors exist that have noise figures below 10 db (experimental devices have been produced with noise figures below 4 db) and a life expectancy measured in years rather than in hours—a life expectancy of forty years is estimated by some authorities. Transistors have been produced that will operate at temperatures of 375°C (centigrade) and may be stored at temperatures up to 500°C. Also, as would be expected with a solid device, the transistor is free from shock and vibration effects to a great extent.

Stargazing

In the future, transistors will influence many aspects of electronics. Commercial computers, to keep rapid and accurate store inventories, will be possible. Portable radios that require no power other than that received from the sun or small atomic batteries are already envisaged. There is some indication that transistors and atomic batteries may be combined so that the transistor would have a built-in power supply good for about twenty-five years.

Many concepts, still seeming far-fetched, have been made more feasible by the transistor. For example, automatic highways upon which the driver may relax after dialing the location to which he wants to travel are feasible. The nation-wide telephone dialing system, which is partially completed already, is being made possible in part by the transistor. The earth satellites, like Vanguard, will probably employ transistorized equipment because of its light weight and small power consumption.

In totality, it is expected that the transistor will make possible many new devices that will make everyday living easier and more enjoyable.

No, not yet (1991) ditto

2

Physics Review

In this chapter the salient points of basic physics are reviewed. Since the transistor is a semiconductor device, and since these devices are still generally unfamiliar, their operation is explained by utilizing the fundamental laws of physics.[1]

The basic building block of all matter is the atom; therefore this physics review is directed toward providing an understanding of the structure of the atom. In order to accomplish this understanding Newtonian physics and the concepts of energy are considered. Following consideration of the atom, the action of combined atoms in a solid is studied. This leads to considering three types of solids: conductors, semiconductors, and insulators. Of these, the semiconductor is of interest here, but comparison to the other two is useful.

Newtonian Physics

It is maintained by many authorities that Newton's formulation of the fundamental physical laws was the beginning of modern science. Newton's studies, although originally directed toward the movement of the planets in the universe, led to the development of the funda-

[1] The initial material in this review may be unnecessary for those readers having adequate background in elementary physics. The purpose of this material is to act as a refresher for those whose physics training is far in the past and to establish a consistent, continuous development of the physical action of semiconductors. For the readers of adequate background the authors suggest merely scanning the initial material and beginning with the section on "The Isolated Atom."

9

mental laws of all motion. These laws have remained unchanged since Newton's time in spite of the fact that refinements are necessary when dealing with extremely small quantities at high velocity, such as the quantitative behavior of individual atoms. Since we are interested here in acquiring a fundamental concept of the atom, we shall rely on Newton's basic laws without delving into quantitative calculations requiring the refinements mentioned.

Newton's four laws consist of three laws of motion plus one law concerning gravitation.

Newton's first law of motion:

A body at rest will remain at rest, and a body in motion will remain in motion with constant velocity as long as no unbalanced external forces act on it.

Newton's second law of motion:

If an unbalanced force acts upon a body, the body will be accelerated; the magnitude of the acceleration will be proportional to the magnitude of the unbalanced force and the direction of the acceleration will be in the direction of the unbalanced force.

Newton's third law of motion:

If one body exerts a force on a second body, the second body exerts a force of equal magnitude but in the opposite direction on the first body.

Newton's law of universal gravitation:

Every body in the universe attracts every other body with a force which is directly proportional to the product of their masses and inversely proportional to the square of the distance between them.

It is worth while to utilize common experience in obtaining an understanding of these four laws. Newton's first law specifies that every body possesses a resistance to a change of motion. Inertia is the measure of this tendency of a body to remain in its present state of motion. This occurs when the body is at rest as well as when it is moving. The property of inertia can be demonstrated by placing a coin on a slip of paper and then pulling the paper out from under the coin with a quick jerk. Although the paper has moved, the position of the coin remains unchanged. It is the inertia of the coin that keeps it from moving when it is initially at rest.

Another common experience exhibits the property of inertia in a moving body. When riding in a car in which the brakes are suddenly applied, the car will stop quickly. The rider will continue forward however, unless he is braced. This forward movement continues until he places his hand against the dashboard or some other object to check his motion. It is this property of inertia that causes a person to be thrown through the windshield or suffer a serious chest injury when an accident occurs in which the car is almost instantly stopped.

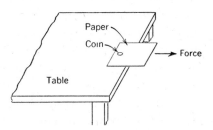

Fig. 2-1. Demonstration of the property of inertia for a body at rest. Pull the paper rapidly and the coin remains on the table top.

To restate Newton's first law, we can say that a body tends to remain in its present state of motion unless acted upon by an unbalanced external force.

Newton's second law specifies the magnitude and direction of the change in motion when an unbalanced external force is applied to a body. This change in motion is measured by the acceleration of the body. When a force is applied, the acceleration will be proportional to the force, and inversely proportional to the mass of the body. Before proceeding further it is useful to consider the property of mass.

The mass of an object is a measure of the amount of material it contains as indicated by its inertia. Since weight is often confused with mass, it is necessary to note the distinction. Mass is an intrinsic

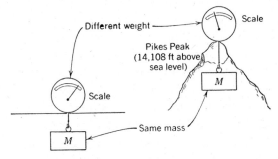

Fig. 2-2. Difference between weight and mass. Weight depends on position; mass is independent of position.

property of a body, whereas weight is the property which specifies the effect of the earth's gravitation on the mass. If the weights of a number of bodies are measured at sea level, the weight and mass of each body will be related by a single constant. If now measurements are made at Pike's Peak on the same bodies the weight and mass will again be related by a constant; but this constant is different from the former constant. The masses of the bodies remain the same but the measured weights change. This is shown in Figure 2-2 and results from the fact that the effect of the earth's gravity varies with different altitudes. This difference, however, is so small as to be negligible in practically all cases where the body is relatively close to the earth's surface.

Returning to Newton's second law then, the acceleration experienced by a body is proportional to the force applied and inversely proportional to its mass. In the usual set of units the proportionality factor is unity so that acceleration equals the force divided by the mass. The acceleration of a body is expressed as the rate of change of velocity. Thus the force on a body can be determined by noting its mass and the rate of change of its velocity. An easily demonstrated example of this consists of rolling a ball bearing across a table top and causing it to strike a block of wood. It is the motion of the wood which will be studied. As shown in Figure 2-3, the ball bearing will apply a force to the block of wood upon striking it. Depending upon the mass of the wood, the block will be accelerated from a velocity of zero to some finite velocity. In this example the ball bearing acts as the source of external force which causes the block to experience an acceleration. This same experiment can be done with two coins on a smooth surface.

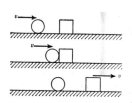

Fig. 2-3. Example of acceleration resulting from an external unbalanced force.

Whereas the first two laws consider the properties of a single body, Newton's third law of motion deals with the forces associated between two bodies. This law may be restated thus: For every action there is an equal and opposite reaction. Although the forces on the two bodies are equal and opposite, they do not cancel each other since they act on different bodies. Thus when one steps from a boat the person is moved toward the shore while the boat is propelled backward. In order to move forward one exerts a force on the boat; the boat exerts an equal and opposite force on the person. In spite of the equality of forces, the boat will move a smaller distance than the person if the boat's effective mass is greater.

Another example of action and reaction is experienced when walking across a smooth floor upon which a rug is placed. The rug tends to move backward when one tries to push forward on it. The reason for the rug movement lies in the fact that since there is little friction between the rug and the floor, there is no sufficient force available to push back on the person. Therefore, the rug moves according to its mass and the force applied. Figure 2-4 depicts two familiar situations which illustrate this third law of motion. Part (a) shows a weight lying on the earth; the force exerted on the earth by the body's weight is equaled by the force which the earth exerts on the body. In (b) the same condition applies to the vertical forces of the automobile tires. In the horizontal direction, the tire exerts a force (F_7) on the road. The road in turn exerts a force (F_8) on the tire so

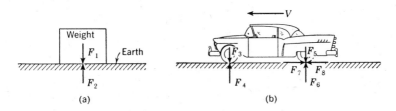

(a)   (b)

Fig. 2-4. Diagrams showing the forces associated with a weight at rest upon the earth and the forces between a moving car and the earth: in (a) $F_1 = F_2$; in (b) $F_3 = F_4$, $F_5 = F_6$, and $F_7 = F_8$.

that $F_7 = F_8$. If F_7 were greater than F_8 the tire would be spinning on the road; if F_8 were greater than F_7 the tire would be skidding. *tough to visualize*

It has been noted that the first three laws deal with motion; the fourth law concerns the attraction between any two bodies of the universe. This law states that all bodies of the universe experience an attraction toward each other. When one of the bodies concerned is the earth, this attraction is simply gravity. It was stated earlier that the weight which a body possesses is the effect of the earth upon the mass of the body. This effect is caused by the attraction between the earth and the body (gravity). Newton's law states that the magnitude of the weight determined by gravity is equal to the product of the mass of the earth and the mass of the body divided by the square of the distance between the body and the center of the earth. Although gravity is the clearest example of this universal attraction between bodies, it must be remembered that all bodies attract each other. Thus two books lying on a table attract each other; however, because the attraction between the earth and each of the books (their weight) causes a much greater frictional force on the table, the force between the books is hardly measurable.

An example of the application of this universal law of gravitation is depicted in Figure 2-5. Two situations are depicted: a certain mass is shown lying on the surface of the earth, and the same mass is considered on the surface of the planet Jupiter. The product of the mass of the earth and the mass of the body divided by the square of the distance between the body and the center of the earth determines the force (weight) which the body experiences on the surface of the

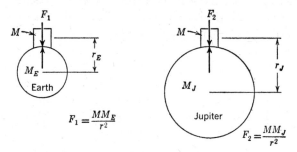

Fig. 2-5. Universal gravitation. F_2 is $2\frac{1}{2}$ times F_1 due to the larger mass of Jupiter.

earth. If this same quantity is calculated, using the mass of Jupiter and the distance to its center, the weight experienced on the surface of Jupiter would be $2\frac{1}{2}$ times as much as in the case of Earth. This is caused by the fact that the mass of Jupiter is much larger than the mass of Earth. Thus if one weighs 200 pounds on Earth, one would experience a weight of 500 pounds on Jupiter. It should be noted that one's own mass remains unchanged but the force experienced would increase.

This concludes the review of Newtonian physics. Since the goal of this physics review is to obtain an understanding of the atom, Newtonian laws will be applied to the solar system. The conventional representation of the atom is similar in many respects, on a much smaller scale, to the construction of the solar system. Therefore, Newton's laws applied to the solar system will be considered next.

Application of Newton's Laws to the Solar System

Before considering Newton's explanation of the solar system, it is interesting to trace the various concepts which preceded Newton's discovery. Ptolemy explained the action of the planets and the sun from the standpoint that the earth was the center of the solar system and the other planets and sun revolved about the earth in circular paths. This appeared correct until refined measurements proved that the orbits of the planets are not circular. Copernicus expounded the theory that the sun is the center and the planets, including the earth, revolve around the sun. Kepler proved that this was true and postulated laws which, he contended, govern the motion of the planets. These laws, which will not be stated here, led Newton to discover his law of universal gravitation and his three laws of motion.

The current concept of the solar system is as follows. The sun is the center of our solar system and the planets revolve about the sun in elliptical orbits. The forces which hold the planets in their relative positions can now be developed from Newton's three laws of motion and his law of universal gravitation.

Without considering the philosophical question of how the universe was started, we shall assume that the planets are located in their orbits and possess their respective velocities. Thus we are dealing with the question of how the planets maintain this original movement. In accordance with Newton's universal law of gravitation each planet exerts an attractive force on all the other planets. The forces between the planets, however, are small in comparison with the forces between the planets and the sun; therefore we may neglect all forces except those between any planet and the sun. The forces between planets do affect the respective orbits but this is a minor consideration.

We shall consider the application of Newton's three laws of motion to the solar system by considering the earth. Newton's first law, specifying that a body maintains its present motion unless acted upon by a force, predicts that the earth will tend to continue in a straight path with its present velocity. The attraction between the sun and the earth, however, provides the force which causes the earth to follow a curved orbit about the sun. This is somewhat analogous to the action that takes place when a weight is whirled around on the end of a string. Here the tension force provided by the string keeps the weight in a curved path. Newton's second law which specifies that the result of any unbalanced force is an acceleration is fulfilled when it is realized that the continuously changing direction of the earth's velocity represents an acceleration (of the earth) toward the sun. Figure 2-6 illustrates the force that acts upon the earth and the continuously changing direction of its velocity. The velocity is always tangent to the orbit at any position on the path. The third law of motion dealing with action and reaction is already illustrated. The force exerted by the sun on the earth is exactly equal and opposite to the force required by the earth to keep it in the curved orbit. If these forces were not equal, the earth would move closer to or farther from the sun until the forces became equalized.

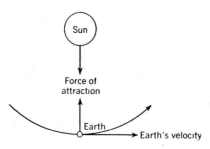

Fig. 2-6. Earth's orbit and gravitational force. Force of attraction pulls earth into a curved orbit around the sun.

The same conditions described for the earth also apply to the other planets. Their initial velocities, their distances from the sun, the sun's mass, and their masses determine their orbits as required by Newton's laws of motion. As stated before, this scheme of the planets and sun will later be extended to the atom, where we deal with electrons instead of planets, a nucleus instead of the sun; and the force of attraction will be electrostatic instead of gravitational.

Energy

The concepts of energy are a necessary consideration in any physical problem and they are especially vital in understanding the action in atoms. The properties of semiconductors will later be illustrated by considering the energies of electrons. For these reasons the basic concepts of energy will now be reviewed.

Having discussed forces from the standpoint of Newtonian physics, we may now consider what happens when a force acts over a given distance. If we push a block of wood across a table top we are doing work. Work is defined as the product of a force and the distance over which it operates. It should be noted that distance is an important concept in work; if we hold a weight stationary, no work is being done on the block even though our muscles will tire. Energy is closely related to work, for energy is a measure of the ability to do work. Energy is generally considered in terms of three basic types: potential energy, kinetic energy, and heat energy.

Kinetic energy is the measure of the ability of an object in motion to do work. A simple illustration of how a moving object can perform

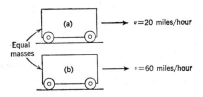

Fig. 2-7. Kinetic energy. Object (b) has the larger kinetic energy as its velocity is higher than that of object (a).

work by exerting a force over a distance is afforded by considering the action when the moving body strikes another stationary body. Upon impact, the second body will experience a force and will move accordingly. Thus the first body has exerted work on the second body. The amount of work which a moving body can perform is proportional to the product of the square of its velocity and its mass:

$$\text{Kinetic energy} = \text{K.E.} = \tfrac{1}{2}mv^2$$

Figure 2-7 shows two bodies of equal mass but with different velocities. The second object can perform more work than the first since its kinetic energy is higher.

Potential energy is an energy of position. Position here refers to distance from an ever-present force. The most familiar force in this respect is the gravitational force. This force is ever present in the sense that it is a permanent force which acts everywhere in the vicinity of the earth. If the surface of the earth is considered the reference point or datum plane, we can see how any body positioned above the surface is capable of doing work. If a book is resting on a table of one foot height, work can be done by allowing the book to drop to the floor. If the book is tied to a heavy object on the table, the falling of the book will exert a force over a distance on the heavy

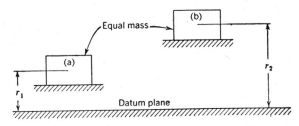

Fig. 2-8. Potential energy. In this diagram, object (b) has the larger potential energy because it is located higher above the datum plane than object (a).

object. If the table is now made three feet in height more work can be done by the book. In this manner, position above the earth determines the potential energy of a body in the gravitational field. Figure 2-8 is an illustration of the potential energy of two objects.

Although heat energy is one of the basic forms of energy, heat energy is not usually considered in terms of its ability to do work by exerting a force over a distance. Usually heat energy is considered in terms of its equivalent mechanical ability for exerting such a force. A familiar example will illustrate, however, the manner in which heat can do work directly. If heat is applied to an air-filled balloon, the air will expand and increase the volume of the balloon. The force exerted in expanding times the distance expanded is the measure of the work performed by the heat. A frequent source of heat energy in physical motion problems is friction. Whenever two objects are caused to slide on each other the friction, which produces a force that opposes the sliding, causes the sliding objects to receive heat energy.

Having discussed three of the basic types of energy, we may now consider a very important relationship between the three forms. The first law of thermodynamics specifies that energy cannot be destroyed but only converted from one form to another. This is also called the *law of conservation of energy.*

The changing of energy from one form to another can be illustrated if the following simple experiment is conducted. Place a piece of paper as a bridge between two books which are separated about two inches. Place a pencil on each end of the paper where it lies on the book. If another pencil is now held about two inches above the paper, the pencil possesses a certain amount of potential energy. If the pencil is released, it immediately gains kinetic energy by virtue of its motion; meanwhile its potential energy is decreasing since the pencil is losing height. In this manner potential energy is converted into kinetic energy. When the pencil has struck the paper and stopped, the kinetic energy has decreased to zero. A measure of the kinetic energy possessed by the pencil is the amount by which the paper is deflected. When the kinetic energy is reduced to zero, that energy is converted to heat energy (frictional) at the points of support on the book and the heat energy of impact of the falling pencil onto the paper.

Another example of the energy conversions is exhibited by tossing a box onto a shelf. The stored energy in the body is converted into kinetic energy of the box as it leaves the hand. As the box goes higher in the air some of the kinetic energy is converted to potential energy due to the continually increasing height. When the box reaches its maximum height it has zero kinetic energy and maximum potential energy. As it descends toward the shelf potential energy is changed to kinetic energy due to the downward motion. Upon striking the shelf, the accrued kinetic energy is changed to heat energy of impact.

The Isolated Atom

Since the most fundamental unit of all matter is the atom, we shall begin consideration of materials eventually leading to semiconductors by studying the properties of single atoms as they would appear if they were isolated. We shall then proceed to investigate the action when many atoms are combined to form a crystal of a solid material.

The arrangement and action of the separate components of an isolated atom are similar in many respects to a minute solar system. In analogy to the sun of the solar system, which is the center of attraction, each atom possesses a nucleus which is the center of attraction forces. Corresponding to the planets of the universe the electrons of an atom rotate in orbits about the nucleus. The forces and relationships between the nucleus and electrons of an atom are similar to those existing between the sun and its planets.

In spite of the similarity of the solar system and atoms, three major differences should be noted. The most obvious is the extreme difference in size; whereas the solar system is several billion miles in diameter, the diameter of the atomic solar system is so small that 1×10^{23} (1 with 23 zeros following) such systems can be placed in a cubic centimeter. The second way in which they differ is the nature of the attraction forces. The action of our solar system is determined by gravitational forces. The forces existing in the atomic system are electrostatic forces; electrostatic forces are the attractional force which always exist between two electric charges. The attractional forces referred to here pertain to Coulomb's familiar law which specifies that like charges repel and unlike charges attract each other. The charges may be either single charges such as electrons, or may be solid objects which possess an excess or deficiency of electrons. If a body is uncharged it is said to be electrically neutral. The electrostatic forces act much like the gravitational forces; a charged object creates a field which affects any other charges in the field much like gravity affects any bodies with mass. One difference lies in the fact that an electric field may repel another charge, whereas the gravitational field always attracts objects. A third difference distinguishing the solar system and the atom is a matter of orderliness. The electrons corresponding to the planets all possess the same mass; the planets of the solar system do not have equal masses. Noting these differences, it should be remembered that the basic model of the two systems are the same.

The electron may be pictured as being an extremely small particle with a known mass and possessing one unit of negative electronic charge. It is important to note that every electron has exactly the same mass and charge. The nucleus, the center of the atom, is made up of protons and neutrons. The proton has a mass 1800 times that of the electron and has one unit of positive charge. Thus electrically the proton is equivalent to the electron except for the difference in mass and the opposite sign for the charge. The neutron has a mass approximately equal to the proton but has no electric charge. These two quantities, the proton and the neutron, combine to form the nucleus.

In accordance with the analogy to the solar system, the atom is made up of a nucleus around which one or more electrons are spinning in orbits. For all atoms there are a certain number of orbits available. These orbits also represent energy levels for the electrons; each orbit corresponds to a certain energy, and no more than two electrons may exist in one level or orbit. It is very important to note that these energy levels, or orbits, exist in discrete levels for the atom. No electron may exist at any level (or orbit) other than one of the permissible levels. Thus the electrons are restricted in the sense that their energies must occur in one of the permissible levels for the atom. For purposes of considering the chemical properties of the atoms a group of permissible orbits are combined into electron "shells." The amplitude difference in energy between shells is much greater than the difference between energy levels within a shell. Thus the shells can be regarded as appropriate groupings of the possible orbits. The number of electrons which appear in the various shells determine the chemical properties of the atom and the state of the energies or orbits within the shells determine the electrical properties of the atom.

There is a definite maximum to the number of electrons which may appear in each of the shells. A smaller number than this may appear but not a larger number. The first shell, or inner shell, may possess two electrons. The second may have up to eight electrons, and the third, eighteen. The fourth shell may have as many as 32 electrons. The atoms or elements that we shall be concerned with do not have more than four shells. A law that holds for the first three shells is that whenever one of these shells has any electrons it is certain that the lower shells are filled. The fourth shell may have electrons after the third one has at least eighteen. Each of the existing atoms or elements differs in the total number of electrons which occur in the various shells; there are 98 different elements and each one differs in this manner. For example, hydrogen has one electron in the first shell; helium contains two electrons in the first shell (this is the maximum for the first shell); lithium has two electrons in the first shell and one in the second shell; neon contains two in the first shell, and eight in the second shell.

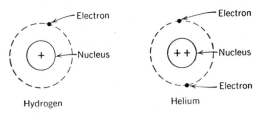

Fig. 2-9. Hydrogen and helium atoms.

A very important property of all atoms is that the electric charge on the nucleus is always equal to the negative charge as determined by the number of electrons. Thus for hydrogen the nucleus has a positive charge of one unit, helium has a positive charge of two units, and lithium has a charge of three units. This means that the atom by itself is always electrically neutral; however, if an atom gains or loses some electrons it will be in a charged condition. If an atom is in the charged state it is said to be an *ionized atom* and it is called an *ion*. Figure 2-9 represents the electron shells and nuclei of the hydrogen and the helium atoms. It is seen that the charge on the nucleus equals the number of electrons in the atom.

The electrons which exist in the outermost shells (the higher-order shells) are called *valence electrons*, because it is these electrons which determine the action of the atom when it combines with atoms of another element to form compounds. When the outermost shell of an atom is completely filled, that element is stable and not capable of combining with the atoms of another element to form a compound. If this outer shell is not completely filled, however, the atom is susceptible to forming a compound. The general nature of these formations is that an atom will accept valence electrons from another atom so that the combined electrons will fill the outer shell. In turn an atom may contribute its valence electrons to those of another atom to form a compound. A general rule is that if the atom contains more than four valence electrons it will usually receive valence electrons from another atom. If the atom contains fewer than four valence electrons it will usually contribute its electrons to those of the other atom.

Having considered the construction of the various elements in terms of the electrons and nucleus we can now consider those forces and actions which bind the atom together. As mentioned earlier, the forces acting within the atom are similar to the forces acting in the solar system. The nucleus contains an electric charge which is greater than the charge of any one electron (except for the case of hydrogen); it will be remembered that the total charge of the nucleus is equal to the total charge of all the electrons of the atom. The electric attraction between the nucleus and any one of the electrons exerts a force on the electron which is very similar to the gravitational force exerted by the sun on the planets. Therefore the electrons are made to follow curved orbits much as the planets. All the considerations of Newton's laws applying to the planet motion apply to the motion of the electrons. The inward force needed to constantly change the direction of motion of the electron is supplied by the force of attraction between the electron and the nucleus. As in the case of the solar system the law of action and reaction must hold; the orbit is determined by the energy which the electron possesses. In other words, the force needed to change the direction of the electron (to keep it moving in a curved orbit) must be exactly equal to the force of attraction provided by the electrostatic force of attraction. If by some means the electron is provided with more energy, the orbit, and hence the energy level, of that electron must change. Since it is very easy to give additional energy to an atom, it should be clear that any one electron has the ability to have its orbit or energy level changed. When it is thus changed, however, the energy supplied must be of such a value that the electron energy can jump from one permissible level to another.

The energy that an electron possesses in any orbit consists of two parts. The electron has kinetic energy due to its motion, and potential energy due to its position with respect to the nucleus. When energy is added to an electron, both the kinetic component and the potential component are increased. It can easily be seen that, since any electron must jump from one discrete level to another, the amount of energy which it is capable of receiving is discrete in value. This reaffirms the fact that electrons cannot exist between permissible orbits.

To reiterate the essential facts concerning the orbits or energy levels of the electrons in an isolated atom: the atom possesses many levels corresponding to orbits in which it is permissible for an electron to be and there are many more possible orbits than electrons. All the electrons of the atom must exist in one of the permissible energy levels. For purposes of defining chemical composition these many orbits are grouped into collections of orbits called electron shells. Those electrons in the orbits of the outermost shell are called valence electrons, and these are active in forming compounds. Since there are many more orbits then electrons, the implied fact is that electrons may move from orbit to orbit if proper energy is provided.

The application of heat is one of the most convenient ways to apply energy to an atom. If we can envisage having a single atom isolated in space the application of heat would act to raise the energy level, and thus change the orbit, of some electrons in the atom. The determination of which electrons will receive an increase in energy is decided by the ease with which they can receive the energy; those electrons which previously had the highest energy will be the first to have their orbits changed. It is these electrons which exist in the outermost orbits of the atom. If the proper reference is taken it can be shown that those electrons which are in orbits closest to the nucleus have less energy than the electrons which are in the farther orbits. Thus it is the electrons which are in the outermost orbits that will have their orbits changed first by the application of external additional energy such as heat.

Since the electrons must exist in certain discrete levels, it is seen that when the energy is applied to an atom the amount of heat absorbed will be in discrete quantities. These discrete quantities, called *quantums of energy*, correspond to the difference in energy between the permissible levels for the electrons. If a sufficient amount of heat energy is absorbed by any one electron, that electron can be completely removed from the influence of the atom. This process is called ionization and will be considered in the next chapter.

When an atom absorbs heat energy then, the energy levels of some of the electrons are raised and the atom is said to be *excited*. The energy level which an electron possesses should not be confused with the permissible energy levels of the atom; the permissible levels for the atom do not change with heat. The electron moves from one permissible level to another when heat energy is applied.

Another way to increase the electron energy of the atom is to direct light onto the atom. Light represents the visible portion of the entire electromagnetic spectrum. Thus light consists of the same radiation as radio waves but the frequency (of vibration of the electric and the magnetic fields) is higher for the visible portion. Whenever a body absorbs electromagnetic radiation, the radiation absorbed will be converted into energy. Thus electromagnetic radiation represents a source of energy for raising the electron levels of an atom.

Because the electrons have discrete energy levels at which they may exist, the energy (as for the case of heat) must be absorbed in *quanta*. The electromagnetic field may be considered as possessing little bundles or *quanta* of energy. The amount of energy in a quantum depends upon the frequency of the radiation; the higher the frequency, the higher the energy. In order for the radiation to excite an electron of an atom, the quantum of energy of that radiation must be equal to or greater than the energy needed to raise the electron to the next permissible level. It is for this reason that only a portion of the entire electromagnetic spectrum is capable of giving energy to the electrons of solids. Thus the application of light is a suitable method of applying energy to the electrons of an atom. In the energy sense, the effect of light on an atom is similar to the effect of heat.

The two elements that we are interested in to the greatest extent in this text are silicon and germanium. Silicon is number 14 of the elements. This means that an atom of silicon contains fourteen electrons and thus the nucleus contains a positive charge of fourteen. The two inner shells of electrons are filled and the third shell contains four electrons. Thus silicon has a valence of 4 since it has four electrons which may be used in combining with another element to form a compound. Germanium is element number 32 and also has four electrons in its outer orbit. In this case the outer orbit is the fourth shell; the first three shells are filled with the first having two, the second eight, and the third eighteen. It can be seen that electrically the atoms of silicon and germanium are similar since they each have a valence of 4. Figure 2-10 represents the electron shells and nuclei of the three atoms silicon, germanium, and carbon. Carbon is included in this group because it too has four valence electrons. The

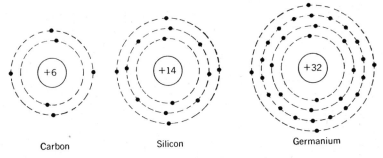

Carbon   Silicon   Germanium

Fig. 2-10. Carbon, silicon, and germanium atoms.

three atoms have an additional property in common; they all assume the shape of the diamond crystal when more than one atom (of the same element) are combined. This, of course, applies to material in the solid state. A great deal more shall be said about silicon and germanium in the chapter on semiconductors.

Atoms in Association to Form Crystals

Having discussed the properties of single isolated atoms we are now in a position to consider combinations of atoms as they occur in nature. We refer here to combinations of atoms of the same material and the combination of atoms of different materials to form compounds. Also, we shall here be interested only in the solid state of any material without considering the properties of gases or liquids.

The first fact to be noted about atoms in combination is that the solid state of any inorganic material possesses a *crystal* state; this means that in the solid state the atoms of the material are oriented with respect to each other in a definite orderly manner. Thus, if one views a single crystal of a solid material, one sees a definite arrangement of all the atoms within that crystal; if one views another crystal of the same material, the identical arrangement of the atoms will be noted as formerly. Although the structure within the crystal is always defined, it should be noted that crystals may be oriented with respect to each other in various ways. The area where one crystal is joined to another crystal is called a grain boundary. Another way to define a single crystal is to state that it is the smallest repetitive structure of atoms found in any solid material.

The combination of atoms to form a crystal in a solid material should not be confused with another combination of atoms, the molecule. A molecule is a unit which specifies the number of single atoms required to form a basic unit of chemical composition. Thus the common gas, oxygen, contains two atoms per molecule and is written O_2. Carbon dioxide, CO_2, requires one atom of carbon and two atoms of oxygen to form one molecule of carbon dioxide.

When discussing a single atom we considered the forces which bind the components of the atom together. It is now pertinent to discuss those forces which bind the atoms within a crystal together and also the forces which bind the crystals themselves together. The forces which bind atoms together are electrostatic in nature, and therefore are similar to the forces operating within the atom. These electrostatic forces can be divided into three categories: (1) ionic binding forces, (2) covalent binding forces, and (3) metallic binding forces. Although our interest shall be chiefly in the covalent type, all three will be discussed briefly.

The ionic binding forces occur when the valence electrons from one atom are joined to those of another atom to fill the outer shell of the latter atom. If an atom has four or more valence electrons (in a shell where the normal number is eight) it has a tendency to gain additional electrons when joining with other atoms. When this happens the outer shell contains the filled amount of eight, and the binding forces are considered ionic. It is these binding forces which usually occur when compounds are formed as mentioned earlier. The term *ionic* is derived from the fact that ions are always formed when this interaction of valence electrons takes place. An ion is defined simply as an electrically charged atom. If an atom, which is always intrinsically electrically neutral, acquires any additional electrons (or loses some) its resultant charged state is called an ion. If an atom has four valence electrons and receives four more to fill its shell it becomes an ion of four negative charges, and the atom contributing four electrons becomes an ion of four positive charges. An example of an ionic bound molecule is salt, or sodium chloride. Sodium, having one valence electron, gives the valence electron to the chlorine atom with seven valence electrons. Thus the chlorine atom acquires a filled shell of eight electrons. Meanwhile, the sodium, in losing one electron, has become positively charged and the chlorine atom has become negatively charged due to the additional electron. Thus each atom has become an ion and the forces which bind them together are regarded as ionic forces.

Covalent forces occur when the valence electrons of neighboring atoms share their electrons with each other. If an atom of a material contains four valence electrons, it may share one electron from each of four neighboring atoms. The concept of sharing valence electrons should be distinguished from the previous situation of gaining (or losing) valence electrons. One important difference is that no ions are formed when the binding forces are covalent. The covalent forces are set up when two electrons coordinate their motions in a manner so as to produce an electrostatic force between the electrons. More will be said about covalent binding forces in the chapter on semi-conductors.

The concepts dealing with the atomic binding forces in metals include metallic binding forces. Here neither ion forces nor covalent forces are the major consideration. Metallic forces are construed as occurring when positive ions float in a cloud of electrons. There is a constant electrostatic force present between the positive ions and the negative electrons. The important feature here is the great mobility of electrons of a metal. Since they move about relatively freely, the electrons cannot be associated with particular atoms. Thus a more or less stable state occurs where ions are continuously being formed by electrons leaving any particular atom, but the atoms are held in place by the attraction between the resulting ions and the electron cloud.

Referring to the previous section concerning a single atom, it was stated that any atom possesses many permissible energy levels in which electrons can exist. It was also pointed out that no electron can exist at an energy level other than one of these permissible levels. This situation remains the same for atoms in combination if the spaces between the atoms are large enough. For example, the atoms of a gas fulfill this condition. In any solid, however, the atoms of the material are very close to each other and important changes occur in the state of the energy levels.

When atoms are brought into close proximity as in a solid, the energy levels which existed for single isolated atoms break up to form *bands* of energy levels. Within each band there are still discrete permissible levels rather than a continuous band. The important fact is that many more energy levels are now permissible, and these levels are grouped into separate bands. For a comparison of the energy levels in a relatively isolated atom and in a solid, Figure 2-11 and Figure 2-12 show the levels for an isolated hydrogen atom and for an atom in a germanium crystal, respectively.

Figure 2-12 shows only the two upper bands of energy levels. There are numerous bands below the level of the *valence bond* band shown in this figure. In considering electrical properties, however, only the two upper bands are of interest. The two upper bands are called the *conduction band* and the *valence bond band*.

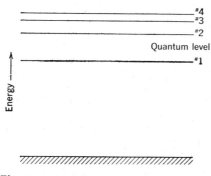

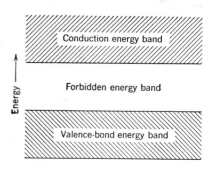

Fig. 2-11. Principal quantum energy levels of a hydrogen atom.

Fig. 2-12. Energy levels of germanium in a crystal structure.

The conduction band is a band of energies in which the level of energy (of the electrons) is high enough so that electrons in these levels will move readily under the influence of an external field. If the electrons are thus mobile, they are capable of sustaining a current if an external field in the form of a voltage is applied. For our purposes here, an electric current is defined as the familiar concept of moving electrons. The more general concept is that any moving charge constitutes an electric current; this will be dealt with later. Therefore solids which have many electrons in the conduction levels are known as conductors.

The valence band is a band of energies in which the energy is of the same level as the energy of valence electrons. The electrons in these levels are more or less attached to individual atoms and are not free to move about as were the former conduction electrons. This valence band would be of little interest if it were not for the fact that, with proper addition of energy, electrons in the valence band may be caused to be elevated to the conduction band. In order to do this, they have to bridge the gap between the valence band and the conduction band. This gap is known as the *forbidden energy band.* It is the energy difference across this forbidden region that determines whether a solid acts as a conductor, a semiconductor, or an insulator.

A conductor is a solid which contains many electrons in the conduction band at room temperature. In fact, there is no forbidden region between the valence band and the conduction band of a conductor; the two bands may be considered to be joined. A semiconductor is a solid which contains a forbidden gap as shown in Figure 2-12. Normally, it would be considered that a semiconductor has no electrons in the conduction band. However, by virtue of the energy provided by the heat of room temperature, there is sufficient energy available to overcome the atomic force on a few valence electrons so that some appear in the conduction band. Therefore at room temperatures semiconductors are capable of sustaining some electric current. It is the semiconductors in which we shall be interested, but not the pure material; we shall be concerned with semiconductors in which certain impurities are placed.

To complete the picture of energy bands, insulators are those materials in which the forbidden gap is so large that practically no electrons can be given sufficient energy to bridge this gap. Therefore, unless extremely high temperatures are available, these materials will not conduct electricity.

A Brief Survey of Modern Physics

The part of the physics review just completed has been directed toward acquiring a simple concept of the nature of atomic action. Our explanation has been based on the classical theories of motion as defined by Newton, and it is felt by the authors that this approach is most profitable for the purposes of this text. However, it is worth while to mention some of the modern refinements which must be used when attempting to explain some physical phenomenon.

The fact that only discrete energy levels are available in an atomic structure is described by a basic formulation of quantum mechanics. Newton's concepts considered alone would imply that any of a continuum of energy levels would be permissible. However, problems such as those posed by the photoelectric effect and black-body radiation led to Planck's discovery of the discrete energy levels in atomic structure. The basic unit in this theory is the *quantum of energy*, which is the energy difference between adjacent levels. Since the concept of levels of energy was used in describing an atom previously, there is no need to alter this concept.

Although it is usually satisfactory to consider an electron as a small charged corpuscular particle having a mass, there are some physical phenomena which contradict this concept. Because of this, a modern concept was evolved which pictures the electron as a *wave packet*. Since our interests here are to gain an understanding of the action in atomic structures, it is not necessary to investigate this refinement of concept; in fact, such investigation is beyond the scope of this book. Another modern concept which is important to physicists is Heisenberg's uncertainty principle. In essence, this principle states that it is impossible, by either calculation or measurement, to establish simultaneously both the exact position and the exact momentum of an electron at any one time. Thus, instead of speaking about an electron being in a certain orbit (at a specified time) if it has a certain energy, the physicist speaks about the probability of the electron being in that orbit if it has the specified energy. One consequence of this is that, instead of depicting one orbit for an electron with a certain energy, one should consider that many orbits are possible at that energy; but that the one initial orbit is the most probable.

References

1. *Proceedings of I. R. E.*, December 1955, p. 1787.
2. *Practical Physics*, White, Manning, Weber, Cornett, McGraw-Hill Book Company, Inc., 1953.
3. *Electronic Engineering Principles*, Ryder, Prentice-Hall, Inc., 1947.
4. *Mechanics*, Slater and Frank, McGraw-Hill Book Company, Inc., 1947.
5. *General and Applied Chemistry*, Currier and Rose, McGraw-Hill Book Company, Inc., 1948.
6. *Transistors—Theory and Applications*, Coblenz and Owens, McGraw-Hill Book Company, Inc., 1955.

Problems

1. Explain Newton's laws of physics and give an example of these laws in operation that you have experienced.
2. Explain Newton's law of universal gravitation.
3. What is the difference between weight and mass?
4. What is acceleration and when does it occur? (Explain this with respect to the forces acting upon a body.)
5. How do Newton's laws apply to the solar system?
6. What is energy? Describe its two most common forms (potential and kinetic).
7. Compare the isolated atom to the solar system (point out their differences).
8. What are electron shells?
9. Sketch the energy diagrams of isolated hydrogen and helium atoms.
10. Sketch the energy diagrams of isolated carbon, silicon, and germanium atoms.
11. What is the main change in the energy diagrams of the electrons from an isolated atom to atoms associated in a crystal structure?
12. Explain what insulators, conductors, and semiconductors are.
13. What are valence and conduction electrons?
14. What is the forbidden region of a semiconductor?

3

Semiconductors

The transistor is a device that utilizes the semiconducting properties of such elements as germanium or silicon. Although transistors are a relatively recent development, semiconductors have been used for decades in such devices as dry rectifiers of the selenium and copper oxide type. In spite of the frequent use of such semiconductors, understanding the theory of operation had to await the development of the transistor.

It is the goal of this chapter to clarify the physical principles of semiconductors and prepare for studying their application in transistors. The structure and properties of intrinsic semiconductor crystals will be considered first. Since certain impurities are essential to the transistor semiconductors, the study will proceed to crystals containing impurities and consideration of single crystals possessing two types of impurities in two distinct regions. At this point we will be ready to study the physical action of a junction transistor.

Crystal Structure and Properties

The heart of a transistor is a piece of single crystal germanium or silicon. It is very important that the piece of semiconductor be part of a single crystal. The concepts of a crystal in a solid state material were mentioned in the previous chapter on physics review but will be repeated here for the specific case of germanium and silicon.

A single crystal of any material specifies that all the atoms are oriented with respect to each other in a definite orderly manner.

Every atom in the crystal is related to its neighbors in exactly the same way. The *lattice* of a crystal refers to the geometrical arrangement which the atoms assume in the crystal. Germanium and silicon have a lattice structure of the crystals that is called the *face-centered cubic lattice*. This type of cubic lattice occurs when each atom has four neighbors which are all at an equal distance from it, and the neighbors are all at an equal distance from each other. Figure 3-1 shows a three-dimensional representation of the atoms of the cubic lattice. It is interesting to note that the diamond also has the face-centered cubic lattice for its crystal structure.

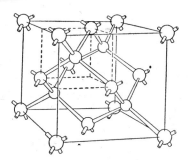

Fig. 3-1. Structure of atoms in face-centered cubic lattice.

In the natural state, any piece of a solid material would contain many crystals. Thus the material would be made up of many units as shown in Figure 3-1, and these units would be oriented with respect to each other in various ways. The boundary between such crystal units is called a *grain boundary*. Therefore if a material contains any grain boundaries it is necessarily polycrystalline; that is, it contains more than one crystal. All the crystals will be identical in structure (except size), but they will have various orientations with respect to each other. As stated then, a solid material usually is polycrystalline. Only by careful processing can a large piece of single crystal material be formed. Producing large single crystal specimens was one of the early difficulties in manufacturing transistors.

The crystal structure shown in Figure 3-1 is held in place by forces between the atoms. As is the case for most semiconductors, germanium and silicon crystals are bound by the forces resulting from *electron-pair bonds*. Forces resulting from such bonds are called *covalent forces*. An electron-pair bond or covalent bond is formed when a valence electron of one atom coordinates its motion with a valence electron of another atom in a manner so as to produce an electrostatic force between the electrons. This bond is often described as a sharing process. Thus an atom shares one of its valence electrons with a valence electron of another atom.

Germanium and silicon are both from the fourth column of the periodic table; this means that their atoms possess four valence electrons. In a crystal of pure germanium or silicon, each atom shares one of these valence electrons with each of its four neighbors. Instead of depicting this electron sharing on a three-dimensional diagram such as Figure 3-1, we can consider a representation of that figure.

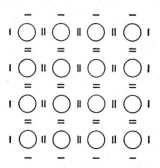

Fig. 3-2. Germanium and silicon crystal structure.

Figure 3-2 shows the resultant two-dimensional representation of the cubic lattice. It will be noted that the status of each atom having four equally spaced neighbors remains true for this representation, so that this simplified view is quite valid. The circles in Figure 3-2 represent the nucleus of the atoms, and the short lines represent the valence electrons. The valence electrons which appear adjacent to each other are involved in covalent bonds. The electrons other than the valence ones are not shown. In this figure it is seen that each atom shares one of its valence electrons with each of four neighboring atoms.

In order to understand the physical action in semiconductors it is necessary to investigate the energies of electrons in the crystal. In Chapter 2 the permissible energy bands of both isolated and crystalline atoms were considered. There it was noted that when atoms are in extremely close proximity as in a solid material, the discrete energy levels of the isolated atom are converted into bands of energy levels with finite gaps between the bands. Although there are a great number of energy bands available, only the valence and the conduction bands enter into the consideration of electrical properties. Both of these bands in turn contain many discrete levels, but for most purposes they can be considered as continuous bands. Figure 3-3

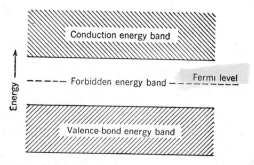

Fig. 3-3. Energy diagram of a silicon or germanium crystal.

shows the same diagram as Figure 2-14 of Chapter 2 and depicts the conduction band and the valence bond band for a crystal of germanium or silicon. It is noted that the gap between the valence and the conduction bands, called the forbidden energy band, is a region in which no electrons can exist.

Thus far we have described those energy bands in which electrons can exist in semiconductors, but have not specified under what conditions they do exist in any of these bands. Let us begin by saying that if the atomic structure of the crystal is exactly as shown in Figure 3-1, then all the electrons of the crystal are involved in covalent bonds. This situation also specifies that each electron is associated with its parent atom. The two foregoing facts clearly indicate that each electron has an energy equivalent to the energy of valence electrons. Therefore, referring to Figure 3-3, the valence band of energy levels will be filled, and no electrons will appear in the conduction band. The situation just described occurs if a crystal is at a temperature of 0° Kelvin (273° centigrade below 0°).

It was stated earlier that the application of heat is an effective method of adding energy to the electrons of any material. If a crystal is at room temperature (25°C) some electrons will have energies above those of a temperature of 0°K due to the effect of the added heat. This room temperature heat is sufficient, in a semiconductor, to break some of the covalent electron bonds. The electrons freed in this process are now capable of moving about in the crystal. The energy added accomplished two things: it broke the bond between two electrons, and also freed the concerned electrons from the electrostatic attraction of the parent atomic nucleus. Since energy had to be added to accomplish this, the affected electrons necessarily have a higher energy than in the bonded state. It is these electrons then which will appear in the conduction band of Figure 3-3, and it is seen why the conduction band is at a higher level than the valence band. The number of electrons which are thus moved from the valence band to the conduction band is determined both by the width of the forbidden region and the energy given the electron as evidenced by its temperature (assuming heat is the only source of energy).

When any electrons go from the valence band into the conduction band the crystal is said to be in an ionized state. This is based on the fact that when the conversion is made, the electron in effect leaves the parent atom. Therefore that atom is missing one unit negative charge and hence is ionized. Although we have here considered heat as the source of external energy, an electric field or incident light can also provide this ionizing energy. It should also be noted that when an electron leaves the valence band for the conduction band an empty energy level occurs in the valence band.

A semiconductor, by definition, is a material whose forbidden gap is such that at room temperature only a small current is conducted. Since electrons are one of the current carriers, this specifies that only a small number of electrons appear in the conduction band of a pure semiconductor at room temperature. A conductor, on the other hand, possesses a forbidden energy gap whose width is zero; therefore many electrons are available for current conduction at room temperature.

It is useful to introduce here a very important concept concerning energy levels. This concept is the *Fermi level* of a material, and is a property of every solid material; we shall here be interested in semiconductors only. This property is especially important whenever two different materials are joined, or when a single material has two types of impurities (as we shall encounter later). The Fermi level is a reference energy level from which all other energies may be conveniently measured. The Fermi level can be defined as that energy level at which the probability of finding an electron n energy units above the level is equal to the probability of finding an "absence" of an electron n energy units below the level.

This level, for a crystal of a pure semiconductor, falls midway in the forbidden region between the valence and the conduction bands. This seems reasonable when it is considered that for every electron in the conduction band there is an empty level in the valence band. It is not likely that an electron from a lower band will enter the valence band. Therefore the status of having an electron in the conduction band correspond to an empty level in the valence band fulfills the above definition of the Fermi level. This reference level of energies is shown for the pure crystal in Figure 3-3.

Having considered the structure and the energy levels of a pure semiconductor, we now wish to study the methods of current conduction. However, before entering the topic of current conduction in a semiconductor crystal it is useful to clarify the concepts of current conduction in any solid. We are all familiar with the use of Ohm's law[1] to calculate the current in a circuit where $I = V/R$. We are

---

[1] The basic circuit laws are briefly reviewed in the initial parts of Chapter 6, "Electrical Review."

usually not so familiar with considering current in solid materials where the dimensions of the conducting element become important. For the case of a circuit resistance we consider the voltage as being the force which, when applied to the resistance, causes a movement of conduction electrons. The current specifies the amount of electrons moved and could be measured, at a certain point on the wire, by counting the number of electrons which passed per unit time. The resistance of the material determines the difficulty with which the electrons are moved, and thus

$$I = \frac{V}{R} \qquad (1)$$

In the case of solid materials the current is again expressed by Ohm's law, but slightly different quantities are used.

When discussing the current in a solid where the dimensions of the conductor are important, current density is the parameter used. The current density is the current per unit cross-sectional area of the conductor. Instead of speaking of voltage, the electric field is used as the force quantity. Conductivity, instead of resistance, is used as the measure of the difficulty with which the current carriers are moved. Figure 3-4 shows a portion of a solid conductor in which we wish to study the current. Ohm's law for the current expressed in terms of the above quantities is:

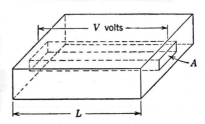

Fig. 3-4. Current-carrying element of a solid.

$$J = \gamma \varepsilon \qquad (2)$$

where J = current density in amperes per square centimeter,
γ = conductivity of the solid in mhos per centimeter,
ε = electric field in volts per centimeter.

The electric field (for a homogeneous medium) is defined as the voltage per unit length. Conductivity is equal to the reciprocal of resistivity and therefore, is proportional to the inverse of the resistance. In order to convert current density J to total current I we have to multiply J by the cross-sectional area:

$$JA = I \qquad (3)$$

and

$$I = \gamma A \varepsilon = \frac{V}{R}$$

Equation (3) shows the analogy between the two forms of Ohm's law.

In conclusion then, we shall be speaking of the conductivity and the electric field when discussing the current in a crystal of a semiconductor. It is to be remembered that the electric field varies as the voltage, but the conductivity varies as the inverse of the resistance. Also, the electric field ε is regarded as the force which causes movement of the charge carriers in a solid material.

We now return to the current conduction which occurs in a crystal of a pure semiconductor. It was stated earlier that when some covalent bonds are broken and the affected electrons are raised to the conduction band, these electrons are capable of supporting a current. If an electric field is applied to the crystal these conduction band electrons are capable of moving and this movement constitutes a current. The movement of these conduction electrons, under the influence of the electric field, is identical to the movement of the electrons in a metallic conductor. There is still another method of supporting a current in a pure semiconductor, however. When a covalent bond is broken, the removal of the electron leaves a vacancy in the parent atom since that atom has now only three valence electrons. It has been found to be the case that an electron from a nearby covalent bond may break its own bond and move to fill the previous vacancy. When the electron arrives at the vacancy, it enters into a covalent bond. The electron, to make this jump, does not have a conduction band energy; rather its energy has remained in the valence band. When the electron moves from the nearby bond to the original vacancy, a new vacancy is created at the bond which the electron left. Another electron, in turn, may leave its bond and move into this new vacancy. In this manner current is supported by electrons which are not in the conduction band; rather their energies lie in the valence band. Even though the movement has been that of an electron moving from one bond to another bond, the more important effect is that the vacancy has moved. Thus this manner of conduction resembles more the movement of the vacancies than the movements of the electrons themselves. This type of conduction is called *conduction by holes*.

It has been noted that this conduction by holes occurs in the valence energy band; the electrons concerned with the movement of the holes do not have conduction band energies. Since the absence of an electron from a normal covalent bond represents a localized positive charge (the atoms are electrically neutral only when all valence electrons are present) the hole may be thought of as a particle similar to the electron but having a positive charge. On this basis, the hole is considered a particle which moves much like the electron under the influence of an electric field, but in an opposite direction to that of the electrons. For this conception the hole is regarded as possessing a definite mass, like the electron. It should always be remembered, however, that the concept of a hole is simply a convenient device for describing the "jumping" movement of the electrons described above. The concepts of conduction by holes will again be considered when discussing current conduction in semiconductors in which certain impurities have been added.

We have just seen that, for a crystal of a pure semiconductor, current may be conducted by two processes. One process is the normal one in which electrons are allowed to move (more or less) throughout the crystal. The other process is one in which the movement of the electrons is relatively restricted—they move from one atom to another—and therefore resembles the movement of the holes, which may be depicted as positive charges with properties similar to the negative electron.

We have already noted that when a covalent bond is broken, both an electron and a hole are made available for carrying current. The process of elevating the electron to the conduction band creates a hole at the region where the electron was freed. These charge carriers, when created by the breaking of covalent bonds, are called electron-hole pairs. Since, in a semiconductor containing no impurities, the only charge carriers are such electron-hole pairs, the number of holes is always equal to the number of conduction electrons. This condition is expressed by saying that the semiconductor is intrinsic. The term *intrinsic* is used to distinguish a pure crystal from one containing impurities.

Since, in the intrinsic crystal, the number of holes is equal to the number of conduction electrons, the Fermi level can be defined in terms of the two charge carriers thus: the Fermi level is the average energy of the charge carriers. A little thought will show that this definition is equivalent to the one stated earlier.

It is necessary to note that the current conduction in an intrinsic semiconductor is dependent on both temperature and the electric field applied. At absolute zero temperature there is no conduction by either method since no covalent bonds are broken. At a higher temperature small currents will flow, by both electron and hole movement, depending on the applied electric field. At excessively high temperatures a pure semiconductor can be made to act like a conductor since more and more covalent bonds are broken to furnish the current carriers.

Crystals with Impurities

Thus far we have been concerned with the crystal structure and the properties of an intrinsic semiconductor; that is, no impurities were considered to be present. For transistors, however, a semiconductor in this pure state is of little value. To be used in a transistor the semiconductor has to possess a small, but nevertheless important, quantity of impurities. The amount and type of such impurities have to be closely controlled during the preparation of the single crystal. We shall now consider crystals which contain impurities. As was done for the pure crystal, the concepts of energy and the conduction properties will be considered.

There are two types of impurities which, when added to a crystal of germanium or silicon, produce either N-type material or P-type material. A transistor is made of a crystal which contains regions of both impurities and these impurities are very important to the operation of the device. We shall consider the alteration of the energy states and the conduction properties of both of these impure crystals.

N-type crystal. It will be remembered that both germanium and silicon are in the fourth column of the periodic table and that this specifies that each of their atoms has four valence electrons. If, during the preparation of a single crystal of material, some atoms from the fifth column of the periodic table (5 valence electrons) are inserted, these atoms will take various positions throughout the crystal. They will supplant some atoms of the pure germanium. The two-dimensional representation of a crystal containing such impurities is shown

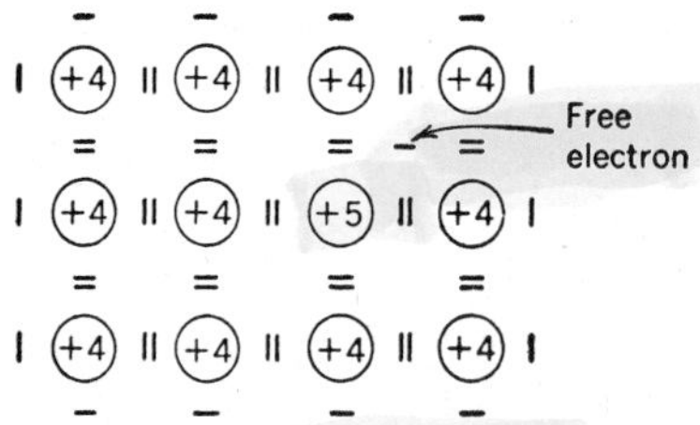

Fig. 3-5. N-type semiconductor.

in Figure 3-5. Because any one atom has only four immediate neighbors, there are four valence electrons from these neighboring atoms available for forming covalent bonds. This means that one of the electrons from the impurity atom is not utilized in a covalent bond.

This electron represents a surplus particle in the regular structure of the crystal. For this reason, an impurity of this type is called a *donor* since it donates an extra electron. Also, the crystal resulting from the addition of this donor impurity is called N-*type*, where N is derived from the negative charge of the surplus particle. This unbound electron is not immediately free to move about, however. Since the foreign atom has a nucleus containing a positive charge of 5, an electrostatic force is exerted on the unbound electron to keep it in the immediate vicinity of the foreign atom. This force, however, is reduced from what would normally be expected by the dielectric effect of the crystal; i.e., the surplus electron is partially shielded from the attraction to the parent atom. The result is that this electron is only loosely bound to the parent atom. Therefore we would expect that, although the energy of the donor electron (in the unionized state) is

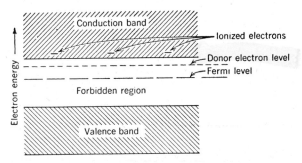

Fig. 3-6. Energy diagram for an N-type semiconductor.

not in the conduction band, it is not far below this band. This has been found to be the case and Figure 3-6 shows the position of the energy of the donor electron. Its energy is 0.05 electron volt below the conduction band of energies, in the forbidden region. (The term "forbidden" applies only to the energies of a pure crystal.) Thus it is seen that, in terms of energy, the donor impurity has added an energy level to the levels of the pure crystal. In addition, this added level appears in a region which was excluded to the pure crystal.

These donor electrons require 0.05 electron volt (of energy) to raise them to the conduction band; for germanium, 0.7 electron volt is required to elevate an electron from the valence band to the conduction band, and silicon requires 1.1 electron volts. Thus it is seen that the energy required to ionize a donor atom is much less than that required to break a covalent bond.

With the addition of impurities to form N-material, it would be expected that the Fermi level will change. It moves, from midway in the forbidden region for the pure crystal, to a place between this position and the conduction band. This is shown in Figure 3-6. For a crystal with impurities, the Fermi level will vary both with the amount of impurities and with the temperature of the crystal. More will be said of this when studying the effects of temperature on a semiconductor.

For this N-type semiconductor, current will again be conducted by the electrons and holes as for the pure crystal, where the electron-hole pairs are derived from broken covalent bonds. However, in this case there are many electrons available which require only a small energy to elevate them to the conduction band. Therefore when an electric field is applied to a crystal of N-type material the effect of the donor electrons will greatly overshadow the effect of the electron-hole pairs achieved by the breaking of covalent bonds. For most purposes, then, the current in N-type material may be considered to be completely carried by the donor electrons. With the exception of the small energy needed to raise these electrons to the conduction band, this current resembles that of an ordinary conductor.

Since there are now more electrons than holes, the electrons in an N-type material are called the *majority* carrier. The hole, of course, is the *minority* carrier. Although both carriers play a role in the conduction, the status of majority and minority depicts the predominance of the one over the other.

The amount of impurity necessary for proper operation of an N-type semiconductor varies, but the order of magnitude is 10^{15} atoms per cubic centimeter. This means that, for every impurity atom there are about 10^7 atoms of germanium or silicon. Thus it can be readily seen that extreme care must be taken in the manufacture of semiconductor devices in order to hold the impurity concentration to the desired values. Any impurity from the fifth column of the periodic table will theoretically result in an N-type semiconductor. However, the larger heavy atoms are not generally used. The most common types of N-type impurities are arsenic and antimony.

P-type crystal. The other type of impurity crystal is called a P-*type* material. P-type material is formed by adding an impurity from the third column of the periodic table to the crystal of the semiconductor. An element from the third column has three valence electrons in the outer orbits of its atoms. When such atoms are added to a pure crystal the foreign atoms will replace some of the germanium or silicon atoms. Since the foreign atom has only three electrons to share with the four neighboring semiconductor atoms, one electron

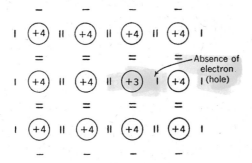

Fig. 3-7. P-type semiconductor.

will be missing from a potential covalent bond of the impurity atom. This situation is shown in the two-dimensional representation of Figure 3-7. Since the impurity atom has a nucleus containing a positive charge of three, that atom is electrically neutral if the empty covalent bond is not filled. The fact that a neighboring atom (of the impurity atom) possesses an electron which is available for forming a covalent bond means that a hole exists in that region. The concept of holes was first encountered when discussing the current conduction methods of the pure crystal. The presence of this hole, in turn, creates

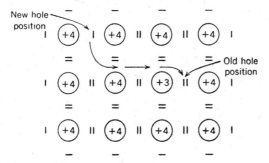

Fig. 3-8. Conduction process in a P-type semiconductor.

the possibility for an electron to jump into this region and form the covalent bond. It is remembered that electrons may leave an existing bond to fill the vacant bond without possessing a conduction band energy. If an electron leaves a covalent bond to fill the bond of the foreign atom, it leaves a hole at the region which it left. That hole may in turn be filled by another electron, and so forth. This method of hole movement is depicted in Figure 3-8. The line with the arrows represents the motion of the electrons. Careful attention to this motion will show that the hole may be considered as moving in the opposite direction of the electrons.

We are now in a position to understand more clearly the concept of current conduction by holes. Usually current is taken to be the movement of electrons through a solid or a wire, and the electrons must be free to move. In this situation, however, the electrons are continuously going from a bound state in one covalent bond to a bound state in another covalent bond. Thus in this case it is not profitable to consider the action of the electrons in causing the current. Rather it is more useful to consider the hole—the absence of the electron—as being the charged particle carrying the current. Although in a P-type material there are always some electrons available for movement, due to the constant breaking up of covalent bonds from the heat energy, by far the greater part of the current is conducted by the manner just described.

The status is that in the P-material, the number of holes present due to the impurity greatly overshadows the number of electron-hole pairs created by the breaking of covalent bonds. Thus when an electric field is applied to a crystal of such material, the current can be considered to be carried completely by the positive impurity particles, the holes. This condition is usually expressed by calling the hole the majority carrier in a P-type material. The electron, of course, would be the minority carrier. The properties of the majority and the minority carriers will be utilized later when discussing the complete crystal of a transistor. The name P-type is derived from the positive charge of the majority carrier of this material. An impurity which results in P-type material is called an acceptor impurity since it accepts one electron to complete its covalent bonds.

Figure 3-9 shows how the presence of the P-type impurity atoms affects the energy levels of the semiconductor. It is seen that the presence of this impurity can be represented as holes having energies slightly above the upper edge of the valence band. As in the case of the donor impurity and its surplus electron, the hole of the acceptor atom is loosely bound to the parent atom. If 0.08 electron volt is applied to this hole, the hole will be freed from its parent atom and will be able to support current. Since a hole is a positive particle, as compared to the negative electron, application of energy to a hole will result in the hole moving downward in the diagram of Figure 3-9. This reaffirms the fact stated earlier that conduction by holes occurs in the valence band.

The effect of the acceptor impurity, it is then seen, is to provide an energy level in addition to those of the pure crystal. Since the only other possible means of achieving a hole is to raise an electron from the valence band to the conduction band, leaving a hole in the valence band, it is seen that the acceptor impurity provides a current carrier. Only 0.08 electron volt is required to ionize the acceptor

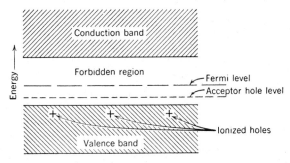

Fig. 3-9. Energy diagram of P-type semiconductor.

impurity, whereas 0.7 electron volt is required to generate a hole by the breaking of a covalent bond in germanium.

As for the case of the N-type material, the Fermi level shifts when P-type impurities are added to a pure crystal. In this case the level is moved from the middle position to a position nearer the valence band. The Fermi level for a P-type material is shown in Figure 3-9. Again this level varies with the amount of impurities and the temperature of the crystal.

The impurities used in P-type semiconductors include indium, gallium, and aluminum. The heavier atoms are not used because of their physical size.

Effect of Heat and Light on Semiconductors

In Chapter 2, when discussing the isolated atom, it was mentioned that the application of heat and light are two methods by which energy can be supplied to an atom so as to raise the energy levels of its electrons. Again when considering current conduction in intrinsic and impurity type crystals in this chapter, it was noted that the heat of room temperature provides sufficient energy to break some covalent bonds of the crystal structure. It is this property of having a few current carriers available, at room temperature, that specifies that germanium and silicon are semiconductors. In this section we are interested in studying more explicitly the effects of heat and light upon semiconductors. As before, we shall investigate the properties of the energy levels and the current conduction. It is felt that the method of energy diagrams provides a convenient way to study the current conduction.

The temperature of absolute zero, or 0°K, is defined as that temperature at which the electrons of any atom are in the lowest possible energy states. It is to be noted that absolute zero is not the absence of all energy, but only the condition of lowest energy. For a semiconductor such as germanium or silicon this means that all the electrons, whether valence electrons or impurity electrons, are bound by electric forces. At this temperature the valence electrons are all associated in covalent bonds. The surplus electrons of N-type impurities are bound to their parent (or donor) atoms, and the holes of P-type impurities are attached to their parent (or acceptor) atoms. Thus no current can flow at this temperature. As the crystal rises to a higher temperature the forces holding the impurity holes and electrons are overcome, so that these carriers are released first. The carriers are released by virtue of the heat energy gained from the rising temperature. At some higher temperature the heat energy gained will be sufficient to cause the generation of electron-hole pairs by the breaking of covalent bonds. At room temperature all the impurity atoms are usually ionized and some covalent bonds have been broken. Thus at room temperature the current is conducted in the manner described in the previous sections for the intrinsic, the N-type, and the P-type crystal.

As temperatures above that of room temperature are reached, the effect produced is that covalent bonds continue to be broken but no additional impurity carriers are released, since they were all ionized previously. This is a very important effect since this condition changes the properties of an impurity type crystal. The consequence of this change is that the impurity crystal begins to become more and more like an intrinsic crystal. As more and more covalent bonds are broken the ratio of electron-hole pairs thus created begins to overshadow the impurity electrons (or holes). Thus the crystal begins to take on the properties of the intrinsic crystal and the effect of the impurities is overcome. This is a completely undesirable effect since the specified amount of impurities is important to the operation of the transistor as we shall see in the next chapter.

The effects of temperature on a crystal of germanium or silicon

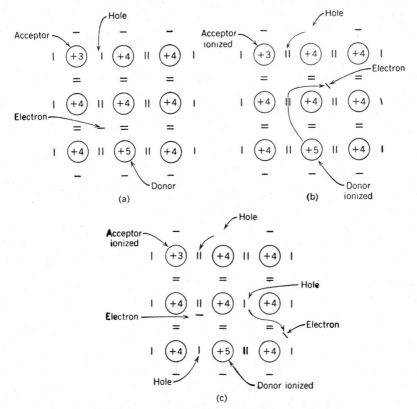

Fig. 3-10. Temperature effects in germanium and silicon. (a) 0° Kelvin. All of the electrons and holes are in their lowest energy state. (b) Middle range of temperature. The acceptors and donors are ionized. (c) High temperature. The donors and acceptors are ionized and also there are electron-hole pairs generated.

are shown in Figure 3-10. The representation here shows both N- and P-type impurities in the crystal. Since the temperature determines the amount of current carriers available, it is seen that the conductivity varies with temperature. It is remembered that conductivity varies inversely with resistance; a high conductivity means a low resistance. At 0°K the conductivity is zero since there are no free holes or electrons. At the normal operating temperature (room temperature, 25°C) the conductivity is determined mainly by impurity carriers—holes for P-type and electrons for N-type material—as discussed earlier. When the temperature increases to the high range (100°C to 500°C) the conductivity increases greatly due to the generation of electron-hole pairs from the breaking of covalent bonds. At these high temperatures then, the current appears the same as for a pure crystal but its value is larger than previously.

Another important effect of high temperatures in an impurity type crystal is that the Fermi level shifts toward the center of the forbidden energy gap. This again results because the electron-hole pairs from broken covalent bonds overshadow the effect of the impurities. Therefore the Fermi level returns toward the Fermi position

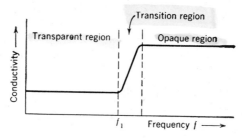

Fig. 3-11. Effects of light of varying frequency upon conductivity.

of an intrinsic crystal. This effect, it will be seen, changes the properties of a crystal containing both N- and P-type regions.

The application of light is another means available for applying energy to a solid material. When light of the correct wavelength or frequency shines upon a germanium or silicon crystal, electron-hole pairs are created. This increase in the number of current carriers will act again to increase the conductivity of the crystal. As mentioned before, light can be considered to contain small bundles of electromagnetic energy, and the amount of energy in a bundle depends upon the frequency of the light. For a quantum of light to be able to create an electron-hole pair, the quantum must possess an energy equal to or greater than the energy of the forbidden gap between the valence and the conduction band of the crystal. If the light is of such a frequency that the energy is less than this amount, it will pass right on through the crystal. The crystal is then said to be transparent to this frequency of light. When the light frequency is above this value, the light energy will be absorbed by the process of creating an electron-hole pair and the crystal is said to be opaque to this light frequency.

Since the generation of electron-hole pairs will result in an increased conductivity, we may consider the conductivity in studying the effect of the band of light frequencies. Figure 3-11 shows how the conductivity of a semiconductor crystal varies with different fre-

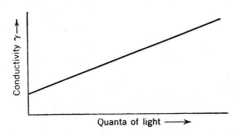

Fig. 3-12. Effects of light strength upon conductivity.

quencies of light. When the energy contained in a quantum of light is below the energy gap of the semiconductor, the material is transparent. When the energy is above this value, the semiconductor is opaque. There is a region of transition between these two conditions as shown in Figure 3-11.

If the frequency of light is above the value of f_1, the amount of light falling on the crystal will affect the conductivity in the manner shown in Figure 3-12. The stronger the light the greater the effect upon the conductivity since more electron-hole pairs are created.

References

1. *Proceedings of I.R.E.*, November 1952, pp. 1289–1313.
2. *Proceeding of Transistor Short Course*, The Pennsylvania State University, 1954, pp. IV-1–VII-7.
3. *Electrons and Holes in Semiconductors*, Shockley, D. Van Nostrand Company, Inc., 1950.

Problems

1. What is a single crystal?
2. How do silicon and germanium form single crystals and what is their crystal structure called?

3. Sketch a two-dimensional diagram depicting the crystal structure of germanium and silicon.
4. Sketch the energy band diagram for a typical semiconductor.
5. What is the Fermi level?
6. What is an electron-hole pair?
7. What is an intrinsic semiconductor?
8. Describe an N-type crystal and sketch its two-dimensional crystal diagram.
9. What is a donor?
10. Sketch the energy diagram for an N-type crystal.
11. Describe a P-type crystal and sketch its two-dimensional crystal diagram.
12. What is an acceptor?
13. Sketch the energy diagram for a P-type crystal.
14. Explain how a hole carries current.
15. What is the effect of heat and light upon a semiconductor, especially with respect to the Fermi level?
16. What is the energy difference between the Fermi level and the valence band in a P-type crystal, and between the Fermi level and the conduction band in an N-type crystal? *Note:* Use room temperature conditions.

4

The Physical Action of Transistors

Having considered the principles of semiconductors, we are now prepared to study the physical operation of transistors. In dealing with this topic we shall direct the major effort toward understanding the physical action of the junction transistor. Although the point contact type was historically the first transistor, the theory of operation of the junction type is considerably better understood. Also, from the view of one who is encountering the subject for the first time, the junction type lends itself to the simpler approach.

The study begins with consideration of P-N junctions, which are the critical areas of a transistor. Following this the N-P-N junction transistor is analyzed in some detail; since the P-N-P type is directly similar to the N-P-N only a brief comment on it is given. A section on the theory of operation of the point contact type is also included.

P-N Junctions

A transistor utilizes a single crystal of semiconductor that contains regions of both N-type and P-type material. Having discussed both types of impurity materials, and the method of conducting current, we are now prepared to consider the interaction when both N-type and P-type materials occur in a single crystal.

When discussing the properties of the pure semiconductor and the semiconductor with impurities, the concept of the Fermi level was used to describe the energy states. The importance of the Fermi level will now become evident. Whenever two materials are joined together in equilibrium conditions *their Fermi levels will always be the same.* Although N-type and P-type materials represent the same basic semiconductor containing different impurities, we have noted that the Fermi level is different for the two materials. The law just stated then demands that their Fermi levels "line-up" when both materials occur in the same crystal. This aligning of the Fermi energy level is somewhat analogous to the situation depicted in Figure 4-1. When

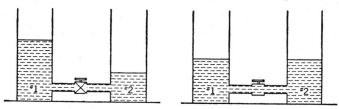

Fig. 4-1. Water levels before and after valve in pipe is opened.

the columns of water are considered separately each may have its own water level; when the two levels are joined, so to speak, the levels of the two columns are no longer independent and they reach a common level. Water flows from the first container into the second container until the water levels in both are equal. The original level of both columns determines the resultant level when the two are joined.

The similar process occurs when an N-type and a P-type material are joined. Figure 4-2(a) shows the energy levels of both the N-type and the P-type material when they are separate. This portion of the figure is a combination of the levels shown previously in Figures 3-6 and 3-9. Figure 4-2(b) shows the resultant energy relations when the two materials are joined. The two situations shown in Figure 4-2 should not lead us to believe that the N- and P-type materials, after

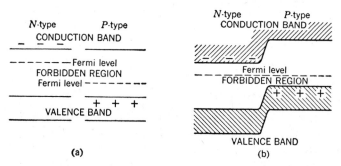

Fig. 4-2. Energy diagram for an N-P junction: (a) energy diagram for N- and P-type semiconductors; (b) equilibrium energy diagram for an N-P junction.

existing separately, may be mechanically joined. A P-N junction can be formed only by a chemical process in which the P- and the N-material are made to form a single crystal. A process for making P-N junctions will be discussed later.

If separate crystals of N-type and P-type materials were mechanically joined, a polycrystalline semiconductor would result and this would not produce transistor action. When attempting to understand transistor action in the simplest terms possible however, it is useful to consider the change from the separate state to the joined state.

In Figure 4-2(b) the region of transition from the N-type to the P-type is the critical region in terms of producing correct transistor action. It is this specific region which is referred to when the term P-N junction is used. We shall now attempt to explain what takes place in the conversion from (a) to (b) in Figure 4-2. Before plunging into this, however, it may be best to repeat the salient facts about the impurity materials in the separate condition as shown in (a). In the N-material the electrons are the majority carriers and therefore the mobile particles; for the P-material, holes are the free particles and therefore the majority carriers. Each material, when considered as a unit, is electrically neutral. This means that in the N-material the negative charge from the free electrons is exactly balanced by the surplus positive charge from each of the impurity atom nuclei; and likewise for the P-material the total positive charge of the free holes is balanced by the total negative charge contributed from each of the impurity nuclei. As a last point, the energy diagrams we have been investigating refer to energies of *electrons*, and energy bands shown depict the permissible energy levels; the *permissible* levels are not necessarily filled with electrons at any one time.

We proceed then to discuss the transition from (a) to (b) of Figure 4-2. The over-all consequence of the transition is that the permissible energy levels of both N- and P-regions have been altered. To wit, the P-region now has higher levels permissible in the conduction band, but some of the levels at the bottom of this band have been removed. The same thing has happened for the valence band. For the N-region, the exact reverse has occurred; this region has lost some of the high conduction levels and gained some levels at the low end. The two actions, the change in the N-levels and the change in the P-levels, occur simultaneously (when the materials have been hypothetically joined) until an equilibrium is reached; that is, until the Fermi levels are aligned. During this period, a very important change in the electrical properties of the junction region has occurred. In order for the P-region to change its permissible energy levels, holes had to leave the P-region and move to the N-region. Likewise for the N-region to change its permissible energy levels, electrons had to leave the N-region and shift to the P-region. Remembering the actual status of holes, both of these actions mean that electrons shifted from the N-region to the P-region. This movement of electrons means that current flowed momentarily when the materials were joined. The current ceases when equilibrium conditions (alignment of Fermi levels) are achieved.

This being the case, it is no longer true that each material is electrically neutral. In the region of the junction, the P-region has more electrons than before, and necessarily the N-region has fewer electrons. This specifies that the P-region has achieved a net negative charge and the N-region a net positive charge. Thinking of the junction momentarily as being two charges of opposite sign, we readily see that an electric field (and hence a voltage) exists at the junction. The voltage caused by this electric field is a permanent feature of the P-N junction and its magnitude depends upon the amount of impurities in both of the regions. This voltage is often called the *potential barrier* of a P-N junction. The current which flowed upon the joining of the two materials was stopped when the potential barrier was high enough to prevent further flow. This is simply another way to view equilibrium conditions. We can alter the magnitude of this junction voltage by applying external bias and this will be considered next. It should be noted, however, that the intrinsic voltage of a P-N junction is the critical feature in determining transistor action. In fact, this voltage difference at the junction of two dissimilar materials has long been exploited. It is this property which is used to produce the ordinary wet cell battery of your automobile or the dry cell batteries used in flashlights.

We shall now consider the influence of applying an external bias to a P-N junction. Since, in any semiconductor, the direction of any applied voltage is significant we shall investigate both forward and reverse bias. It is clear that any external bias will destroy the equilibrium conditions of the P-N junction as depicted in Figure 4-2(b). This being the case, we should expect that current will flow due to the loss of equilibrium.

Figure 4-3 shows the bias direction for both forward and backward bias and the unbiased equilibrium state with the associated energy levels. Figure 4-3(b) shows the unbiased junction and hence is a repetition of Figure 4-2(b). In (a) of Figure 4-3 the forward bias shows that a positive voltage is applied to the P-region. The effect of this, in the energy structure, is to lower the Fermi level, and hence both the conduction and the valence band of the P-region with respect to the N-region. This result is justified when it is remembered that for an unbiased P-N junction, the P-region has a net negative charge. With the external positive voltage applied, the negative charge of the P-region is reduced. With external bias of this polarity, the energy

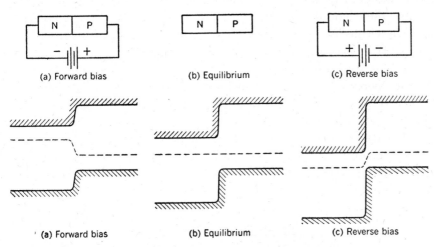

Fig. 4-3. Energy diagrams for N-P junction under forward bias, equilibrium, and reverse bias. *Note:* In (a), (b), and (c) the upper band is the conduction band, the lower band is the valence band; the region between these two bands is the forbidden region, and the broken line is the Fermi level.

bands of the two regions *tend* to become aligned. In effect this reduces the voltage barrier between the N- and the P-region at the junction. With the voltage barrier of the junction thus reduced, additional electrons from the N-region are free to move into the P-region, and holes from the P-region are free to move to the N-region. Again both of these movements constitute a flow of electrons from the N- to the P-region. A continuing supply of electrons from the battery assures that this process continues. Thus the application of forward bias to a P-N junction provides the facility for easy current flow.

Reverse bias, as the name implies, provides also for the flow of current but in this case the polarities are such that the current cannot easily flow. The effect on the energy structure is such as to increase the difference between the energy bands of the two regions. Thus the potential barrier is increased, and it is now more difficult for electrons to move from N to P or for holes to move from P to N. The direction of the external bias is such as to move electrons to the left in the material and move holes to the right. Thus the majority current carriers in both regions move away from the junction producing a *depletion region.* Depletion refers to the reduced number of majority carriers in the region on both sides of the reversed biased junction. At first thought, this would lead one to believe that no current can be carried under these conditions. However, the P-region does contain some electrons (the minority carrier for this region) and the N-region some holes. It is these minority carriers which conduct the current for reverse bias, for these carriers allow movement of electrons from the P- to the N-region and holes from the N- to the P-region. The current which occurs when reverse bias is applied is generally referred to as *back current;* it is also called I_{co} or *cutoff current* for the transistor.

The device just discussed (a P-N junction) is a *diode* of the junction type. To obtain a useful diode (one with extremely small back current) the impurities in the N- and P-regions must be controlled rigorously.

N-P-N Junction Transistor

In essence a junction transistor may be thought of as a single crystal semiconductor which contains two P-N junctions. For proper operation these two junctions must be formed back-to-back. Having considered the energy relations and current conduction of P-N junctions, we now proceed to investigate these properties when two junctions occur in the same crystal. This is merely an extension of the material just discussed and so we proceed directly to the biased N-P-N junction, which fully illustrates the action of a transistor.

Figure 4-4(a) shows the position of the energy levels for the unbiased N-P-N junction transistor. This diagram can be quickly verified by referring to Figure 4-3(b) which shows the diagram for a single junction. As noted before, the Fermi level is aligned throughout the crystal under the equilibrium conditions. The valence and the conduction bands are warped by the amount necessary to assure the constant Fermi level.

The d-c bias conditions necessary to provide transistor action are that one junction be biased in the forward direction (the direction of easy current flow) and the other junction be biased in the reverse direction. The bias of either of the two junctions is stated with respect to the center region, and this center region is called the *base*. The portion of the transistor that is biased in the forward direction (with respect to the base) is called the *emitter* and the portion biased in the reverse direction is called the *collector*. Figure 4-4(b) shows the bias connection necessary to bias the emitter junction in the forward direction and the collector junction in the reverse direction. The positions of the energy levels for the biased transistor are also shown

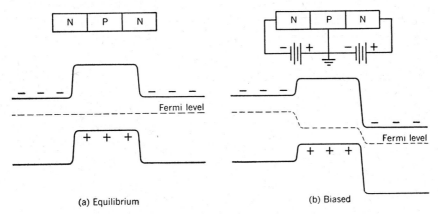

(a) Equilibrium   (b) Biased

Fig. 4-4. Energy diagrams for an N-P-N junction transistor in equilibrium and when biased.

in this figure. Again the positions of these energy levels may be verified by referring to Figure 4-3 (a) and (c).

Figure 4-4(b), then, shows the biases which must be applied to a junction transistor in order to be used in any electronic application. We shall use this figure to study the fundamental action of the charge carriers in the transistor. Although a few separate currents exist, we shall begin by considering the most important one: the current of the base region minority carrier.

Based upon the discussion in the previous section about the currents across biased P-N junctions, it will be seen that the emitter can very easily emit electrons from the N-type emitter into the P-type base region since the emitter junction is biased in the forward direction. These electrons, upon reaching the base region are minority carriers in the base region since the majority carrier of a P-region is the hole. In the base region, since there is no electric field, these

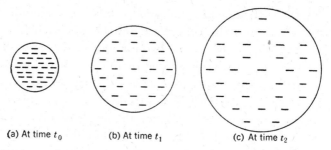

(a) At time t_0 (b) At time t_1 (c) At time t_2

Fig. 4-5. Diffusion process of minority carriers in the base region.

minority carriers move by a process of diffusion. This diffusion process, depicted in Figure 4-5, results from the fact that any bunched group of electrons will diffuse by the same laws as those which govern a group of gas molecules. At time t_0 the electrons are rather compactly spaced after being emitted into the base region. At a later time t_1 the same electrons cover a larger area, and at t_2 they have spread out still farther from each other. If the individual path of an electron could be observed during this diffusion process it might look

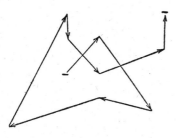

Fig. 4-6. Path of an electron during diffusion process.

like that represented in Figure 4-6. The electron will start off in one direction and retain it until it collides with a crystal lattice or another electron; it will then rebound in another direction until another collision. An erratic motion of this sort is typical of the paths of electrons in any sort of conduction medium. It may seem that this diffusion process is a flimsy sort of basis for transistor action, but remember there are always more electrons entering at the emitter junction, with the result that the minority carriers (electrons) in the base region are crowded toward the collector junction.

When the electrons reach the collector junction they experience a force due to the reverse bias which pulls them into the N-type collector region. It will be remembered that for the reverse bias, the current is carried by minority carriers. If a single N-P junction is being used, there is a very small number of minority carriers available to conduct current with the reverse bias so that only the back (cutoff) current flows—a very small current. In the case here, however, the presence of the emitter junction acts as a continuous *source* of minority carriers for the collector junction. With this supply of minority carriers available the reverse-bias collector junction experiences a relatively large current. In fact, in the manufacture of transistors, an attempt is made to form the width of the base region narrow enough so that practically all the electrons emitted by the emitter junction arrive at the collector junction and pass into the collector region.

We have now seen that the essential physical action of a junction transistor consists of the emitter injecting current carriers into the base region. For the N-P-N transistor these carriers are electrons.

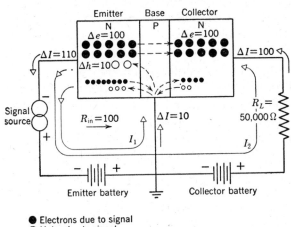

Fig. 4-7. Physical action in an N-P-N transistor in the grounded-base connection.

In the P-type base region the electrons are minority carriers and move by diffusion to the collector junction. Due to the reverse bias of the collector junction the minority carriers of the base region are attracted into the collector region. From this over-all view of the operation we have gained a very important fact: the basic action in a transistor is controlled by current carriers; therefore the transistor is a current-operated device. This is in contrast to the vacuum tube, for example, which is basically a voltage-operated device. For the vacuum tube the basic action is controlled by applying *voltages* to the control grid.

We can now consider the action of the transistor in a simple grounded-base amplifying circuit shown in Figure 4-7. Here we shall consider all the current carriers which enter into the transistor action.

The action will be illustrated by first noting the bias currents[1] and then noting the change when a small signal is applied to the emitter circuit. Figure 4-7 shows the base grounded, the signal applied to the emitter, and the load resistor connected to the collector. This method of connection is known as the *grounded-base* connection. The small solid circles in the diagram represent the electrons which take part in the bias current, and the small unfilled circles represent the bias holes. Since the bias current flows continuously after the batteries are connected, these holes and electrons can be considered to be in continuous movement. The large circles represent those holes and electrons which are made to move due to the small signal applied.

Considering the bias currents, it is seen that electrons flow from the N-emitter to the P-base region. This flow of carriers is justified when it is noted that the emitter junction is biased in the forward direction. From the section on P-N junctions it will be remembered that the current across a junction biased in the forward direction is carried by the majority carriers. Likewise, this accounts for the flow of holes from the P-base to the N-emitter region. The emitter battery has a voltage of the order of 0.1 volt and this causes a current, due to the combined action of the electrons and holes, of about 1.0 milliampere.

For the bias currents across the collector junction, it is seen that electrons flow from the P-base to the N-collector region and holes flow from the N-collector to the P-base region. Again this can be accounted for in terms of the backward bias applied to the collector junction. For backward bias it is the minority carriers which support the current. It was pointed out earlier that the source of these minority carriers are the relatively few holes and electrons generated from the breaking of covalent bonds. A normal collector voltage is about 6.0 volts (from the collector to the base) and this results in a current of the order of 0.010 milliampere. As mentioned before, these currents flow continuously when the batteries are applied to the circuit. For purposes of considering the amplification of the circuit we can disregard these bias currents and concentrate on the *change* in currents when a signal is applied to the emitter. We are interested in discovering what effect this signal has on the output side of the circuit—the load resistor.

[1] The bias concepts for transistors are similar to those for vacuum tubes. The need for bias currents in transistors is first treated on page 128 and is dealt with throughout Chapter 7.

Disregarding the bias currents then, we shall consider the action when a small positive voltage is applied to the emitter. This positive voltage will change the emitter-to-base voltage (from that of the bias) in the forward direction. Therefore electrons will move from the N-emitter to the P-base region. As an example, let us consider that 100 electrons per unit time are moved thus. From the same signal voltage, holes will move from the P-base to the N-emitter. For reasons which will become evident later, it is necessary that this hole flow be less than the electron flow. Let us assume that only 10 holes flow due to the signal. This disparity in amount of electron and hole flow due to the same signal can be controlled mainly by adjusting the amount of impurities in the N- and the P-region. For the above example, the N-emitter region would have approximately 10 times as many impurities as the P-base region.

For good transistor action the P-base region is constructed narrow enough so that practically all the electrons move by diffusion to the collector junction. Since the electrons are minority carriers in such a P-region, there is a tendency for the electrons to combine with the holes of the P-region. However, for our example, we shall consider that all the electrons arrive at the collector junction. When they arrive at this junction they are attracted into the collector region because of the reverse bias of this junction.

In order to clarify the input and output currents of this simple amplifier, let us consider the current in the wires connected to each of the three transistor regions. Since both holes and electrons contribute to the current, the emitter wire is conducting a current of 110 units. The wire connected to the base has a current of 10 units; this current is due only to the hole flow from the base region to the emitter region. It was noted that the electron flow across the emitter junction does not contribute to this base wire current since all the electrons move to the collector region. Since the signal did not change the collector junction current in any manner other than the electron current just noted, the collector wire current has increased by 100 current units. For our example, then, we are applying 110 units to the input and achieving 100 units at the output. The current amplification for this case is 100/110 and this figure would be the α for this transistor.[2] The current amplification α is a very important parameter of the transistor. We have found that the current amplification is less than one, and it is always true that, for a junction transistor

[2] The measurement of α requires a constant collector voltage which is ignored in this simple example; see Chap. 7.

operating in the grounded-base connection, the current gain is slightly less than one.

One might readily wonder how this transistor circuit is capable of exhibiting power gain since we have found that the current gain is less than one. The answer lies in the impedance levels at the input and the output. Because of the forward bias of the emitter, the input impedance is fairly low, let us say about 100 ohms. The output impedance, determined by the collector junction, is very high due to the reverse bias of this junction. For a good junction transistor the collector impedance is in the order of one megohm. Having such a high output impedance for the transistor, we can easily make the load resistor of the same order—for our example we shall make $R_L =$ 50,000 ohms. Assuming that each of the current units we considered corresponds to one microampere, we find, using $P = I^2R$ that the power input to the circuit is 0.0012 milliwatt. Calculating the power in the load resistor we find that 0.5 milliwatt is available. Thus this transistor circuit, for the assumed values, exhibits a power gain of 413.

We have now seen in some detail how the basic transistor circuit provides power gain. Along with this power gain, of course, voltage gain is provided. In the example above, the input signal voltage $(V = IR)$ is 0.011 volt and the voltage across the load resistor is 5 volts. Thus a voltage gain of 455 is available. It is essential to note that the important feature of a transistor is a current carrier, and that the important carrier in a junction transistor is the minority carrier of the base region.

For many purposes it is convenient to consider an amplifying circuit in terms of its control properties rather than in the detailed terms just considered. Any amplifying circuit can be considered to be a control circuit in the sense that, by inserting a small signal at the input, a larger reproduction of the signal is attained at the output. For the transistor circuit shown in Figure 4-7, this concept can be exhibited by considering the current I_1 and I_2 as shown. I_2 flows in the load resistor, I_1 flows in the base lead, and $I_1 + I_2$ flows through the source. We can simplify the concept of the action of this circuit by saying that I_2 is the major current of this circuit and that I_1 controls this current. In this sense the action of the transistor is made analogous to the vacuum tube, where the grid voltage controls the current between the cathode and plate. It is very important to note that, for the transistor, a current controls another current. It may be considered that I_1 effects its control over I_2 by varying the conductivity of the material through which I_2 passes. This effect of varying the conductivity is brought about by the way in which the emitter junction responds to a signal, as was described earlier.

Before leaving the consideration of the physical action of a junction transistor it is useful to consider another basic connection of the transistor. This basic amplifier circuit is called the *grounded-emitter* circuit and is shown in Figure 4-8. For this example we shall assume the same transistor is used and the same biases applied as for the previous case of the grounded-base circuit. Also, the magnitude of the applied signal will be the same. It can be seen then that Figure

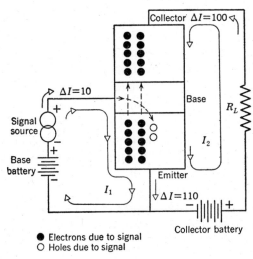

● Electrons due to signal
○ Holes due to signal

Fig. 4-8. Physical action of N-P-N transistor in the grounded-emitter connection.

4-8 is identical to Figure 4-7 except that the signal is applied to the base instead of the emitter. We shall see however, that this change in insertion of signal greatly changes the current gain of the circuit. Since the same value of signal is applied as in the previous case, the emitter junction will experience the same change in forward bias. Therefore the amount of electrons and holes moving across the emitter junction will be the same. (The bias holes and electrons are not shown in Figure 4-8.) The result is that the currents in the transistor leads due to the signal are the same as for the grounded-emitter case.

For this case the input current is 10 current units and the output is 100 units. The current gain, therefore, is $100/10 = 10$. We now see that the grounded emitter connection has a current gain greater than 1. If α is the current gain of the grounded-base circuit, it is always true that the current gain (β_i) for the grounded-emitter circuit is related to α by the equation

$$\beta_i = \frac{\alpha}{1 - \alpha} = \frac{100/110}{1 - 100/110} = 10 \tag{1}$$

The power gain of this connection will also be greater than that for the grounded base. The input resistance is increased over that for the grounded base, and the output resistance is decreased. These changes will be considered in detail when studying the parameters of the transistor. It is sufficient for the purposes here to consider the physical action of electrons and holes in the two basic connections of the transistor.

Considering Figure 4-8 in terms of control, it may be considered that I_2 is the main current of the circuit and I_1 is the control current. If we visualize transistor action in this respect, the operation of the transistor in the grounded-emitter connection is analogous to the physical action of a vacuum tube. The current I_2 may be considered analogous to the current flowing from cathode to plate in a vacuum tube, and the current I_1 can be considered to be the control quantity analogous to the control voltage on a grid. To exert this control, the current I_1 in effect varies the conductivity of the semiconductor path between the collector and the emitter. This is a completely different control concept from the vacuum tube where the voltage on the grid controls the current through the load.

P-N-P Junction Transistor

Since the critical feature of a transistor is the action at the junctions, a P-N-P transistor will operate just as satisfactorily as the N-P-N just discussed. The action in the P-N-P junction transistor is directly similar to the N-P-N if the roles of the N- and P-type semiconductors are reversed. This entails two major differences in the electrical operation: (1) the biasing polarities are reversed (the emitter is biased positive with respect to the base and the collector is biased negative with respect to the base) and (2) the minority carriers in the base region are holes rather than electrons. It is noted that with the biases as stated, the emitter junction is again biased in the forward direction and the collector junction in the reverse direction. In the base region the holes are now the minority carriers since the base consists of N-type material.

Since the holes are the important current carriers involved for the P-N-P transistor, the energy diagram of Figure 4-9 illustrates the energy levels for the holes at the three regions of the semiconductor. Note that all the previous energy diagrams depicted the energy levels of electrons. Careful thought will show that this diagram is similar

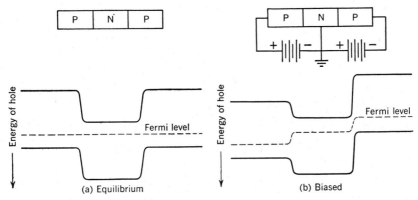

Fig. 4-9. Energy diagrams for P-N-P junction transistor.

to that of Figure 4-4 for the hole energy increases as you go toward the bottom of the diagram. Thus the emitter injects holes into the base region and these holes diffuse to the collector junction where they are collected. The examples of two amplifiers discussed for the N-P-N transistor can be applied here if the roles of the electrons and holes are reversed. There is no difference in physical operation of the two types of junction transistors except for this current carrier reversal.

Point Contact Transistor

The point contact transistor uses the properties of a metal-to-semiconductor contact. When a metal point of small cross section is in contact with a semiconductor, a potential barrier similar to that appearing across a junction is produced. Two such contacts are used in a point contact transistor. One is biased in the forward direction and serves as an emitter and the other is biased in the reverse direction and serves as a collector.

The greatest difference between a point contact and a junction transistor occurs in connection with the collector. The collector in a point contact transistor emits majority carriers into the base region, which further affects the collector current.

The number of majority carriers emitted into the base region by the collector is proportional to the emitter current. The end result is that the current flowing in the collector is larger than that in the emitter, which produces a current gain (α) greater than 1.

Problems

1. Sketch the energy diagram for a P-N junction in a semiconductor.
2. What part does the Fermi level play in a P-N junction?
3. What is the potential barrier in a P-N junction?
4. What are the required polarities for forward and reverse bias on a P-N junction?
5. Sketch the biased and unbiased energy diagrams for an N-P-N junction transistor.
6. What are the required biasing conditions for an N-P-N junction transistor?
7. Explain diffusion in the base region of an N-P-N transistor.
8. Explain the amplifying properties of an N-P-N transistor.
9. Explain the reason for a current gain less than one for the grounded-base configuration.
10. Explain the reason for a current gain greater than one for the grounded-emitter configuration.
11. Sketch the energy diagrams for a P-N-P junction transistor.
12. What is the difference in biasing conditions for an N-P-N and a P-N-P transistor?

5

Summary of Various Transistor Types

In the preceding chapters we have considered the fundamental physical action of the junction transistor. The physical action was built upon a somewhat detailed analysis of the action in semiconductors. It was noted there that the junction type depends critically upon the action in a semiconductor at a *junction* between two impurity materials. The point contact type, on the other hand, utilizes the properties of a *contact* between a semiconductor and a metal, and therefore depends upon the surface states of a semiconductor. Not all transistors, however, are of these types. As we shall see in this chapter, the various other types of transistors may be regarded as variations on the theme of the basic junction or point contact type. Certainly the action of semiconductors is common to all transistors. We shall meet transistors whose physical action is a combination of a junction action and a metal-to-semiconductor action. In another case, the transistor is a junction type, but it contains three junctions instead of two as in the basic unit.

Our purpose here is not to enter into a detailed discussion of each of the variations, but rather to summarize them. It is felt that it is far more profitable to concentrate on a relatively few principles than to provide a breadth of half-understood explanations.

In addition to differences in physical operation, transistors differ in the method of manufacture. This is most evident for transistors which utilize junctions; there are three basically different ways of obtaining the junction.

In this chapter then, we wish to consider the various types of transistors and their methods of manufacture. The methods of manufacture for the basic junction transistor will be considered first. Following this, three devices which utilize a junction but are different from the basic type are considered; they are the P-N-P-N, the field effect, and the surface-barrier transistor. For these three cases a summary of their operation and the manufacturing method will be cited.

Junction-Type Transistors

For purposes of clarification, the term *junction-type transistors* refers to all types which utilize a junction. Thus this category includes the basic type described in the previous chapter plus the allied types mentioned above. We begin by describing the manufacturing methods for the basic N-P-N or P-N-P junction transistor.

N-P-N and P-N-P junction transistor. Referring to the previous chapters, it is remembered that the basic junction transistor consists of two P-N junctions with impurity material arranged in N-P-N or P-N-P fashion. Depending upon the manner in which a single crystal N-P-N (or P-N-P) semiconductor is obtained, the resulting transistor is called a *grown junction*, an *alloy junction*, or a *rate-grown* transistor. Although all three methods of manufacture result in the basic junction transistor, there are noticeable differences in the electrical properties consequent to the three different methods.

The first and most direct method employed in achieving an N-P-N (or P-N-P) semiconductor was by a method of growing the crystal, and is called the grown junction method. This process begins by placing high purity germanium along with granules of N-type impurity into a small graphite crucible which is capable of being heated to very high temperatures. This furnace-like device is equipped with a vertical rod capable of being drawn upward at a very slow rate while turning. In its crudest form, the vertical-pulling furnace resembles a slow-operating drill press with an attached heating unit. After the N-type germanium is heated sufficiently to achieve the molten state, a small seed crystal is lowered into the melt until it just comes in contact with the surface. This seed is a single crystal of germanium in which precaution is taken to cut the crystal perfectly along a face of the cubic lattice. Because of surface tension between atoms of the seed and atoms of the melt, the melt will cling to the seed after contact. The seed is then pulled slowly away from the melt while being rotated. That portion of the melt which is in contact with the seed begins to solidify because of the cooling provided by heat conduction through the seed. Thus, as the seed is withdrawn, a solid piece of germanium is continuously accumulated. The germanium changes from the molten state to the solid state as it rises slightly above the surface of the melt, the cooling always being provided by the solid material preceding it. The material that freezes out of the melt takes on the same crystal orientation as that of the seed. If the process continues smoothly the resultant grown material will be a single crystal specimen.

It is noted that the original material in the crucible was N-type. If now, during the pulling process, some pellets of P-type impurity are dropped into the melt they will counteract the N-type impurity and change the material to P-type. The rotating of the material as it is withdrawn insures that any such additions are properly mixed throughout the melt. In this manner a P-region is formed adjacent to the N-region. After a short length of P-type is grown, N-impurities are again added to form N-material. In this manner a single-crystal N-P-N semiconductor is formed.

This relatively large crystal is then sliced into small pieces, each of which contains the P-layers sandwiched between two N-layers. Metal contacts are then placed on all three regions with the middle P-layers acting as the base. Although the result here is an N-P-N transistor, a P-N-P can be made in exactly the same manner. All that remains to be done is to enclose the semiconductor in a solid plastic material to seal it from the contaminating effects of humidity, etc.

The second method of achieving an N-P-N (or P-N-P) semiconductor is called the rate-grown method. This method is similar to the grown method described above except that several N-P-N (or P-N-P) sandwiches may be obtained from a single growing process. Instead of explicitly changing the material by addition of impurities, the melt always contains both N- and P-impurities. In this case the type of material grown is determined by the rate at which the pulling occurs. When the crystal is being grown, a slow rate of pulling produces N-type material because the P-impurities tend to stay in the molten state. If the rate is increased sufficiently the P-impurities which are being constantly rejected from the growing crystal form a concentration directly under the crystal. The increased supply of P-impurities from this concentration will produce a P-layer. Let us say that the growing rate is adjusted so that an N-type region is being grown. When the rate is changed properly a P-region is grown and a P-N junction is formed. The rate is then returned to that suitable for an N-region. This process may be repeated several times during the growing of a single crystal, which results in a more economical use of materials than for the former method.

The third method of achieving junction transistors consists of an alloy process. Instead of the process of growing a crystal from the molten state, this process depends on an operation similar to soldering.

The essential treatment is to begin with an N-type crystal and "fuse" or "alloy" a P-producing material into the N-region. It was noted in Chapter 3 that indium acts as an impurity to produce P-type

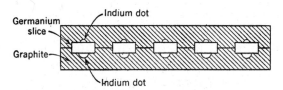

Fig. 5-1. Jig arrangement for alloy transistor.

material when it is combined with germanium. Therefore indium is used to combine with the N-type germanium so as to produce a P-N-P junction transistor. The operation is begun by taking an N-type crystal and slicing it into small wafers about one-quarter inch long by one-eighth inch wide. These slices are then placed in a graphite jig with a "dot" of prepared indium on either side, as shown in Figure 5-1 (showing five such units). The use of a jig is necessary because the indium dots must be perfectly aligned on opposite sides of the slice, and its graphite construction is necessary to withstand the heat.

The jig is placed in a furnace and the temperature is raised to about 500°C for a short period of time. During this heating the jig is surrounded with hydrogen gas in order to prevent contamination. As a result of the extreme heat the indium melts and starts combining with the germanium. The combining action is similar to that of soldering, in that a mechanical bond is created by the heat; however, in this case a much more important effect is the *chemical* bonding that takes place.

After the jig is removed from the furnace and has cooled, metal leads are attached to the three areas. The amount of indium placed on one side of the slice was larger than on the other side. The larger indium dot becomes the collector, the smaller indium portion becomes the emitter, and the N-type slice is the base. The result is a P-N-P junction transistor and is shown in Figure 5-2. It is important to note that, after the alloying process, the indium enters into the crystal structure of the germanium so that the resultant P-N-P junctions form a *single* crystal.

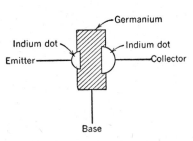

Fig. 5-2. P-N-P alloy junction transistor.

N-P-N transistors may also be constructed by this alloying process if a P-type slice is used and antimony or arsenic is substituted for indium. In the past it has been the usual practice to construct P-N-P transistors by the alloying method and N-P-N transistors by the grown or rate-grown method. For the grown junction method it has been found that the impurities can be controlled better if the operation is started with N-type material; thus an N-P-N junction results. For the alloying process, germanium heavily dosed with indium provides a convenient material to alloy to a central N-layer, thus providing a P-N-P junction. It is possible, however, to obtain P-N-P from the grown method, and N-P-N from the alloy method.

In the past, most commercial transistors have been made by the alloy method. Although this method is somewhat less controllable than the grown junction method, it does lend itself to mass production more readily. Thus, unless a high degree of accuracy is needed—accuracy in amount of impurities and width of the center region—the alloy method is used. If the accuracy is necessary, the grown junction method is used.

P-N-P-N junction transistor. The first special type of junction transistor that we shall consider is the P-N-P-N type, commonly called the *hook* transistor. Its basic operation rests upon junctions, but there are three junctions instead of two. It will be our purpose here not to entail in lengthy description, but to summarize the operation in relation to the more detailed material presented in Chapter 4.

The various regions and the biasing conditions for the hook transistor are shown in Figure 5-3. The valence and conduction bands are also shown in the figure; they depict the same type of information as Figures 4-4 and 4-9 of Chapter 4. For purposes of clarity, we have marked the various regions P_1, N_1, etc. and have numbered the junctions 1, 2, 3. It may be noted that this transistor acquired the name *hook* because of the hooklike appearance of the energy diagram.

It will be remembered from Chapter 4 that the important current carrier in a transistor is the minority carrier in the base region. Since the base region here is N-type, the important carrier is the hole. For that reason it is necessary to remind the reader that the energy diagram of Figure 5-3 is to be interpreted in terms of holes. Like the

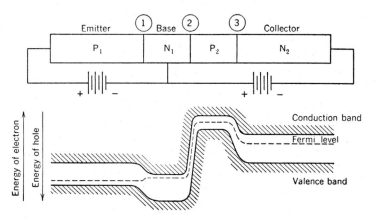

Fig. 5-3. Energy diagram for a P-N-P-N hook transistor when biased.

P-N-P diagram of Figure 4-9, the hole energy increases toward the bottom of the diagram.

With this in mind, it is seen that junction 1 is biased in the forward direction and hence holes are emitted by the P-region into the N-base region. These holes experience a collecting action at junction 2 due to the shape of the energy diagram (compare with Figure 4-9). When arriving at junction 3, the holes experience a repelling voltage barrier, again due to the shape of the energy diagram. Consequently the emitted holes become trapped in the P_2-region.

The trapped holes accomplish the critical operation of the hook transistor. As a result of being trapped near junction 3, they *lower* the voltage barrier of this junction—in effect they put a forward bias on junction 3. As a direct result, electrons from the N-collector region (the majority carrier of this region) will cross junction 3 to the left. These released electrons pass through the P_2-region and are collected by the N-base. A current amplification is involved in this process, for the amount of electrons released is greater than the number of trapped holes needed to accomplish this release. It will be remembered that the basic type of junction transistor always has a current amplification of less than unity; by use of this special type, a gain factor, α, of greater than unity is possible.

The essential action, then, is that the holes emitted by the P_1-emitter control the electron current of the N_2-P_2-N_1 regions. It is implicit that this special type is more difficult to manufacture than the basic type. Also, a higher noise level is prevalent. For these reasons the hook transistor has not been applied to a great extent.

The field effect transistor. The second special type of junction transistor is the *field effect*, or *unipolar*, transistor. Although the basic structure consists of junctions, its physical operation differs from that

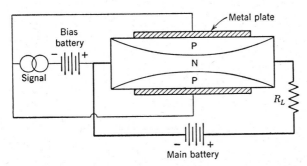

Fig. 5-4. Operation of field-effect transistor in a simple amplifier circuit.

of the basic junction type. As in the previous case of the P-N-P-N type, we are interested here in summarizing the operation in relation to the basic semiconductor phenomenon.

The essential structure of the field effect transistor is similar to that of a P-N-P type as there is an N-type layer between two layers of P-material, as shown in Figure 5-4. The essential operation of this transistor is best explained by considering a main current and a control voltage. In Figure 5-4 the path of the main current, which contains the load resistor, is exhibited by a heavy line. The connections which provide the control voltage are shown in light lines.

The N-type layer provides the path of main current through the transistor. Since electrons are the majority carrier in N-type, the main current is composed mostly of electrons. It is the function of the signal voltage to *control* the amount of electrons which flow through the N-layer, and thus control the main current. The signal voltage exerts this control by applying reverse bias to both the P-N junctions. (It is seen from the symmetry of the circuit that any action on one junction also occurs on the other; so only one junction will be discussed in this section.)

Our object now is to see why the application of reverse bias affects the control, and how amplification is provided in that the *controlled* signal is greater than the control one. Referring to Chapter 4 (Figure 4-3c) it will be seen that the bias battery of Figure 5-4 does provide reverse bias to the P-N junctions. It will also be remembered that the reverse bias causes the majority carriers, of both the P- and the N-regions, to be drawn away from the junction, and that this results in a depletion region. It is this depletion region which provides the increase in voltage barrier when reverse bias is applied. It is exactly this depletion effect that provides the control in the field-effect transistor. As the reverse bias is increased, electrons in the N-layer are drawn away from the junction. Not only are they physically moved, they are also rendered incapable of conducting current. The depletion region acts much like a capacitor: the charges are moved and effectively stored in the battery. For example, a capacitor plate which has a positive charge has been robbed of some of its normal electrons.

The effect, then, is that the reverse bias causes the electrons normally near the junction to be withdrawn as available current carriers. When the reverse bias is varied, the volume of the depletion region is varied, so that the number of electrons affected varies with the bias. The total effect is that the area of the N-type material which provides current carriers is varied by the signal. Therefore the main current varies with the greater or less number of carriers available.

Having established the manner of control, it is now easy to see why amplification results. Since the signal is providing reverse bias, only a very small current flows in the input. The output current, on the other hand, is not even passing through a junction. It is passing straight through an N-type material. Its magnitude is limited only by the size of the main battery and the impurity density of the N-material. Thus a small signal controls a much larger output signal.

Although the field effect transistor shows possibility of being a very useful device, its application thus far has been limited by a comparatively high noise figure.

The surface-barrier transistor. The surface-barrier transistor is the third type which utilizes a junction for its operation, but operates in a different manner than the basic junction type. This transistor departs from the basic type also in the manner in which it is manufactured. Although it differs both in manufacture and physical operation, its electrical behavior is essentially the same as for the basic junction type.

The junctions, for the surface-barrier type, are supplied by a metal and a semiconductor rather than the conventional two impurity types of semiconductor. To achieve such junctions, two jets of an electrolyte are squirted against a small slice of N-type germanium. From basic chemistry it will be remembered that an electrolyte is any solution capable of conducting electricity. With current of the right polarity through the electrolyte, the jet acts as an abrasive and etches the surface of the germanium. This is continued until the germanium thickness is reduced to a desired value, and then the polarity of the current through the electrolyte is reversed. This stops the etching action and the jet begins plating the germanium with a metal electrode. The use of this electrolyte method permits a great degree of accuracy in controlling the thickness of the germanium slice. It is for this reason that the surface-barrier transistor can be operated at very high frequencies.

In the manner described then, a thin slice of N-type germanium is obtained between two metal electrodes. Figure 5-5 shows a cross section of the surface-barrier transistor. Like the point contact transistor the surface-barrier type depends for its operation upon the surface states of the germanium. At the surface of a piece of pure germanium an electric field exists such that both holes and electrons are excluded from a thin region near the surface. For N-type germanium, the field is such as to repel the free electrons (majority carrier) away from this surface region. If a metal is joined to the germanium, the free electrons are still repelled, but a concentration of holes (minority carrier) is produced directly under the surface.

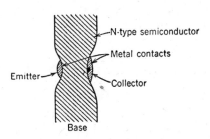

Fig. 5-5. Cross section of surface-barrier transistor.

When the emitter contact is biased positive with respect to the base some of these holes will move into the region between the emitter and the collector. These holes then diffuse across the base region, as in the P-N-P transistor. If the collector contact has a reverse bias the holes will be collected. In this manner the signal on the emitter controls the current through the collector.

P-N-I-P and N-P-I-N transistors. These two devices are variations of the basic junction transistor, their main difference being an intrinsic region between the base and collector regions. This intrinsic region serves two purposes: it reduces the collector to base capacitance and places a region that has the effect of isolating the collector junction from the base. This permits a smaller base region to be used without collector-to-base punch-through.

The drift transistor. The drift transistor is similar to that of the N-P-I-N or P-N-I-P device. In place of the intrinsic region, the impurity concentration is allowed to decrease exponentially from the emitter junction to the collector junction. The two devices accomplish basically the same ends, by different methods.

Diffused-base transistor. The diffused-base transistor obtains its name from its manufacturing process. A slice of germanium is placed in an oven, where a layer of impurity is deposited on the surface. This impurity diffuses into the germanium, forming usually the base region. The emitter is then alloyed onto this diffused base, and the original material is the collector. With this process very thin base regions are possible, thus permitting very high-frequency operation.

Other Semiconductor Devices

It was mentioned previously that semiconductors were utilized as circuit devices long before the appearance of the transistor. It is of interest here to summarize these various other applications. The devices we shall consider are: diodes or varistors, double-base diodes, Zener diodes, thermistors, and photodiodes.

One of the earliest forms of a semiconductor diode was the *crystal detector*. The chief characteristic of any diode is that it readily conducts current in one direction, but offers a very high resistance to current of the opposite direction. If a diode and resistor are connected to an alternating voltage source, only that half of the alternating voltage of the correct polarity will appear across the load resistor; if a capacitor is added in parallel to the load resistor, a basic power supply is formed. In terms of a transistor, a junction diode consists of one-half of a transistor; that is, only one junction is used instead of two. From our previous study of P-N junctions, it is easily seen that a single junction acts as a diode. When the junction is biased in the reverse direction the junction offers a high impedance, and little current flows. If forward bias is applied the junction will permit a relatively large current to flow. In this way a semiconductor junction acts as a diode, and can be used as a circuit device.

A semiconductor diode may also be of the point contact variety.

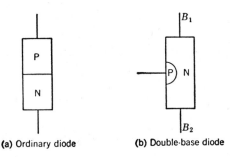

(a) Ordinary diode   (b) Double-base diode

Fig. 5-6. An ordinary diode and a double-base diode compared as to physical structure.

In this case the diode may be considered to be formed out of one-half of a point contact transistor; that is, a semiconductor and one point contact. Although the basic action is the same, the point contact diode does not offer as high a "reverse impedance" as does the junction type. For this reason the junction type is the more efficient of the two.

Another useful semiconductor device is the *double-base diode*. The double-base diode has only one junction as does the ordinary diode, but two base connections are present. Figure 5-6 shows a comparison of a double-base diode and an ordinary diode. The double-base diode exhibits an interesting phenomenon under the following biasing conditions. A current flowing through B_1 and B_2 causes a voltage drop to appear along the length of the N-region (base), due to the distributed resistance along the path. If the P-region at the center of the diode is biased with a potential that is equal to the voltage of the center of the base, one portion of the P-region will experience a forward bias and the other portion will experience a reverse bias. As a result one portion will act as an emitter and the other portion will act as a collector. Thus the action is somewhat like that of a transistor; however, there is no gain associated with this device and the operation is very nonlinear. This device finds application in pulse and switching circuits.

The *Zener diode* is another useful circuit device. This type of diode makes use of the breakdown properties of a P-N junction. If the reverse voltage applied to a P-N junction is progressively increased, a value will be reached at which the current will increase greatly from its normal cutoff value. The voltage at which this occurs is called the

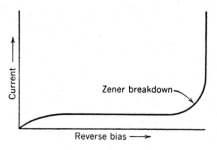

Fig. 5-7. Zener effect in a P-N junction diode.

breakdown voltage or the *Zener* voltage and occurs at 250,000 volts/cm for germanium. If, in biasing a transistor, the reverse bias is high enough to induce the Zener effect, the transistor may be ruined. In a Zener diode, however, the construction of the junction is such that the Zener effect may be used repeatedly in a circuit application. A graph showing the current characteristic of a Zener diode is given in Figure 5-7.

A *thermistor* is any electronic device in which the proper operation is dependent upon temperature. If a particular electronic circuit has to operate over a temperature range that causes the circuit to show undesirable effects of temperature, a thermistor may be used in such a manner that it compensates, by its own temperature dependence, the undesirable properties of the rest of the circuit. A P-N junction, biased in the reverse direction, is intrinsically temperature sensitive. It was noted earlier that temperature affects the amount of minority carriers within an impurity semiconductor because of the generation of electron-hole pairs. It is also remembered that, when reverse bias is applied, the minority carriers are the current bearers. A thermistor, then, is a semiconductor diode in which special attention has been given to emphasize the temperature dependence of the current for any particular voltage. We shall meet the thermistor again when considering the bias stabilization of transistor circuits.

Still another useful circuit device is a semiconductor junction which makes use of the effects of light upon the junction. Such a device is called a *photodiode* and is simply another application of a P-N junction in which special care has been taken to emphasize the light effects upon the junction. It is remembered that light, like temperature, is effective in generating electron-hole pairs in a semiconductor. Therefore if a diode is biased in the reverse direction, any incidence of light will modify the conductivity of the junction and thus provide a device which enables the incidence of light to control some desired function.

Problems

1. What are the types of junction transistors?
2. Explain the method of producing the grown-junction transistor.
3. How does the rate-grown method differ from that of the plain grown junction method?
4. Describe the alloy process of manufacturing transistors.
5. How does the P-N-P-N transistor operate?
6. Describe the field-effect transistor.
7. Describe the manufacturing process used in fabricating the surface-barrier transistor.
8. How does the surface-barrier transistor differ from the normal junction type?
9. What is the N-P-I-N or P-N-I-P transistor?
10. What is a diffused-base transistor?
11. What are some other devices that are basically semiconductors?

Part Two

CIRCUITS

6

Electrical Review

In order to provide a consistent approach to the circuit aspects of transistors, it is necessary to rely on the basic electric circuit theory. For this reason it is desirable to review, as briefly as possible, this basic circuit theory in the light of the material to follow. It is intended that this material act as a refresher and give the reader a frame of reference upon which the remaining chapters of this text are based. This chapter begins with the fundamental quantities of electricity and electric circuits. While the basic material is included only for easy reference, the more advanced material on frequency response, equivalent circuits, and impedance matching will be covered more completely.[1]

Basic Circuit Quantities

Current. Current is the measure of *flow* of electric charge in any conductor and is measured in amperes. The amount of current flowing corresponds to the number of coulombs of electric charge which pass a given cross section of conductor per unit time. In an ordinary conductor the current is carried by electrons so that the current flow-

---

[1] The reader should note that, like the Physics Review, this chapter begins with a brief restatement of the most basic electric theory. For the reader who is quite familiar with these basic concepts the initial material will be unnecessary. For such readers the authors suggest skipping the first sections and beginning with the section on "Methods of Circuit Analysis."

ing is directly related to the number of electrons flowing. The two major types of current are direct current and alternating current.

A *direct current* is a current in which the *direction* of flow of the electric charges is always the same. Although the direct current may vary in magnitude, it usually is constant. Therefore the equation for a direct current may be written

$$I = k \tag{1}$$

Alternating current is a current in which the direction of flow of the electric charges changes periodically. Thus in a circuit the electrons flow to the right for one-half cycle and to the left for the other half cycle. The most common alternating current is a sine-wave current, and its equation is written

$$i = I_m \sin \omega t \tag{2}$$

where i = instantaneous value of current,
I_m = maximum current value,
$\omega = 2\pi f$ = electrical angular frequency in radians per second,
t = time elapsed from some starting time.

This equation states that, in a circuit containing a sine-wave current, the current at any instant of time will be given by the product of the maximum value of the wave and the sine of an angle. It is noted that the product ωt indicates an angle measured in radians.

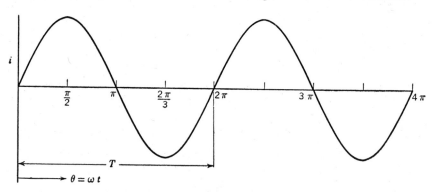

Fig. 6-1. Graph of a sine-wave alternating current.

Figure 6-1 shows a graph of the instantaneous value of a sine-wave current. The *frequency* (f) of a sine wave is determined by the number of complete cycles which occur in one second. The *period* of a sine wave (T) is defined as the time required to complete one cycle. Thus the period is equal to the reciprocal of the frequency:

$$T = \frac{1}{f} \qquad (3)$$

Although it is sometimes necessary to know the equation of the current in a circuit, it is usually sufficient to consider only the effective value of a sine-wave current. The *effective value* is defined as that value of alternating current which produces the same amount of work (or heat) in a circuit as does a direct current. Thus one ampere of effective alternating current does the same amount of work as one ampere of direct current. The effective value of a sine-wave current is equal to

$$I_{\text{eff}} = \frac{I_m}{\sqrt{2}} = 0.707 I_m \qquad (4)$$

When dealing with any alternating currents for the rest of this text, the effective value will always be used unless noted otherwise. Because of the manner of deriving the effective value, it is also called the *root mean square* or *rms* value.

It is important here to consider combinations of alternating and direct current. A unidirectional current that varies in magnitude is composed of both a-c and d-c components. In this case the d-c component is larger than the peak value of the a-c component. If the a-c component is larger, we no longer have unidirectional current flow, but alternating current with unequal periods. There may also be alternating currents composed of more than one sine wave.

Voltage. Voltage plays two roles in electric circuit theory. In the one sense, voltage is the electromotive force (emf) that produces current in a circuit. In this sense the voltage of a battery, for example, is the force which produces a flow of current; the letter E will be used to designate a voltage source. Voltage is also used in the sense of describing the *effect* of a current passing through any passive circuit element. It is in this sense that we speak of the voltage across a resistor, a capacitor, or an inductor. This is also called voltage drop and will be designated by V.

Since voltages are directly related to currents, there are direct and alternating voltages. The equation for a direct voltage will be

$$E = k \qquad (5)$$

Corresponding to the current case, the equation for an alternating voltage is

$$e = E_m \sin \omega t \tag{6}$$

where e = instantaneous value of voltage,

E_m = maximum voltage value,

$\omega = 2\pi f$ = electrical angular frequency in radians per second,

f = frequency or number of alternations per second,

t = time in seconds.

The effective or rms value of a sine-wave voltage is again calculated by the equation

$$E_{\text{eff}} = \frac{E_m}{\sqrt{2}} = 0.707 E_m \tag{7}$$

Power. The remaining basic electrical quantity is power. There are two aspects of power in electric circuit theory. The first aspect concerns the rate of work done when electric power is converted to some form of mechanical power. Thus, in a motor, electric power is converted to mechanical rotation; in a radio speaker electric energy is converted to acoustical energy. In both cases the electric energy consumed is the measure of the work done by the converting device.

The second aspect of power concerns the time rate of loss of energy in the form of heat. Whenever current flows through a resistance such as that of a transmission line, electric energy is changed to heat energy and is dissipated into the surroundings. This consumption of energy represents a loss of energy to the electric circuit, and is comparable to friction in mechanical systems.

In both of the above cases the *consumption* of energy implies that electric energy is changed to some other form of energy and is lost to the electric system. In the case of the motor the consumption can be regarded as intentional and useful, whereas in the second case it is unintentional and represents a loss of efficiency for the electric circuit.

Having considered the basic electrical quantities—current, voltage, and power—the review continues to the circuit relations for the three passive circuit elements.

Passive Circuit Elements

In considering the basic circuit elements, we are interested in the relation between the applied voltage and the resulting current for resistance, inductance, and capacitance.

Resistance. A resistance is an element which offers opposition to the flow of current and consumes power. Resistance is measured in ohms, and if a voltage is applied, current will flow according to the relation

$$I = \frac{E}{R} \tag{8}$$

where I = current in amperes,
 E = voltage in volts,
 R = resistance in ohms.

Equation (8) is the statement of Ohm's law, and is one of the fundamental equations of electric circuitry. Ohm's law states that one volt impressed across one ohm of resistance results in one ampere of current flow. The power consumed by a resistance when a current flows through it is given by

$$P = I^2R \tag{9}$$

where P = power in watts.

Equations (8) and (9) apply for either direct or alternating currents. It must be remembered, however, that for the a-c case the effective or rms values must always be used.

Capacitance. A *capacitor* is an element which offers opposition to the flow of current but in which no power is consumed. A capacitor, in its simplest form, consists of two conducting plates separated by a dielectric. At any instant of time the voltage across a capacitor is related to the electric charge on the plates by the equation

$$E = \frac{Q}{C} \tag{10}$$

where E = voltage across capacitor in volts,
 Q = charge on capacitor in coulombs,
 C = amount of capacitance in farads.

One of the important properties of a capacitor is that it is capable of *storing* an electric charge. Thus if a direct voltage source is applied to a capacitor, a charge will be stored whose amount is determined by Equation (10). If now the source is removed, the capacitor will retain the charge and a voltage will remain across the capacitor equal to the applied voltage. For this reason the capacitor has two applications in a circuit: (1) as an element capable of storing charge; and (2) as an element offering opposition to the flow of current in the same sense as a resistor.

If we are interested in the first application, we must consider the "transient" situation. That is, we want to know how long it takes to charge the capacitor and how long to discharge it after another element is applied. We note that, in the storage application, current flows as long as the capacitor is either charging or discharging. Current continues to flow until the conditions of Equation (10) are met.

If we are interested in the capacitor as a circuit element offering opposition to the flow of current, we deal with it in terms of a steady direct or alternating current. From the previous paragraph it is noted that, if a steady direct voltage is applied to a capacitor, no current will flow after the initial transient charging current. *Thus a capacitor blocks the flow of steady direct current.* If an alternating voltage is applied to a capacitor the continuously changing value of voltage specifies that a continuous current flows. The fact that a capacitor blocks a steady direct current but allows an alternating current to flow makes it a very useful element for separating direct and alternating currents. This function represents its most important use in electronics.

If an alternating voltage is applied to a capacitor, a current will flow of value

$$I = \frac{V}{X_C} \tag{11}$$

where X_C = capacitive reactance in ohms.

Equation (11) states that X_C is the opposition which the capacitor offers to the flow of alternating current. X_C in turn, is defined by

$$X_C = \frac{1}{2\pi f C} \tag{12}$$

where f = frequency of the alternating current,
C = capacitance in farads.

Note that Equations (11) and (12) may be used for direct currents also if a direct current is regarded as an alternating current of zero frequency. Then $X_C = \infty$ and no current flows.

X_C is measured in ohms and is called capacitive *reactance*. A reactance differs from a resistance in that a phase angle is associated with reactance; the phase angle refers to the angle between the voltage and the current. For a pure capacitance, the current leads the voltage by 90°. Thus if an alternating voltage is applied to a capacitor, the resulting current, at any time, will lead the voltage by one-quarter of a cycle. Another difference between a reactance and a resistance is that a pure reactance consumes no power.

A capacitor, then, does not consume power. When an a-c source is applied, the capacitor will store energy during one-half of the cycle and return the energy to the source during the other half cycle.

Inductance. Inductance is another passive element that offers opposition to the flow of current but in which no power is consumed. If an alternating voltage is applied to an inductor, a current will flow, given by

$$I = \frac{V}{X_L} \tag{13}$$

X_L, in turn, is given by

$$X_L = 2\pi f L \tag{14}$$

where X_L = inductive reactance in ohms,
L = inductance in henries.

From Equations (13) and (14) it is noted that, for a direct current ($f = 0$), the inductor offers no opposition. For direct current then, a pure inductor is a short circuit.

X_L is called *inductive reactance* and is measured in ohms. The phase angle associated with inductive reactance is 90°, and the current lags the voltage. It is noted that this angle is opposite to that for the capacitor, where the current leads the voltage.

Basic Circuits

Series circuits. Whenever resistances are connected in series, the total resistance is simply the sum of all the resistances. If a resistance is in series with a reactance, either capacitive or inductive, the resistance and reactance must be added vectorially. The combination of resistance and reactance is called *impedance*. Since impedance generally has reactance present, a phase angle will be

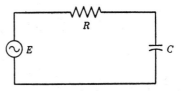

Fig. 6-2. Series *RC* circuit.

associated with it. Therefore, when specifying the impedance we must give the magnitude and the phase angle.

Figure 6-2 shows a series RC circuit. For an applied voltage, E, the magnitude of the current will be given by the impedance form of Ohm's law:

$$I = \frac{E}{|Z|} \tag{15}$$

where $|Z|$ = the magnitude of the impedance in ohms.

The magnitude of the impedance is found by the relation

$$|Z| = \sqrt{R^2 + (-X_c)^2} \tag{16}$$

The minus sign preceding X_c is necessary to distinguish the *lead* phase angle of the capacitor from the *lag* angle of the inductor.

Note that a resistance and a reactance can never be added directly, but must be combined in the manner shown in Equation (16).

If we wish to know the phase angle between the current and the voltage of the circuit, we have to find the phase angle of Z. This is given by

$$\theta = \tan^{-1} - \frac{X_c}{R} \tag{17}$$

To write the complete expression for the impedance, then,

$$Z = \sqrt{R^2 + (-X_c)^2} \,\Big|\underline{\tan^{-1} - \frac{X_c}{R}} \tag{18}$$

This equation gives the magnitude and the angle of the impedance phasor.

The phase relationship between the current and voltage is shown in Figure 6-3(a). It is seen that the current leads the voltage by an angle θ, and this is the impedance angle as defined by Equation (17). Figure 6-3(b) shows a phasor representation of the current and volt-

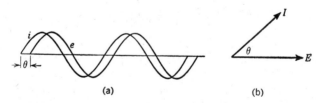

(a)   (b)

Fig. 6-3. Phase angle between current and voltage in an RC series circuit. (a) Actual waveform of current and voltage. (b) Phasor diagram representation.

age. A phasor diagram of this sort is very useful, in a-c circuitry, for providing a visual picture of the current-voltage relations. Such diagrams are usually used as an aid for the calculations.

The impedance itself may be represented by a phasor diagram. This is shown in Figure 6-4. From such a diagram Equations (16) and (17) can be verified by using simple trigonometry. The magnitude of the impedance is given by the hypotenuse of a right triangle, and the phase angle is determined by the angle whose tangent is $-X_C/R$.

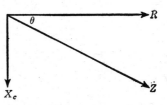

Fig. 6-4. Impedance phasor diagram of an RC series circuit.

A useful notation that fits the vector representation of Figure 6-4 is the following:

$$Z = R - jX_C \qquad (19)$$

The j will always precede a reactive term when this notation is used and indicates that the reactance is to be plotted at right angles to the resistance component. The negative sign appears because the current leads the voltage in a capacitive reactance, and on the phasor diagram, indicates that the Z phasor lies below the horizontal axis.

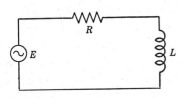

Fig. 6-5. Series RL circuit.

A circuit consisting of a resistor and an inductance in series is shown in Figure 6-5. Again the current is given by Equation (15) and the magnitude of the impedance is given by

$$|Z| = \sqrt{R^2 + X_L^2} \qquad (20)$$

Since reactance is present, a phase angle will be associated with this circuit. This phase angle, which specifies the phase between the current and the voltage, is given by

$$\theta = \tan^{-1} \frac{X_L}{R} \qquad (21)$$

The complete expression for the impedance then, is

$$Z = \sqrt{R^2 + X_L^2} \left| \tan^{-1} \frac{X_L}{R} \right. \qquad (22)$$

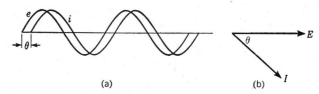

(a)   (b)

Fig. 6-6. Phase angle between current and voltage of an *RL* series circuit. (a) Actual waveform of current and voltage. (b) Phasor representation.

This equation gives the magnitude and the angle of the impedance phasor.

For the *RL* circuit, the current *lags* the voltage; it is remembered that current leads the voltage in the *RC* circuit. Figure 6-6(a) shows the actual waveforms of the current and voltage, and it is seen that the current lags the voltage by the impedance angle θ. The phasor representation of the current and voltage is shown in Figure 6-6(b).

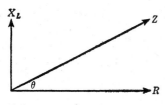

Fig. 6-7. Impedance phasor diagram of an *RL* series circuit.

The impedance phasor, for the series *RL* case, is shown in Figure 6-7. It is noted that in this case the X_L is plotted upward, and that the resultant Z lies above the horizontal axis.

Again the impedance can be written in the form

$$Z = R + jX_L \tag{23}$$

We can now state a general rule concerning elements in series. When reactances and resistances are connected in series, *add the resistances separately, and then add the reactances by using a positive sign for inductive reactance and a negative sign for capacitive reactance.* The total impedance is found by the relation

$$Z = \sqrt{(R_1 + R_2 + R_3 + \ldots)^2 + (X_{L_1} + X_{L_2} - X_{C_1} - X_{C_2} - \ldots)^2}$$
$$\left| \tan^{-1} \frac{X_{L_1} + X_{L_2} - X_{C_1} - X_{C_2} - \ldots}{R_1 + R_2 + R_3 + \ldots} \right. \tag{24}$$

If all the circuit elements are in series, the current flowing through each element is the same. The voltage across each element, of course, depends upon the impedance of the element. The total voltage across the series circuit is equal to the phasor sum of the element voltages. It is important to remember that, for elements containing reactance, the voltages cannot be added directly but must be added vectorially.

Figure 6-8 shows a series circuit consisting of three series impedances. The phasor sketch shows how the three voltages add to form the total applied voltage. Since the same current is common to

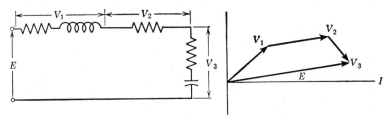

Fig. 6-8. Phasor diagram showing the voltage addition in a series circuit.

all elements in a series circuit, the current is used as the reference for the phasor diagram.

Whenever a circuit contains reactance, the power consumed can be calculated by the relation

$$P = VI \cos \theta \qquad (25)$$

The angle θ here is again the impedance angle. This equation can be applied to either a single impedance or a total circuit. Since any power is consumed only in resistance, the following relation must be true:

$$P = I^2R = VI \cos \theta \qquad (26)$$

Thus the power can be calculated by either of the two methods.

Parallel circuits. When resistances are connected in parallel the total resistance can be found by first adding the reciprocals of all the resistances, and then inverting the result. Likewise, if reactances are connected in parallel, the total reactance is found by adding the reciprocals of all the reactances, and then inverting the result. For reactance, it is necessary to note the sign: a positive sign for inductive reactance and a negative sign for capacitive reactance.

When both resistance and reactance appear in a parallel circuit, the total resistance and total reactance must be found separately and then these totals must be combined according to the laws of a resistance and a reactance in parallel. Since this is relatively complicated, it is easier to deal with the *admittance* of a parallel circuit than with the impedance. The admittance is defined as the reciprocal of the impedance:

$$Y = \frac{1}{Z} \tag{27}$$

where Y = admittance in mhos,
     Z = impedance in ohms.

Since the admittance Y is the reciprocal of a phasor quantity, it will itself be a phasor and it is measured in mhos.

By substitution we find that Ohm's law can be written in terms of admittance thus:

$$I = EY \tag{28}$$

where I = total current from source,
     E = applied voltage.

We shall use a parallel RC circuit, shown in Figure 6-9, to illustrate the use of admittance. The essential step in using admittance is

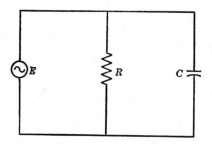

Fig. 6-9. Parallel RC circuit.

to take the reciprocal of the resistances and the reactances. The reciprocal of a resistance (G) is called a *conductance* and is found by:

$$G = \frac{1}{R} \tag{29}$$

where G = conductance in mhos,
     R = resistance in ohms.

The reciprocal of a reactance is called a "susceptance" and is found by:

$$B_C = \frac{1}{X_C} \tag{30}$$

where B_C = capacitive susceptance in mhos,
$\quad X_C$ = capacitive reactance in ohms.

The conductance is analogous to the resistance of an impedance, and the susceptance is analogous to the reactance of an impedance. The magnitude of the admittance then, is found by combining the conductance and the susceptance in the following manner:

$$|Y| = \sqrt{G^2 + B_C^2} \tag{31}$$

where Y = admittance in mhos,
$\quad G = 1/R$ = conductance in mhos,
$\quad B_C = 1/X_C$ = capacitive susceptance in mhos.

Similar to the case for impedance, the phase angle between the voltage and the current is found by:

$$\theta = \tan^{-1} \frac{B_C}{G} \tag{32}$$

The complete expression for the admittance, which contains the magnitude and the phase angle, is then given by:

$$Y = \sqrt{G^2 + B_C^2} \left| \tan^{-1} \frac{B_C}{G} \right. \tag{33}$$

As for the impedance, the admittance can also be written in the form:

$$Y = G + jB_C \tag{34}$$

A phasor diagram showing the current and voltage of the parallel RC circuit is shown in Figure 6-10(a). Figure 6-10(b) shows the

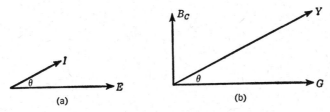

(a) (b)

Fig. 6-10. Diagrams for a parallel RC circuit: (a) vector diagram of current and voltage; (b) vector diagram of admittance.

vector representation of the admittance. Although this diagram is similar to that of Figure 6-4 for impedance, it should be noted that capacitive susceptance (B_C) is plotted upward, whereas capacitive reactance (X_C) is plotted downward. It is this difference which accounts for the use of the positive sign in Equation (34).

We have just seen that the use of admittance, for parallel circuits, is essentially a laborsaving device. The method consists of using the reciprocal quantities directly in Ohm's law rather than converting the reciprocal quantities to impedance and then using the impedance form of Ohm's law. It is important to note that, when an impedance is stated, the elements are effectively in series. When an admittance is stated, the elements are in parallel. In fact, if the impedance of a parallel circuit is found, this can be regarded as a series equivalent of the parallel circuit.

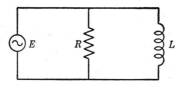

Fig. 6-11. Parallel RL circuit.

A parallel RL circuit is shown in Figure 6-11. If the voltage E is applied, the current flowing will be

$$I = EY \tag{35}$$

For the case of a resistance in parallel with an inductance, the magnitude of Y is given by

$$|Y| = \sqrt{G^2 + (-B_L)^2} \tag{36}$$

where Y = admittance of the circuit in mhos,
$G = 1/R$ = conductance in mhos,
$B_L = 1/X_L$ = inductive susceptance in mhos.

The phase angle between the voltage and current is given by

$$\theta = \tan^{-1}\frac{B_L}{G} \tag{37}$$

As a result of Equations (36) and (37), the complete expression for Y is

$$Y = \sqrt{G^2 + (-B_L)^2}\ \bigg/\!\tan^{-1}\frac{B_L}{G} \tag{38}$$

As before, the admittance Y may be written in the form:

$$Y = G - jB_L \qquad (39)$$

Figure 6-12(a) shows the phasor diagram of the current and voltage in the parallel RL circuit. Figure 6-12(b) depicts the phasor diagram of the admittance. It is noted that B_L is plotted downward,

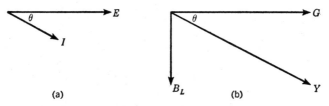

(a)   (b)

Fig. 6-12. Diagrams for a parallel RL circuit: (a) phasor diagram of current and voltage; (b) phasor diagram of admittance.

whereas X_L (in impedance) is plotted upward. This agrees with the negative sign preceding the j term in Equation (39).

In circuits that contain many elements in parallel the general procedure is to add all the conductances, add all the susceptances (paying attention to sign) and then find the admittance by using the equation:

$$Y = \sqrt{(G_1 + G_2 + G_3 \ldots)^2 + (B_{C_1} + B_{C_2} - B_{L_1} - B_{L_2} \ldots)^2}$$
$$\left| \tan^{-1} \frac{B_{C_1} + B_{C_2} - B_{L_1} - B_{L_2} \ldots}{G_1 + G_2 + G_3 \ldots} \right. \qquad (40)$$

If all the circuit elements are in parallel, the voltage across all the elements is the same. The total current flowing into the circuit consists of the *phasor* sum of the element currents. Again it is necessary to stress the fact that the currents must be added vectorially whenever susceptance appears in the circuit.

As in the series circuit, the power is all consumed in resistances and can be found by

$$P = I^2R = VI \cos \theta \qquad (41)$$

where θ = the admittance angle.

Resonance. In a circuit that contains both inductance and capacitance, the inductive reactance may cancel the capacitive reactance. When this occurs, the circuit is in *resonance*. Resonance may occur in series circuits or in parallel circuits.

If a series circuit contains R, L, and C, as shown in Figure 6-13, the impedance is given by

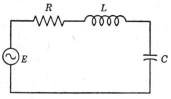

Fig. 6-13. *RLC* series circuit.

$$|Z| = \sqrt{R^2 + (X_L - X_C)^2} \quad (42)$$

If X_L is equal to X_C, then the reactive term in Equation (42) goes to zero, and the impedance for the resulting series resonance is

$$Z_r = \sqrt{R^2} = R \quad (43)$$

It is easily seen that for such a circuit the lowest value of impedance is experienced at resonance. If a circuit contains inductance and capacitance, resonance can be achieved by: (1) varying the inductance, (2) varying the capacitance, or (3) varying the frequency. In any case, the basic condition that must be met is that

$$X_L = X_C \quad (44)$$

If the inductance and capacitance are held constant, and the frequency is varied, the frequency at which resonance occurs is found by setting $X_L = X_C$ and solving for f.

$$X_L = X_C, \quad 2\pi f_r L = \frac{1}{2\pi f_r C}, \quad f_r = \frac{1}{2\pi\sqrt{LC}} \quad (45)$$

At a frequency slightly higher than f_r, X_L will be greater than X_C, and the circuit appears inductive. At a frequency lower than f_r, the X_C predominates and the circuit appears as a capacitive circuit. The variation of impedance, as f is varied, is shown in Figure 6-14. The

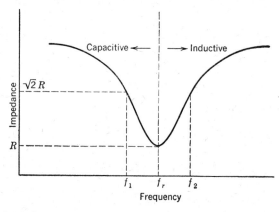

Fig. 6-14. Impedance versus frequency for an *RLC* series circuit.

capacitive and inductive regions are shown there, and it is seen that the lowest possible impedance is encountered at resonance.

The frequency-selective properties of a series resonant circuit are also shown by this figure. At the resonant frequency, and in its neighborhood, the circuit offers a low impedance. At any other frequencies the circuit offers a much higher impedance.

The selectiveness of a resonant circuit depends upon the sharpness of the peak. If the peak, such as in Figure 6-14, is very narrow the circuit will select only a narrow range of frequencies and reject the others. The parameter that measures the sharpness of the peak is the Q, and is defined by

$$Q = \frac{\text{resonant frequency}}{\text{frequency bandpass}} = \frac{f_r}{f_2 - f_1} \qquad (46)$$

The f_2 and f_1 of Equation (46), which specify the frequency bandpass, are those frequencies where the impedance curve is $\sqrt{2}$ times the minimum value of the curve. Here f_2 is the higher frequency and f_1 is the lower frequency; the bandpass is shown in Figure 6-14.

For the series resonant circuit, Q is also equal to

$$Q = \frac{X_{L_r}}{R} = \frac{X_{C_r}}{R} \qquad (47)$$

Although the parameter Q applies basically to the entire resonant circuit, many times the Q of an inductance alone is specified. In this case the Q is

$$Q = \frac{X_{L_{inductor}}}{R_L} \qquad (48)$$

where R_L = resistance of the inductor.

If an inductor whose Q is given is used in a resonant circuit with no additional resistance inserted, the Q of the coil closely approxi-

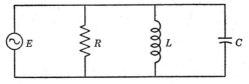

Fig. 6-15. Parallel RLC circuit.

mates the Q of the circuit no matter what resonant frequency is used.

If an inductance and a capacitance are connected in parallel, as in Figure 6-15, the phenomenon of *parallel* resonance may be experienced. Since it is a parallel circuit, we shall deal with admittance. The admittance is found by

$$|Y| = \sqrt{G^2 + (B_C - B_L)^2} \qquad (49)$$

When the capacitive susceptance B_C is equal to the inductive susceptance B_L, parallel resonance will occur and the admittance will be a minimum, equal to

$$Y_r = \sqrt{G^2} = G \qquad (50)$$

Since admittance is the reciprocal of impedance, we see that parallel resonance exhibits *maximum* impedance. This is opposite to the case of series resonance, where minimum impedance occurs. Resonance may

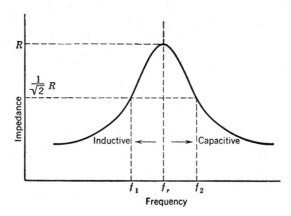

Fig. 6-16. Impedance function of a parallel *RLC* circuit.

be achieved by the three means stated for the series case. If frequency is varied and the inductance and capacitance contain no series resistance, then the resonant frequency will be given by Equation (45), which was stated for the series case.

Figure 6-16 shows the curve of impedance versus frequency for a parallel resonant circuit. As noted, the impedance is maximum at resonance. Note also that the circuit is inductive below resonance and capacitive above. This is reversed from the case of series resonance.

Also shown in Figure 6-16 are the frequency-rejection properties of a parallel resonant circuit. At resonance the circuit offers a high impedance, but offers a lower impedance to the frequency bands on either side. As in the series resonance, the measure of the rejection property is the Q. The Q is defined in Equation (46). For the parallel resonant circuit, the Q may also be found by the equation:

$$Q = \frac{R}{X_{L_r}} = \frac{R}{X_{C_r}} \qquad (51)$$

It should be noted that Equation (51) differs from Equation (47).

Voltage and Current Sources

Although all sources in an electric circuit are essentially power sources, they are called *voltage sources* or *current sources* depending upon whether they resemble an ideal voltage source or an ideal current source.

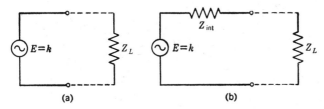

Fig. 6-17. Voltage sources: (a) ideal voltage source; (b) practical voltage source.

An ideal voltage generator is a power source that contains no internal series impedance. The concept of ideal stems from the fact that, no matter how much current is drawn, the voltage always remains the same. Figure 6-17(a) shows an ideal voltage source connected to a load; the voltage across the load will remain constant for any value of load impedance.

Any physical source of power necessarily has an internal impedance, so that a practical voltage generator appears as in Figure 6-17(b). The internal impedance is in series with the ideal generator. The voltage across the load now depends on the value of Z_L and is equal to

$$E_L = \frac{Z_L}{Z_{int} + Z_L} E_g \qquad (52)$$

As long as the internal impedance (Z_{int}) is small with respect to any load impedance (Z_L), the output voltage remains essentially constant with changing load. However, when Z_L is of the same order of magnitude as Z_{int}, the output voltage will change when the load impedance changes.

An ideal current generator is a power source that contains an infinite internal parallel impedance. It is ideal in the sense that it will force a constant current through a circuit no matter what the load impedance. An ideal current generator is shown in Figure 6-18(a), and the current through the load will remain constant for any load.

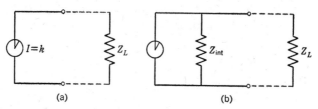

(a)   (b)

Fig. 6-18. Current sources: (a) ideal current source; (b) practical current source.

A practical current generator will have a finite impedance in parallel with the ideal current generator and is shown in Figure 6-18(b). The current through the load will now depend on the value of the load, and is given by

$$I_L = \frac{Z_{int}}{Z_{int} + Z_L} I \qquad (53)$$

As long as the load impedance (Z_L) is small compared with (Z_{int}), the load current will be essentially independent of the value of the load. If the value of Z_L is of the same order of magnitude as Z_{int}, however, the current will vary as the load impedance is changed.

Although the series representation is usually used for the voltage source, and the parallel representation for the current source, each can be converted from one form to the other. In conclusion, then, a voltage source is a power source that possesses a relatively low internal impedance, and a current source is a power source that has a relatively high internal impedance.

Before leaving the topic of "sources," it is useful to define *active* and *passive* circuits. An active circuit is one that contains an internal source. "Internal" here refers to being internal with respect to the input and output terminals defined for the circuit. Usually an active circuit implies that the internal source voltage (or current) is dependent upon other circuit quantities, and is not fixed. A passive circuit, of course, is one that does not contain such internal sources.

Methods of Circuit Analysis

In general, electric circuits are not of the simple series or parallel type. For these more complicated circuits general methods of analysis are required. There are two general methods of analyzing circuits; the mesh method and the nodal method; both are based on Kirchhoff's circuit laws. The mesh method is based on Kirchhoff's first law, which states that "the sum of all the voltage drops around a loop is equal to zero." The nodal method is based upon Kirchhoff's second law which states that "the sum of all the currents into a node is equal to zero." We shall treat the mesh method first.

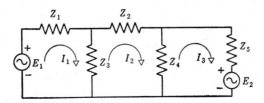

Fig. 6-19. Series-parallel circuit.

Figure 6-19 shows a series-parallel circuit which we shall use to illustrate the mesh method. The first step is to assume a separate positive direction of current for each mesh (or loop) of the circuit. The curved lines of Figure 6-19 show the assumed positive directions. It should be noted here that no attention need be paid to the direction of any current; the direction may be chosen in any manner. The second step consists of writing an equation for each of the meshes; this equation consists of setting the sum of the voltage drops in each mesh equal to zero. We write the equation by starting at one point in the mesh and summing the voltage drops until the starting point is reached. If any voltage rises (batteries, etc.) are encountered, they may be written as negative voltage drops, and transferred to the other side of the equation. The three mesh equations which result from the circuit of Figure 6-19 are

First loop: $\quad E_1 = I_1(Z_1 + Z_3) - I_2Z_3 + I_30$ $\qquad$ (54)

Second loop: $\quad 0 = -I_1Z_3 + I_2(Z_3 + Z_2 + Z_4) - I_3Z_4$ $\qquad$ (55)

Third loop: $\quad -E_2 = I_10 - I_2Z_4 + I_3(Z_4 + Z_5)$ $\qquad$ (56)

These three equations, taken together, represent the equations necessary to analyze the circuit. They are three simultaneous equations, and hence must be solved by either the method of elimination or the method of determinants.[1] We note that, from the mathematics viewpoint, the voltage sources on the left side of the equations are the constants, and the three currents I_1, I_2, and I_3 are the three unknowns. It is remembered that as many equations are required as there are unknowns. In the three equations we may say that the voltages are written in terms of the currents.

We may solve, then, for each of the three currents by the use of the method of determinants. The current I_1 is found to be

$$
I_1 = \frac{\begin{vmatrix} E_1 & -Z_3 & 0 \\ 0 & Z_2 + Z_3 + Z_4 & -Z_4 \\ -E_2 & -Z_4 & Z_4 + Z_5 \end{vmatrix}}{\begin{vmatrix} Z_1 + Z_3 & -Z_3 & 0 \\ -Z_3 & Z_2 + Z_3 + Z_4 & -Z_4 \\ 0 & -Z_4 & Z_4 + Z_5 \end{vmatrix}} \tag{57}
$$

In this manner the currents I_2 and I_3 can be determined. After the three currents have been evaluated, the current flowing in any element of the circuit can be found by noting the assumed currents on the diagram. For example, the current flowing through Z_3 is $I_2 - I_1$. The voltage across any element is found by multiplying the element current by the impedance.

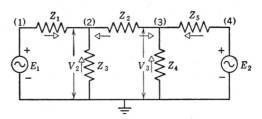

Fig. 6-20. Same circuit as that of Fig. 6-19.

We can now see why any positive direction may be chosen for the mesh currents; the currents will appear with a phase angle with respect to the assumed positive direction when evaluated.

The other general method of solving electric networks is called the *nodal* method. The object here is to write the currents of the circuit in terms of the voltages; thus the voltages are the unknowns in this

[1] The solution of simultaneous algebraic equations is treated in Appendix 1.

case. To illustrate the use of the nodal method we shall use the same circuit as was used for the mesh method. The circuit is shown repeated in Figure 6-20. Since we are here dealing with nodes it is necessary to define a node. A node is simply the junction of two or more wires. Further, a node is called an *independent node* if its voltage is not determined by an external source. In Figure 6-20 we see that there are five nodes: four of them are numbered and the fifth is the ground node. In the nodal method one node is always selected as the reference node, and we have chosen the grounded node of Figure 6-20.

In using the nodal method, as many nodal equations must be written as there are independent nodes. Consequently, after the reference node has been selected, it is necessary to determine which of the remaining nodes are independent. Referring to Figure 6-20 we note that nodes 1 and 4 are not independent since both are already determined by the voltage sources E_1 and E_2, respectively. Thus the two nodes which must be considered are nodes (2) and (3). Writing the equation for node 2, we set the sum of the currents into the node equal to zero (see arrows).

$$\frac{E_1 - V_2}{Z_1} - \frac{V_2}{Z_3} + \frac{V_3 - V_2}{Z_2} = 0$$

rearranging, we have

$$V_2\left(-\frac{1}{Z_3} - \frac{1}{Z_1} - \frac{1}{Z_2}\right) + V_3\left(\frac{1}{Z_3}\right) = \frac{-E_1}{Z_1} \tag{58}$$

Using the same process for node 3, the original and rearranged equations are

$$\frac{V_2 - V_3}{Z_2} - \frac{V_3}{Z_4} + \frac{V_4 - V_3}{Z_5} = 0$$

$$V_2\left(\frac{1}{Z_2}\right) + V_3\left(-\frac{1}{Z_4} - \frac{1}{Z_2} - \frac{1}{Z_5}\right) = -\frac{V_4}{Z_5} \tag{59}$$

Combining the equations for the two nodes, the two resulting simultaneous equations are

Node 2: $\quad -\dfrac{E_1}{Z_1} = V_2\left(-\dfrac{1}{Z_3} - \dfrac{1}{Z_1} - \dfrac{1}{Z_2}\right) + V_3\left(\dfrac{1}{Z_3}\right)$

$$\tag{60}$$

Node 3: $\quad -\dfrac{V_4}{Z_5} = V_2\left(\dfrac{1}{Z_2}\right) + V_3\left(-\dfrac{1}{Z_4} - \dfrac{1}{Z_2} - \dfrac{1}{Z_5}\right) = -\dfrac{V_4}{Z_5}$

It is seen that Equations (60) are two simultaneous equations in which the currents are written in terms of the voltages. Thus the voltages are the unknowns and the currents are essentially the constants. We can solve for both V_2 and V_3 by the use of determinants.

$$V_2 = \frac{\begin{vmatrix} -\dfrac{E_1}{Z_1} & \dfrac{1}{Z_3} \\[2ex] -\dfrac{V_4}{Z_5} & \left(-\dfrac{1}{Z_4} - \dfrac{1}{Z_2} - \dfrac{1}{Z_5}\right) \end{vmatrix}}{\begin{vmatrix} \left(-\dfrac{1}{Z_3} - \dfrac{1}{Z_1} - \dfrac{1}{Z_2}\right) & \dfrac{1}{Z_3} \\[2ex] \dfrac{1}{Z_2} & \left(-\dfrac{1}{Z_4} - \dfrac{1}{Z_2} - \dfrac{1}{Z}\right) \end{vmatrix}} \tag{61}$$

The value of V_3 can be found in an identical manner. After the node voltages are thus found the current in any element of the circuit can be evaluated by taking the difference in voltage across the element and dividing by the impedance.

It is important to recognize that the mesh method and the nodal method are different ways of performing the same task: analyzing a given electric network. We also note that, in the example used, three mesh equations were required whereas only two nodal equations were needed. This is often the case, and in such cases much labor can be saved by using the nodal method even though it may be less familiar, at first, than the method of meshes. The best method to use in any situation is determined by comparing the number of meshes to the number of independent nodes.

In conclusion let us stress the fact that the mesh and the nodal methods are the basic tools for solving any electric network.

Circuit Theorems

Many times in dealing with an electric network, we are interested, not in the entire network, but in some single part of it. It is often the case that we are interested mainly in what takes place at the load impedance or what may be called the *output* of a network. When this is the case, two circuit theorems, Thevenin's and Norton's, are valuable tools. The essence of both of these theorems is that they greatly simplify that portion of the circuit which is of lesser interest, and enable us to view the action on the output part directly.

Figure 6-21 illustrates the application of Thevenin's theorem. Let us assume that, in the circuit of Figure 6-21(a), we are interested only in the current flowing through the load resistance.

As shown in Figure 6-21(b), all the circuitry except the load resistance
has been simplified to a single generator and series impedance. No
matter how complicated the original circuit, it can be simplified in
this manner so that a single generator and series impedance form the

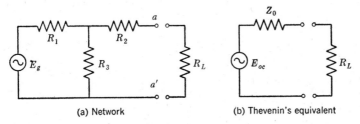

(a) Network   (b) Thevenin's equivalent

Fig. 6-21. An electrical network and its Thevenin equivalent.

equivalent of that part of the circuit connected to the output. Stated
formally, Thevenin's theorem specifies that "any linear circuit may
be replaced by an equivalent circuit consisting of a voltage generator
in series with an impedance."

The open-circuit voltage (E_{oc}) is found by determining the voltage
across points a-a' when R_L is disconnected. Since, with R_L disconnected, there is no drop across R_2, the voltage will be

$$E_{oc} = \frac{R_3 E_g}{R_1 + R_3} \qquad (62)$$

where E_{oc} = the open-circuit voltage of the Thevenin's equivalent.

The equivalent impedance is found by looking back from the
points a-a'. In this process all sources are assumed to be zero and are
replaced by their internal impedance: the Z_0 for Figure 6-21 with
the ideal voltage generator shorted, is thus

$$Z_0 = R_2 + \frac{R_1 R_3}{R_1 + R_3} \qquad (63)$$

where Z_0 = the series impedance of the Thevenin's equivalent.

In a like manner the Thevenin's equivalent circuit can be found
for any network as seen through two terminals. The procedure is to:
(1) find the open-circuit voltage (i.e., the voltage with the output
disconnected), and (2) determine the impedance looking back from
the output terminals, with all sources replaced by their internal
impedance—an ideal voltage source is short-circuited and an ideal
current source is open-circuited. If the concerned network has no

source in it, then the Thevenin's equivalent reduces to merely finding the equivalent impedance.

Norton's theorem deals with a similar situation. In this case, however, the resultant equivalent circuit contains a current generator instead of a voltage generator. Figure 6-22 shows the same circuit as that of Figure 6-21, but this time Norton's theorem is applied to form the equivalent circuit. Again the effect has been achieved that all the circuitry except the output has been simplified to a single current generator and a parallel impedance. The magnitude of the current generator in the equivalent circuit (I_{sc}) is found by short-

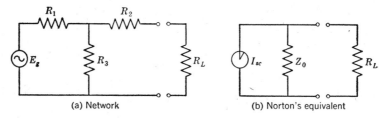

(a) Network   (b) Norton's equivalent

Fig. 6-22. An electrical network and its Norton equivalent.

circuiting the output terminals. The current generator is made equal to the current flowing through the short-circuited terminals. In Figure 6-22 this can be shown to be

$$I_{sc} = \frac{E_g R_3}{R_1 R_2 + R_1 R_3 + R_2 R_3} \tag{64}$$

The parallel impedance is found by exactly the same manner as for the Thevenin's case: the equivalent impedance is found by looking back from the output terminals. For doing this, all sources are short-circuited and replaced by their internal impedances. For Figure 6-22, the parallel impedance is, as before,

$$Z_0 = R_2 + \frac{R_1 R_3}{R_1 + R_3} \tag{65}$$

It seems clear that, since Thevenin's and Norton's equivalent circuits perform essentially the same function, we should be able to convert from one type of equivalent circuit to the other. This is the case, and Figure 6-23 shows the two types of circuit with the quantities to convert from one to the other.

It is interesting to relate the use of the theorems just described to that of the basic mesh and nodal methods. The mesh and nodal methods are used to analyze a circuit completely in the sense that every current and every voltage of the circuit is found. The circuit theorems, on the other hand, find their greatest use in the special case where only the current and voltage at an output are sought.

Thus far we have considered the two theorems in the application where a *known* electric network is simplified in order to be able to attack the output part of the circuit directly. There is still another aspect of the two theorems. This aspect concerns the taking of measurements to determine the electrical operation of an *unknown* network or electric device. Thevenin's theorem tells us that, for any two-terminal circuit or device, we can ascertain the electrical operation by making two measurements: (1) the open-circuit voltage, and

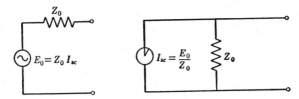

Fig. 6-23. Equivalence of Thevenin's and Norton's circuits.

(2) the input impedance with all sources replaced by their internal impedance. It is necessary, of course, that we be able to short-circuit (or open) any sources in the circuit or device.

In conclusion then, Thevenin's and Norton's theorems enable us to reduce any two-terminal network to a single generator and impedance. This can be done by manipulation of a known network or by taking measurements on an unknown network or device.

Black-Box Concept

Another situation that frequently occurs in electronics is that we are interested in both the input side and the output side. That is, we have a known generator on the input side and a known load on the output side, and we are interested in what output is produced by the generator. For this situation we wish to simplify the intervening network as much as possible in order to be able to view the generator and the load directly. We can regard the intervening network as a circuit having two input terminals and two output terminals. Thus this intervening circuit is called a four-terminal or a two-terminal pair circuit.

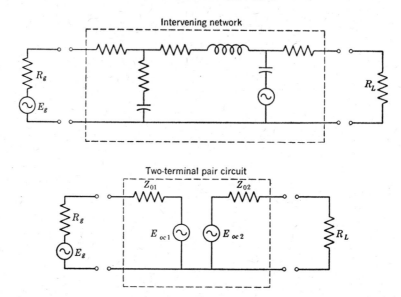

Fig. 6-24. Circuit showing use of two-terminal pair concept.

We have just seen, in the preceding section, that the circuit connected to a terminal pair can always be replaced by a single voltage generator and series impedance. It follows, then, that for the intervening circuit between a known source and a load, the circuit can be replaced by one Thevenin equivalent on the input side and another equivalent on the output side. Therefore, no matter how complex the intervening circuit, the resultant equivalent can consist of no more than two generators and two impedances. Figure 6-24 shows an example of the application of this concept. (Note that, since Thevenin's and Norton's theorems are defined only for linear circuits, all the material in this section also implies *linear* circuits.)

The concept of treating an intervening circuit in this manner is called the *black-box* concept because we need not know the actual circuit. We need only take two measurements on the input side and two on the output side to determine the action of the circuit. These measurements, as stated previously, are the open-circuit voltage and the impedance looking back into the circuit. For this reason, then, we can think of the intervening circuit as being in a black box whose contents we cannot examine directly.

This concept is most essential when dealing with electric devices. Any physical device most certainly has both input and output terminals. We can find the electrical operation of any device, then, by taking the measurements stated above and inserting the resulting equivalent circuit between the input source and the output load. This process can be regarded as a *method* for determining the electric equivalent circuit of a physical device such as a vacuum tube, a transistor, etc.

We can now apply this method to the derivation of an equivalent circuit for the transistor. By taking measurements on the input side—the open circuit voltage with a known voltage applied to the output, and the impedance looking into the transistor with the output short-circuited—we find the values for the Thevenin's equivalent of the in-

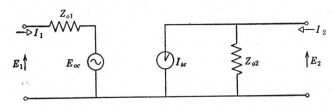

Fig. 6-25. General equivalent of a two-terminal circuit.

put side, as shown in Figure 6-24. We do the same thing for the output side, except that this time we shall use a Norton's equivalent instead of Thevenin's. It was found earlier that a Thevenin's circuit can always be replaced by a Norton's. The reason for doing this is that, for a transistor, the measurements are much more appropriate to determining the Norton's values on the output side.

Since we have a series circuit and a voltage generator on the left-hand side of Figure 6-25, it is logical to write a mesh equation for this side. The equation will be

$$E_1 = Z_{0_1}I_1 + E_{oc} \tag{66}$$

For the output side, the presence of the current generator and the fact that it is a parallel circuit suggests the use of a nodal equation. The equation for the output side is

$$I_2 = I_{sc} + \frac{E_2}{Z_{0_2}} \tag{67}$$

The two equations which describe the electrical operation of the circuit of Figure 6-25, then, are

$$E_1 = Z_{0_1}I_1 + E_{oc}, \quad I_2 = I_{sc} + \frac{E_2}{Z_{0_2}} \tag{68}$$

It was mentioned earlier that the circuit of Figure 6-25 can be used to represent *any* electric circuit or device that has two input terminals and two output terminals. Therefore, the two Equations (68) are valid for *any* two-terminal pair circuit or device, provided that the proper values for the generators and resistances are found.

Equations (68) are of little use yet because there are more unknowns than equations. From Equation (62) it will be remembered that the open-circuit voltage is always related to the driving voltage; in Equation (68) the driving voltage, for the input side E_{oc}, is equal to a constant times E_2. Similarly, the current generator on the output side is related to the driving current; therefore I_{sc} is equal to a constant times I_1, because I_1 is the driving current for the output side measurement. With these substitutions, Equations (68) can be written

$$E_1 = h_{11}I_1 + h_{12}E_2, \quad I_2 = h_{21}I_1 + h_{22}E_2 \qquad (69)$$

It is seen that $h_{12}E_2$ has replaced E_{oc} and $h_{21}I_1$ has replaced I_{sc}. It is also seen that we have simply relabeled Z_{0_1} and called it h_{11}; also, $1/Z_{0_2}$ has been called h_{22}. Equations (69), then, are exactly the same as Equations (68) with the above substitutions.

It is interesting to note why the symbol h was selected to represent the values of the circuit constants. It is remembered that one of the two equations is a mesh equation and the other is a nodal equation. Thus these two equations make use of both the mesh method and the nodal method. For this reason they can be thought of as hybrid equations. The symbol h then is simply the abbreviation for the word hybrid.

Referring to Equations (69), we note that we now have two simultaneous equations. The unknowns are I_1 and E_2, and the constants for the equations are E_1 and I_2. It is remembered that these equations were written for the equivalent circuit of Figure 6-25. We can now change the labels of that circuit to suit the symbols which appear in the equations. The equivalent circuit appears as shown in Figure 6-26. It is necessary to repeat that this equivalent circuit can be used

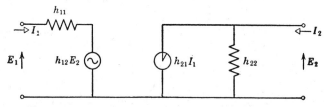

Fig. 6-26. Equivalent circuit in terms of h parameters.

to represent *any* electric circuit or device which has two input and two output terminals. However, for our purposes, we are interested in this circuit as the equivalent circuit of a transistor. This circuit will be used throughout this book to represent the electrical operation of the transistor. Thus we will be using the h parameters to describe the transistor operation.

Referring to Figure 6-26 it is seen that h_{11} is the input resistance seen when the output side is short-circuited, and h_{22} is the output conductance (reciprocal of resistance) when the input side is open-circuited. The factor h_{12} is a dimensionless constant and relates the open-circuit voltage of the input to the voltage appearing across the output; h_{21} is the constant factor that shows the current which appears in the output side when a current exists in the input side.

If we have a two-terminal pair circuit or device, such as a transistor, we can find the h parameters by taking the proper measurements. Looking at Equations (69), h_{11} may be measured by short-circuiting the output terminals (making $E_2 = 0$), applying a voltage E_1 to the input, and then measuring the resulting input current. Then h_{11} will be given by the ratio of the input voltage to the input current:

$$h_{11} = \frac{E_1}{I_1}\bigg|_{E_2=0} \tag{70}$$

In a similar manner, h_{21} is measured when $E_2 = 0$ by taking the ratio of the output current I_2 to the input current I_1.

$$h_{21} = \frac{I_2}{I_1}\bigg|_{E_2=0} \tag{71}$$

Values of h_{12} and h_{22} are measured when the input side is open-circuited ($I_1 = 0$) and a voltage is applied to the output. The equations for h_{12} and h_{22} are

$$h_{12} = \frac{E_1}{E_2}\bigg|_{I_1=0} \qquad h_{22} = \frac{I_2}{E_2}\bigg|_{I_1=0} \tag{72}$$

In conclusion, then, the black-box or two-terminal pair concept is essentially the concept of simplifying the intervening network between a source and a load. Additionally, from the standpoint of measurements, this concept is useful in finding the electric equivalent circuit of a physical device. We have here treated the equivalent circuit in terms of h parameters, but it should be noted that other parameters can be used. The h parameters were chosen because they are most appropriate for transistors.

The two-terminal pair concept is also the basis of the matrix treatment of electric networks. This treatment is beyond the scope of this book and will not be considered.

Maximum Power Transfer

Whenever two circuits are connected together, or a device is connected in an electric network, the concept of *maximum power transfer* becomes important. This concept has to do with matching the impedances of both circuits so that the maximum possible power is transferred from one circuit to the other.

When dealing with connected circuits we can think of the one circuit as being a source and the other circuit as being the load on that source. The source part of the circuit may be either an actual voltage or current source, discussed previously, or it may be the output terminals of any electric network. From Thevenin's and Norton's theorems we remember that the output terminals of any network can be represented by a single generator and impedance. Therefore, whether the source part is an actual generator or the output of a network, it can always be written as an ideal current generator in parallel with an internal impedance.[1] For the load part of the circuit, we may have a single load impedance or a complex network. In the case of the latter, we can always find the equivalent impedance which the network presents at the input terminals.

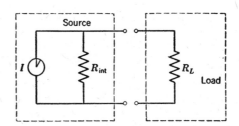

Fig. 6-27. Diagram showing two connected circuits in terms of a source and a load.

Figure 6-27 shows a diagram which depicts two connected circuits in terms of a source and a load where both the internal impedance and the load are resistive. As noted before, this diagram can be applied

[1] The use of Norton's theorem is selected instead of Thevenin's because the output of a transistor is essentially a current source.

to any two connected circuits, as well as to a generator connected to a single load.

In order to achieve the maximum amount of power in the load of Figure 6-27, *the load resistance must be equal to the internal resistance of the source.*

$$R_{int} = R_L \qquad\qquad (73)$$

If the load resistance is either higher or lower than the internal resistance of the source, the power achieved in the load resistor will

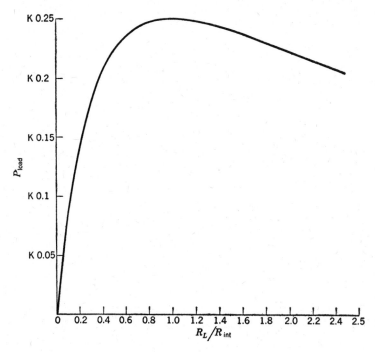

Fig. 6-28. Power output versus ratio of load-to-source resistance.

be less than for the case where Equation (73) is fulfilled. This is shown in the graph of Figure 6-28, where the load power is plotted versus the ratio of R_L to R_{int}. It is seen that maximum power occurs when the ratio is equal to one.

If the resistances are matched according to Equation (73), the power achieved in the load resistance is

$$P_L = \frac{I^2 R_L}{4} \qquad\qquad (74)$$

where P_L = power consumed in R_L,

I = current from the current generator.

This is the maximum power available from any source, whether it be an actual generator or the output of a network.

If the internal impedance of a source *is not a pure resistance*, then slightly different matching conditions are needed. For a source impedance containing a reactive element, the load impedance should be

$$Z_L = R - jX \quad \text{if} \quad Z_{\text{int}} = R + jX \qquad (75)$$

We note that the resistance of the load is equal to the resistance of the source, and that, additionally, the reactance of the load is equal to the reactance of the source. However, the reactance of the load is of *opposite* sign from that of the source. Hence, if source impedance is

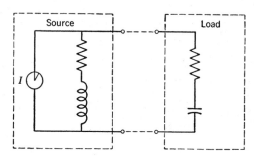

Fig. 6-29. Impedance matching if source is reactive.

inductive, the load impedance should contain a capacitance whose reactance is equal to that of the source inductive reactance. A source with an inductive reactance and consequent capacitive load is shown in Figure 6-29. If the source impedance were capacitive, then the load impedance would have to be inductive. The maximum power is transferred to the load, then, when Equation (75) is fulfilled.

Many times the source impedance is reactive, but it is not possible to make the load impedance matched by the use of Equation (75) because the load is restricted to a resistance. In this case the best solution is to make the *value* of the load resistance equal to the *magnitude* of the source impedance. This may be written

$$\sqrt{R_{\text{int}}^2 + X_{L_{\text{int}}}^2} = \sqrt{R_L^2} = R_L \qquad (76)$$

The conditions described above must be fulfilled if maximum power transfer is to be accomplished. In many cases, however, it is impractical or too costly to match the source to the load. In this case the closest match will have to suffice. We shall find that stage-to-stage matching is a prominent problem in the use of transistors

Frequency Response

In dealing with electronic circuits, one of the most important problems arising is the response of the circuits to signals of varying frequencies. If an amplifying electronic circuit, for example, is to reproduce faithfully a complex input signal, the circuit must amplify equally a variety of frequencies with sufficient accuracy to avoid distortion.

Electronic circuits generally consist of devices, such as vacuum tubes and transistors, and interstage networks. The interstage networks are necessary to provide the proper biases to the devices and to enable connection of one stage to another. The problem of frequency response exists in both the electronic devices and the interstage networks. The frequency response of the transistor will be taken up later; we will here consider the frequency response of circuits which are typically used as interstage networks.

Whenever a circuit contains a reactance, the action of that circuit will vary with frequency since the reactance itself is dependent upon frequency. Before going into a mathematical analysis, let us investigate the general effect of capacitors and inductors. Capacitive reactance, it is remembered, is inversely proportional to frequency. Therefore, as the frequency goes up, the X_C approaches zero. Figure

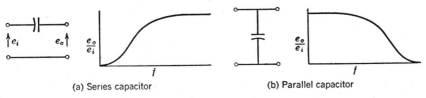

(a) Series capacitor   (b) Parallel capacitor

Fig. 6-30. Capacitor circuits and sketch showing frequency response.

6-30(a) shows a series capacitor connected between the input and output terminals of a simple circuit. Let us assume that a voltage (e_i) of constant magnitude but of varying frequency is applied to the input. We wish to know how the output voltage varies with frequency. Figure 6-30(a) shows a sketch of the variation in output voltage (e_o) with frequency. It is seen that, at zero frequency (direct current), the

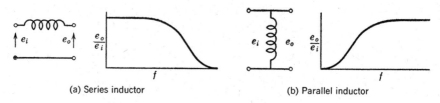

(a) Series inductor   (b) Parallel inductor

Fig. 6-31. Inductor circuits and sketch showing frequency response.

voltage all appears *across* X_C and hence e_o equals zero. As the frequency goes up, X_C decreases and less voltage drop appears across it. Finally, at a high enough frequency, X_C becomes effectively zero and all the input voltage appears at the output. Thus *a series capacitor tends to block the low frequencies* because of the high impedance it offers.

A parallel capacitor is shown in Figure 6-30(b). From the sketch shown it is seen that, *at high frequencies, the capacitor tends to short out the input signal.* At low frequencies, the X_C is high enough to exert no load on the signal.

Considering an inductance, it is remembered that X_L is proportional to frequency. Therefore, as shown in Figure 6-31(a), *a series inductance blocks the signal at high frequencies.* At low frequencies the inductive reactance causes little voltage drop and the entire input signal appears at the output.

A parallel inductor is shown in Figure 6-31(b). It is seen that a *parallel inductor tends to short out the input signal at the low frequencies.* For the high frequencies, the X_L is sufficiently large to cause no appreciable load on the signal.

These, then, are the general frequency relations for series and parallel reactances. We now proceed to show the analysis method used for interstage networks containing series and parallel reactances. The first circuit to be considered is shown in Figure 6-32(a). It is

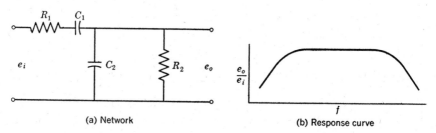

(a) Network   (b) Response curve

Fig. 6-32. An interstage network having a series and parallel capacitance: (a) network; (b) response curve.

noted that both a series and a parallel capacitor are included. From our previous survey, we know that the frequency response will drop off at the low end because of C_1 and at the high end because of C_2. Thus we expect to find the frequency response as sketched in Figure 6-32(b).

The established procedure for solving the frequency response problems of circuits, in general, is to break the problem up into the three frequency areas; low frequency, mid frequency, and high frequency. Thus in Figure 6-32(a), we do not solve the circuit as is, but

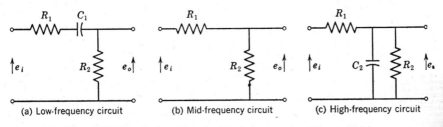

(a) Low-frequency circuit   (b) Mid-frequency circuit   (c) High-frequency circuit

Fig. 6-33. Equivalent circuits for the network of Fig. 6-31(a).

first alter the circuit appropriately for each of the three frequency areas. Figure 6-33 shows the resulting three circuits, derived from Figure 6-32. It is seen that, for low frequencies, the parallel capacitor is removed; for high frequencies the series capacitor is removed; and for the frequencies between these ranges both reactive elements are dropped.

We will begin the calculation of the frequency response by considering the mid-frequency circuit. For an input voltage (e_i), the output voltage (e_o) of Figure 6-33(b) will be given by

$$e_o = iR_2 = \frac{e_i}{R_1 + R_2} R_2 \qquad (77)$$

The ratio of e_o to e_i will then be

$$\frac{e_o}{e_i} = \frac{R_2}{R_1 + R_2} \qquad (78)$$

This is the maximum response available from the circuit of Figure 6-32.

For the low-frequency circuit of Figure 6-33(a), the e_o will be given by

$$e_o = iR_2 = \frac{e_i R_2}{\sqrt{(R_1 + R_2)^2 + \left(\frac{1}{\omega C_1}\right)^2}} \qquad (79)$$

The ratio of e_o to e_i is then

$$\frac{e_o}{e_i} = \frac{R_2}{\sqrt{(R_1 + R_2)^2 + (1/\omega C_1)^2}} \tag{80}$$

It is seen that, as the frequency decreases ($\omega \to 0$), the response of Equation (80) drops because the denominator is getting larger. Thus the low frequency portion of the sketch in Figure 6-32(b) is verified.

Considering the high-frequency circuit of Figure 6-33(c), the output voltage will be

$$e_o = i \left| \frac{-jR_2/\omega C_2}{R_2 - j/\omega C_2} \right| = \frac{e_i R_2}{\sqrt{(R_1 R_2 \omega C_2)^2 + (R_1 + R_2)^2}} \tag{81}$$

Then the ratio e_o of e_i will be

$$\frac{e_o}{e_i} = \frac{R_2}{\sqrt{(R_1 R_2 \omega C_2)^2 + (R_1 + R_2)^2}} \tag{82}$$

From Equation (82) it is seen that, as the frequency increases ($\omega \to \infty$) the response drops because of the growing denominator. Thus the high-frequency sketch of Figure 6-32(b) is verified.

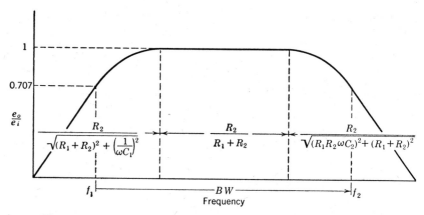

Fig. 6-34. Frequency response curve showing division into three areas.

Figure 6-34 shows the entire frequency response curve with the proper equations shown for each area.

When dealing with circuits in which the response drops at either the low frequencies or the high frequencies, or both, it is necessary to specify over what range the circuit is usable. The *half-power points* of the circuit are used to define that frequency range over which the response is acceptable. The half-power point is defined as "that point at which the power delivered to the load drops to one-half the maximum value." Since power is proportional to the square of voltage, the half-power point corresponds to that point where the voltage has dropped to $1/\sqrt{2}$ of the maximum value.

From Figure 6-34 it is seen that the maximum voltage (hence maximum power) occurs in the mid-frequency range. Therefore we

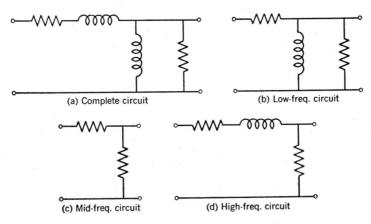

(a) Complete circuit   (b) Low-freq. circuit

(c) Mid-freq. circuit   (d) High-freq. circuit

Fig. 6-35. An interstage network having series and parallel inductances.

can find the half-power points by proceeding along the curve, on both sides of the maximum, until the e_o/e_i ratio has dropped to $1/\sqrt{2}$ of its mid-frequency value. The low and the high half-power points are shown in Figure 6-34 as f_1 and f_2, respectively. The frequency range between f_1 and f_2, for any frequency-dependent circuit, is defined as the *bandwidth*.

$$BW = f_2 - f_1 \tag{83}$$

where BW = bandwidth in cycles per second.

The frequency response of the series-parallel inductance circuit of Figure 6-35(a) will be considered next. The reduced circuits that apply to each frequency range are shown in part (b) of this figure. Note that here it is the parallel inductance that causes the low-frequency drop-off, and the series inductance decreases the high-frequency response.

Without doing the intermediate steps, the response curve and the equations which apply to each region are shown in Figure 6-36. The equations specify the ratio of e_o/e_i for the concerned region. The half-power points may again be found by determining where the response curve has dropped to $1/\sqrt{2}$ of the maximum value. The consequent bandwidth is shown on the figure.

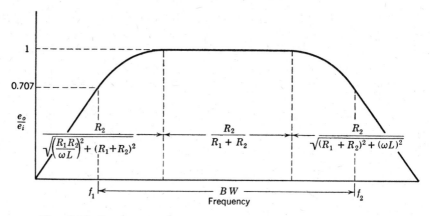

Fig. 6-36. Frequency response curve showing division into three areas.

Although the response curves of Figures 6-34 and 6-36 are typical of the ones encountered, the presence of both capacitors and inductors may cause resonance to occur at some frequency. This will result in the response curve having a peak at the resonant frequency. If such circuits are encountered, the basic ideas used in the foregoing paragraphs will serve to find the response curve. Again the solution is found by dividing the problem into the three frequency areas. The difference is, that in the area containing the resonance peak, the equation will be a corresponding resonance equation rather that the more simple equations given above.

Transformers

The last topic to be considered in this electrical review is the transformer. This device, very important to electronic circuits, consists of two inductances (coils of wire) which are physically adjacent to each other. When an alternating voltage is applied to the one coil, the resulting current induces a voltage in the other coil. The amount of voltage thus induced depends upon the physical construction and the number of wire turns on each coil.

The transformer is used to transform voltages, currents, or impedances to a higher or lower level, and to isolate direct and alternating currents. It should be noted that no voltage is induced if a direct voltage is applied to a coil.

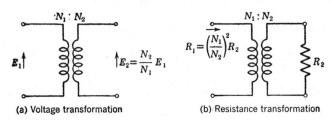

(a) Voltage transformation   (b) Resistance transformation

Fig. 6-37. Action of an ideal transformer: (a) voltage transformation; (b) resistance transformation.

We will consider here only the *ideal* transformer; that is, a transformer in which there are no resistances. As a result, this transformer has no losses, and the power in is equal to the power out. The symbol for an ideal transformer is shown in Figure 6-37(a). If an alternating voltage E_1 is applied to the primary side, the voltage on the output side will be

$$E_2 = \frac{N_2}{N_1} E_1 \tag{84}$$

where E_2 = voltage on second side,
N_2 = number of turns on secondary,
N_1 = number of turns on primary.

If a load is attached to the secondary side, the primary current (I_1) will cause a secondary current equal to

$$I_2 = \frac{N_1}{N_2} I_1 \tag{85}$$

where I_2 = current in secondary and through the load.

One of the most important uses of the transformer in electronic circuits lies in impedance matching. If a resistance R_2 is connected to the secondary, the load *appearing on the primary side* will be

$$R_1 = \left(\frac{N_1}{N_2}\right)^2 R_2 \tag{86}$$

Therefore, if the actual resistance load of a circuit is of an undesirable value, a transformer may be used, as shown in Figure 6-37(b), to transform the resistance to a suitable value. When meeting this situation in a circuit, the analysis procedure is to find the transformed resistance and use this as the load on the circuit.

Problems

1. Define the ampere and explain which particle or particles carry current.
2. What is voltage and how does it produce current flow?
3. What is power? (Explain in terms of current and voltage.)
4. What are resistance, capacitance, and inductance, and explain how they perform differently in a-c and d-c circuits?
5. Explain Ohm's law and how it functions with respect to a-c and d-c circuits.
6. How does inductive and capacitive reactance differ from resistance?
7. What is the definition of a series circuit?
8. What is the definition of a parallel circuit?
9. What is impedance? (Explain with respect to resistance and reactance.)
10. What does a phasor diagram of current and voltage show about an electric circuit?
11. How is admittance related to impedance?
12. How are conductance and susceptance related to resistance and reactance?
13. Define resonance of an electric circuit.
14. What is meant by the Q of a circuit?
15. Describe an ideal voltage source. How does a practical voltage source differ?
16. Describe an ideal current source. How does a practical current source differ?

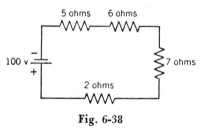

Fig. 6-38

17. What is the voltage drop across each resistor of the circuit of Figure 6-38 and what is the power consumed by each resistor?
18. What is the current through each branch of the circuit of Figure 6-39 and what power is consumed by each branch?

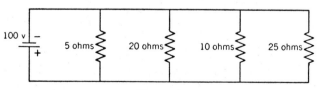

Fig. 6-39

19. What is the total resistance to the flow of current in circuits of Figures 6-38 and 6-39?

20. What are the current, voltage, and power for each resistor of the circuit of Figure 6-40? What is the total current drawn from the 100 v battery?

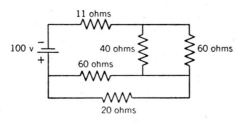

Fig. 6-40

21. There is a set of resistors connected as shown in Figure 6-41. It is desired to know what proportion of the input voltage appears across the 3 K resistor. This is a simulated d-c biasing circuit used in transistor circuits. (Hint: Use nodal method.)

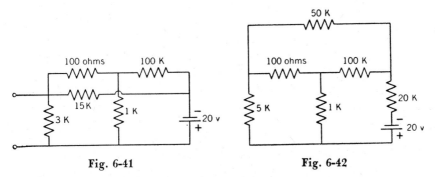

Fig. 6-41   **Fig. 6-42**

22. In Figure 6-42 is shown another transistor biasing circuit. What is the current flowing through the 100 ohm resistor? (Hint: Use mesh method.)

23. What is the Thevenin equivalent of the circuits shown in Figure 6-43?

24. What is the Norton equivalent of the circuit shown in Figure 6-43?

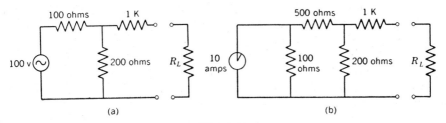

(a)   (b)

Fig. 6-43

25. Find the hybrid equivalent circuit of the four-terminal devices shown in Figure 6-44.

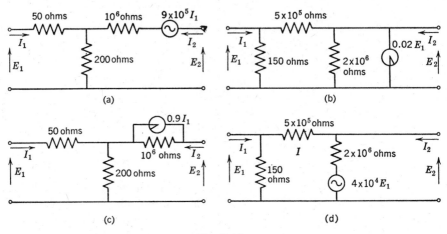

Fig. 6-44

26. What load resistance R_L should be used in the circuits of Figure 6-43 to obtain maximum power transfer to the load?

27. Determine the upper and lower half-power frequencies for the circuit shown in Figure 6-45.

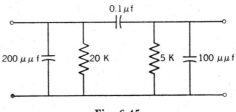

Fig. 6-45

7

The Transistor as a Circuit Element

Thus far, in dealing with transistors, we have concentrated on understanding the physical operation. In Chapter 4 the basic operation of the junction was described. We shall now begin to study the circuit aspects of the transistor; i.e., the transistor as an electric device.

In this chapter emphasis will be placed on the *methods* by which the transistor is analyzed as a circuit element. We shall find that the circuitry methods for the transistor are similar, in some respects, to those for vacuum tubes. Therefore the material of this chapter will seem familiar to those readers proficient in vacuum tube theory. Nevertheless, it is necessary to re-investigate the fundamental methods as applied to transistors.

The first circuitry method considered is the *method of graphical analysis*. After the philosophy and basis of this method is explained, the simple amplifier of Chapter 4 will be analyzed as a circuit element. Following this the *method of equivalent circuits* is treated, and again the simple amplifier is used to illustrate the use of the method.

Method of Graphical Analysis

When dealing with its circuit aspects, the first fact to be noted about a transistor is that it is an *active* device. In the previous chapter on electrical review, an active electric circuit was defined as a circuit that has an internal power source. We can view the transistor as an active circuit element in this way: when a signal is applied to the input, an internal (and amplified) voltage causes an enlarged signal in the output. Thus it is seen that the active property of the transistor is the method of specifying amplification in a circuit.

The second fact to be noted about a transistor is that it is a *biased* active device. Somewhat like the vacuum tube, bias currents must be applied to the transistor in order to operate it as a useful device. It is usually the case that bias batteries (or bias circuitry) are applied to both the input and the output sides of the transistor circuit; however, in some cases the input side is left unbiased.

In order to completely specify the action of a transistor in a circuit then, we must know its action about any and every bias point. The most convenient way of specifying this action is to find the graphical characteristics of the transistor. If we have the characteristics of both the input and the output side we then know the circuit action of the transistor at any and all bias points. One can conclude that the only way to specify the complete electric action of a biased active device is to specify the input and output characteristics.

Junction transistor characteristics. We shall illustrate the use of characteristics by considering the grounded-base connection. For this connection the output side is the collector, as noted in Chapter 4. The output characteristics then will consist of collector current (I_C) plotted versus collector voltage (V_C). Since the emitter is the input for the grounded-base connection, the collector characteristics will

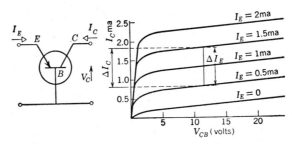

Fig. 7-1. Collector curves for grounded-base junction transistor.

be plotted with emitter current (I_E) as the parameter. The collector curves for a junction transistor along with the symbolic circuit diagram are shown in Figure 7-1. Along any one curve on this graph the input (emitter) current is constant. This series of curves tells us what emitter current must exist to achieve any combination of V_C and I_C. It is noted that these curves are very linear, and practically parallel to the V_C axis. This leads to a very important observation:

the collector current, for constant emitter current does not change appreciably with large changes in collector voltage.

It is interesting to note the reason for not selecting emitter voltage (V_E) as the parameter for the collector characteristics. If the V_C-I_C characteristics were plotted versus V_E they would appear distinctly non-linear. The reason for this is that the input resistance is not linear; i.e., its value changes as the input current increases or decreases. It is for this reason that transistor collector characteristics are always plotted by holding the input *current* constant. As the curves suggest, the characteristics of Figure 7-1 are measured by varying the collector voltage and then adjusting the emitter current so as to keep it constant for any particular curve. In conclusion then, the curves of Figure 7-1 are the output characteristics for a grounded base junction transistor. They give us information only about the transistor; there is no circuitry added thus far.

The current gain (α) of a transistor is determined by the straight line shown in Figure 7-1. As defined in Chapter 4, the current gain is:

$$\alpha = -\frac{\Delta I_C}{\Delta I_E} \tag{1}$$

If, in Figure 7-1, we read the change in I_C and in I_E across the short line, then the α is determined by Equation (1), and it is seen to be .960/1.00. A word of caution is necessary here; the current gain (α) is: (1) a parameter of only the transistor, independent of circuitry, and (2) is valid only for the grounded base connection. Later we shall be dealing with the current gains of various circuits; those should not be confused with α.

The other set of characteristics needed to specify the electrical action is the input set. For the grounded base case they will be a plot of emitter current (I_E) versus emitter voltage (V_E). For this case collector current (I_C) is the variable. The emitter characteristics for a junction transistor are shown in Figure 7-2.

There are two things worthy of notice in these characteristics: (1) the fact that the curves do not continue into the origin and (2) the fact that the $I_C = 0$ curve lies in the negative V_E, I_E region. The reason that the curves do not continue to the origin lies with the fact that variation of collector voltage hardly affects emitter current. It is noted that the curves of Figure 7-2 are measured by first varying the emitter voltage and then adjusting the collector voltage to keep I_C constant. The shortness of the curves of Figure 7-2 show that, as the

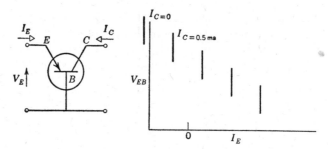

Fig. 7-2. Emitter curves for grounded-base junction transistor.

collector voltage is adjusted over its whole range, the emitter voltage can be changed only slightly if I_C is to remain constant. Thus this reaffirms the earlier statement about the nonvariation of collector current with variation of collector voltage. The $I_C = 0$ curve lying in the negative region appears reasonable when it is remembered that the emitter junction is biased in the forward direction. One apparent way to get the $I_C = 0$ curve would be to open the collector side, making $I_C = 0$. However, this would result in no transistor action since, from Chapter 4, it will be remembered that reverse bias on the collector is essential. Therefore, I_C must be brought to zero by adjusting the emitter voltage with the collector connected. To achieve zero collector current the normally forward bias of the emitter must actually be reversed. We will see later that this does not result in any unusual action on the part of the transistor.

Amplifier illustration. Having the characteristics which specify completely the transistor as a circuit element we can now illustrate the use of these characteristics. For this purpose we will use the same simple amplifier circuit which was used in Chapter 4 to explain the physical action. Figure 7-3 shows the basic grounded base amplifier

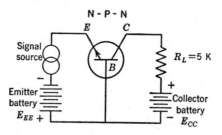

Fig. 7-3. Circuit showing basic biasing method of grounded-base amplifier.

circuit and is the same amplifier as in Figure 4-7. The method of biasing shown in Figure 7-3, in which the bias battery is connected directly in series with the electrode, is the simplest and the most direct. Later we shall consider other more elaborate biasing methods. As in the circuit discussed in Chapter 4, the emitter battery provides forward bias for the emitter junction and the collector battery provides reverse bias for the collector junction.

Since, for both vacuum tubes and transistors, the output circuit is usually the more important, we shall consider the output side first. When using the characteristics to analyze any biased active device, we

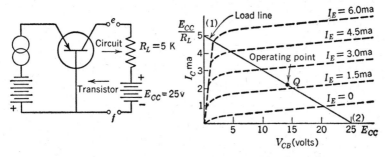

Fig. 7-4. Use of characteristics on output side of transistor.

must in effect also find the graph of the circuit to which the device is attached. Our object then is to find the graph of the output circuit to which the output side of the transistor is attached. Thus in Figure 7-4 we wish to find the I_C-V_C graph of the circuit to the right of points e-f. We get this by taking the limit points; when the circuit is short-circuited and when it is open-circuited. If e is short-circuited to f, the voltage across e-f is zero and the current flowing is

$$I = \frac{E_{CC}}{R_L} = \frac{25}{5000} = 5 \text{ ma} \tag{2}$$

This results in point (1) of Figure 7-4(b). When e-f is open-circuited the current is zero, and $V_C = E_{CC}$, resulting in point (2). The graph of the *circuit*, then is the straight line connected between the two points. This is the "load line" for the circuit shown. Since the circuit to the right of e-f is connected to the transistor to the left, we in effect have to achieve a graphical solution of the two conditions. Thus we superimpose the load line on the characteristics, and have as a result a sort of simultaneous graphical solution.

It is quite profitable, whenever using characteristics and load lines, to consider them in the terms just described. The following summarizes the method: (1) momentarily break the circuit so that the device with the characteristics appear on one side and the attached circuitry appears on the other side; (2) find the graph of the attached circuitry; (3) superimpose the circuitry graph on the characteristics.

We have yet to determine where the operating point is on the load line. This will be determined by the value of I_E, which is dependent on the emitter bias. Let us assume that the emitter battery causes an I_E of 2.0 ma. The operating point will then appear at the intersection of the $I_E = 2.0$ ma curve and the load line as shown in Figure 7-4.

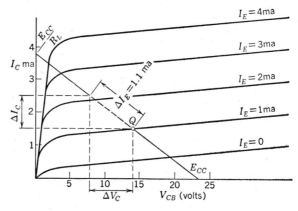

Fig. 7-5. Output characteristics showing basic amplifier action.

Using the output characteristics of Figure 7-5, we can now view the circuit operation of the basic amplifier. In Chapter 4 an input signal was assumed to cause a signal current of 1.1 ma. Electrically this means that the signal has caused the transistor to follow the dotted path of the load line in Figure 7-5. It is seen that the dotted path covers a length corresponding to $I_E = 1.1$ ma. Reading the change in collector current along the vertical axis, we see that the change is $\Delta I_C = 2.5 - 1.5 = 1.0$ milliampere. Reading the change in collector voltage, we find it to be $14 - 8 = 6$ volts. Therefore, using $P = VI$, the power output is 6 milliwatts, which corresponds with the result of Chapter 4. This, then, is the electrical operation which was described physically in terms of electrons and holes in Chapter 4.

Although it is usually sufficient to consider only the output characteristics and load line, the input characteristics may be treated in the same manner. Again the essential idea is to find the graph of the circuitry attached to the input (emitter) side, and superimpose this graph on the emitter characteristics. Since we may consider the signal source to be a pure voltage generator in series with an internal resistance, the input circuitry consists of a bias battery, a resistance, and a voltage source. The input load line, then, will be similar to that for the output side. The voltage generator of the signal source, however, will serve to *move the load line* along the V_E axis. This movement corresponds to the voltage applied by the voltage source. It is in this respect—the presence of the signal source—that the input char-

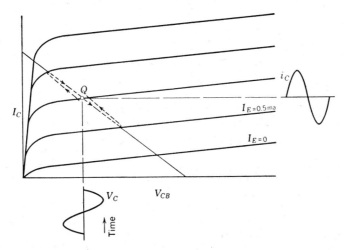

Fig. 7-6. Output characteristics showing sine-wave signal applied.

acteristic analysis differs from the output analysis. Thus, using both the input and the output characteristic method, the entire electrical operation of the transistor can be exhibited graphically.

It has been stated that usually the output characteristics alone have to be considered. This occurs because the appropriate signal source for a transistor is a *current* source rather than a voltage source; i.e., the source should exhibit a very high resistance compared with the transistor input resistance. If the current source is used, then, the excursion in terms of input current is known, and the input characteristics analysis does not have to be used.

Before leaving the discussion of the basic amplifier, it is useful to describe the output characteristic analysis when an a-c sine wave signal is applied. This is simply an extension of the principles just described and is shown in Figure 7-6.

If a current source is supplying a sine wave signal, the transistor will follow the dashed path on the load line of Figure 7-6. This operation results in a variation of collector current I_C shown to the right of Figure 7-6. With this collector alternating current flowing through the load resistor, an alternating voltage will be developed across the load resistor. This voltage V_C can be read directly from the characteristics, and is shown in Figure 7-6.

When considering a-c amplifiers, we are mainly interested in the operation just described. That is, the operation *about* the bias point is of chief interest. Although the load resistor will have a direct voltage due to the bias current, we would be interested mainly in the alternating voltage shown as V_C in Figure 7-6. For the a-c amplifiers then, after the bias point is established, we pay little attention to it, and concern ourselves with the operation *around* the bias point.

Other transistor characteristics. The fundamental methods described in the previous section apply whenever the method of graphical analysis is used. However, if a grounded emitter connection is used instead of a grounded base the transistor characteristics will be somewhat different. Also, the characteristics of the point contact type transistors differ sufficiently from those of the junction type to warrant attention here.

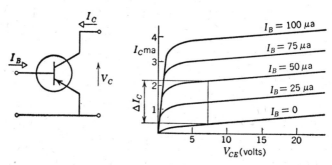

Fig. 7-7. Collector curves for grounded-emitter junction transistor.

If the transistor is operated in the grounded emitter connection the output characteristics appear as in Figure 7-7. Although these curves look similar to those of Figure 7-1 (grounded base), there are two important differences. First, the base current (I_B) is now the input variable instead of I_E. This results from the fact that the signal is now applied to the base. Second, the collector voltage is measured from collector to emitter (V_{CE}). The voltage V_{CE} differs only slightly in value from V_{CB}, so that for most purposes they can be regarded as identical. The load line is constructed on this graph in the identical manner to that for the grounded base.

As a result of I_B being the input current, rather than I_E, the short circuit current gain of the grounded emitter transistor will be

$$\beta = \frac{\Delta I_C}{\Delta I_B} \qquad (2a)$$

As read from Figure 7-7, the current gain is $\beta = 37$, and is greater than one. This is related to α, the current gain of the grounded base, by the equation:

$$\beta = \frac{\alpha}{1 - \alpha} \qquad (2b)$$

This relation was pointed out in Chapter 4, and we see that the current gain of the grounded emitter junction transistor is always greater than that of the grouned base. The current gain β is a parameter of only the transistor, independent of circuitry, and is valid only for the grounded emitter connection.

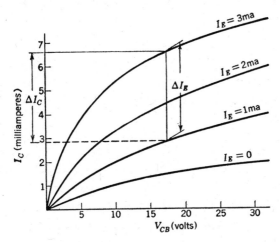

Fig. 7-8. Point contact collector characteristics for grounded-base connection.

The characteristic curves for a point contact transistor in the grounded-base configuration are shown in Figure 7-8 and 7-9. We can gain some insight into the difference in electrical operation between point contact and junction type transistors by comparing Figures 7-8 and 7-9 with Figures 7-1 and 7-2, respectively. We note that for the collector characteristics the point contact curves are not so straight as the junction curves. This means that, for constant emitter current, the collector does vary appreciably with collector voltage. Also, we see that for the grounded-base point contact transistor, the current gain (α) is greater than 1. It is remembered that α is always less than 1 for the conventional junction transistor.

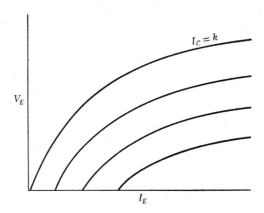

Fig. 7-9. Point contact emitter characteristics for grounded-base connections.

In comparing Figure 7-9 to Figure 7-2, we note that the input characteristics do continue to the origin for the point contact. This again is caused by the fact that, for the point contact, variation of collector voltage does affect emitter current if collector current is held constant.

When using a point contact transistor in a circuit, the method of analysis, of course, is identical to the method described for the junction type. Although the method is identical, the electrical results are somewhat different because of the slightly different properties.

Method of Equivalent Circuits

When considering active devices such as a transistor we are usually interested in the amplification, and in getting the maximum amplification under the prescribed conditions. In general, this demands that we analyze the transistor as an element in an electric network. It is for this purpose that *equivalent circuits* of active devices are required.

In its simplest light, we may consider an equivalent circuit (of a physical device) as a combination of electric elements which, when given the proper values, produces the identical electrical operation in a circuit that the physical element does. Our first object, then, is to find that combination of electric elements which simulate a transistor. Before doing this, however, it is necessary to deal with the subject of bias.

In a biased active device, such as the transistor, the equivalent circuit is always constructed without regard to the bias; i.e., the bias circuit and conditions are left out of the equivalent circuit. The reason for this is quite obvious. Within the operating limits of the transistor, the method of operation is always the same, regardless of bias. Although the operation is identical the *values* of the equivalent circuit elements may change with bias.

Since the values of the equivalent circuit do change with bias, an equivalent circuit must necessarily represent the transistor only for a small variation *about* the operating point. In other words, only when small signals are applied does the equivalent circuit accurately represent the transistor. The change in circuit element value with bias is what specifies that the transistor, like a vacuum tube, is a nonlinear device.

When considering the relation of the equivalent circuit to the characteristics, we can consider the circuit as representing the operation *in a region of a particular operating point*. Now it is seen why we called the characteristics the *complete* specifications of the electrical action; for by use of the characteristics, the operation is depicted at *any* operating point and for any variation about that point. The equivalent circuit, on the other hand, depicts the operation only in the region of a specified bias point. With these restrictions it should not be implied that the equivalent circuit is less useful than the characteristics, for this is certainly not the case. It is our purpose here merely to stress the relationship between the two methods. We shall later specify when and where the two methods are used.

Grounded-base equivalent circuit. We return then to the problem of finding that combination of electric elements which, when connected in a circuit, acts exactly as does the transistor when connected in the same circuit. Since the transistor can be connected in either of three configurations, we have first to decide which connection to use. It has been the practice in the past to use the grounded-base connection as the *reference* connection for the transistor.

For this reason we shall begin with the equivalent circuit of the grounded-base connection. If the circuit for another connection is desired, we can derive it from the grounded-base one.

In finding the equivalent circuit, we might logically start by considering the physics of the device. We know, for example, that the transistor consists of three areas of bulk material (the emitter, the collector, and the base) with the two junctions between these areas. We can represent the emitter and the collector junctions by equivalent resistances, and, in addition, add a base resistance to represent the effective resistance of the base region. Note that the emitter and collector *junctions* are much more influential in the electrical operation

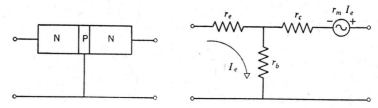

Fig. 7-10. An equivalent circuit which closely resembles the physical construction.

than the properties of the respective emitter and collector bulk materials, while the effective resistance of the base region is determined mainly by the bulk material. Thus we would start with a base resistance, an emitter resistance, and a collector resistance connected in a manner similar to the actual construction of the transistor. In addition, knowing that the transistor is capable of amplification, we are aware that an internal source of voltage has to appear in the circuit. A next logical step would be to place the transistor in a circuit and take measurements. From such measurements it could be ascertained that the equivalent circuit of Figure 7-10 is a valid representation of the electrical operation of the transistor. In this figure the physical construction is also shown to illustrate the similarity between the construction and the equivalent circuit.

In this equivalent circuit, the resistances represent the respective junctions of the physical transistor. The voltage source ($r_m I_e$) is the amplification element. When a voltage is applied to the input a current flows through r_e of value I_e. When this occurs a voltage $r_m I_e$ appears in the source on the output side. Since r_m is very large compared with both r_e and r_b, the voltage on the output is always greater than the applied voltage. Now r_m can be regarded as the mutual resistance that relates the input to the output, or as a forward transfer function. In the last sense r_m plays a role similar to the μ of a vacuum tube.

It is very important to note that, in the circuit of Figure 7-10, the internal voltage source may be placed in other positions. It may be placed in either the r_b branch or the r_e branch. In each case, of course, the value of the voltage source would have to be adjusted accordingly. Such changes can be made by using basic circuit tools such as mesh equations.

Although the equivalent circuit of Figure 7-10 is a valid representation of the electrical operation of the transistor, and it closely resembles the actual physical construction, there are other types of circuits which lend themselves to easier circuit analysis. It is convenient to consider the various *types* of equivalent circuits in terms of the parameters by which the circuits are defined. The parameters, in turn, are determined by the basic circuit method used to analyze the circuit. For example, if mesh equations are used, the voltages are always written in terms of the currents; the currents are the unknowns. The parameters, in this case, are impedances (Z's) of which resistance is the real part. If nodal equations are used, the currents are written in terms of the voltages; the voltages are the unknowns. For this case the parameters are admittances (Y's), since an admittance multiplied by a voltage results in a current. In a particular situation we may combine the nodal and the mesh method. We may write a mesh equation for the input side of a circuit, and a nodal equation for the output side. In this case the parameters will consist of both impedances and admittances. Since impedances of both types are present, such parameters are called hybrid parameters, and it is these in which we shall be most interested. The reason for choosing the hybrid parameters is twofold: (1) the circuit analysis involves less complicated formulas, and (2) the parameters are much easier to measure on an actual transistor.

We shall not stop here to give a mathematical derivation of the conversion from the circuit of Figure 7-10 to an h parameter circuit. We are interested here in what information the equivalent circuit gives us and how it is used. The reader is referred to the equivalent circuit material in the electrical review.

The equivalent circuit which makes use of the h parameters is shown in Figure 7-11. Although this circuit is perfectly general and will depict any electric circuit, we can make it represent the transistor by simply substituting the right values for the four parameters h_{11}, h_{12}, h_{21}, and h_{22}. We note that this equivalent is made up by writing a mesh equation for the input side and a nodal equation for the output side. Therefore h_{11} is a resistance and h_{22} is a conductance; i.e., the resistor labeled h_{22} is a resistance whose value is $1/h_{22}$. Both h_{12} and h_{21} are dimensionless ratios.

We can gain some intuitive notion of how this equivalent works by considering the following. Let us for the moment neglect the voltage source on the input side. Then, when a voltage (E_1) is applied to the input, a current I_1 flows through the resistor h_{11}. This current causes a current, $h_{21}I_1$ to flow in the output current source. Thus h_{21} is the current gain of this equivalent circuit and is equal to $(-\alpha)$.

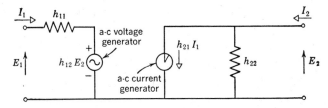

Fig. 7-11. h-parameter equivalent circuit of a transistor.

Placed across the output is a resistor of value $1/h_{22}$. Therefore the current divides between this resistor and that circuitry which is connected to the transistor. A voltage E_2 will be developed across the output as a result of this current and this is the output voltage. We can now look at the voltage generator, $h_{12}E_2$. When any voltage E_2 appears on the output side, a portion of this voltage, $h_{12}E_2$ will be fed back to the input side. Thus the initially applied voltage meets this feedback voltage in addition to the input resistor h_{11}. Thus the transistor may be regarded as having an internal feedback. We shall consider external feedback in a later chapter. It is especially important to remember, both here and for the rest of the book, that h_{11} is a resistance, h_{22} is a conductance, and both h_{12} and h_{21} are dimensionless ratios. In the next section we shall illustrate how the equivalent circuit is used for circuit analysis.

Grounded-base amplifier illustration. It will be our purpose now to treat the basic amplifier, that was considered in the physics section and in the previous section on the graphical analysis method, in the light of equivalent circuits. Figure 7-12 shows the basic grounded-base amplifier and its representation using the equivalent circuit. We note, first of all, that the bias batteries do not appear in the circuit diagram. This agrees with the condition mentioned previously—that the equivalent circuits do not contain the bias conditions. A general rule can be stated thus: when finding the equivalent circuit of an active network, first remove the batteries which provide

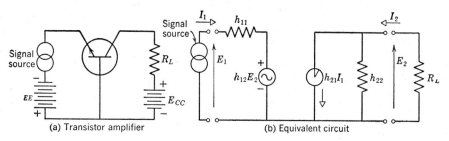

(a) Transistor amplifier   (b) Equivalent circuit

Fig. 7-12. Grounded-base transistor amplifier and its a-c equivalent circuit: (a) transistor amplifier; (b) equivalent circuit.

the bias. We note that, after the equivalent circuit is substituted, a general electric network results. We now have to use the basic network tools to analyze this circuit. For this illustration, we will find the voltage gain by use of mesh and nodal equations. Two simultaneous equations will suffice to analyze this circuit: one mesh equation on the input side and one nodal equation on the output side.

The input equation, since an internal voltage source is present, suggests the use of a mesh equation. Equating the source voltage, E_1, to the sum of the voltage drops, we have

$$E_1 = h_{11}I_1 + h_{12}E_2 \qquad (3)$$

Here it is reaffirmed that $h_{12}E_2$ is a voltage; i.e., h_{12} must be dimensionless.

For the output side a current source is present; therefore a nodal equation is easiest. Using Kirchhoff's current law at the node (1) we can write

$$I_2 = h_{21}I_1 + I_3 = h_{21}I_1 + h_{22}E_2 \qquad (4)$$

where $I_3 = \dfrac{E_2}{1/h_{22}} = h_{22}E_2$.

It is remembered that, in a current source, the current is always constant, regardless of voltage. Therefore the term $h_{21}I_1$ is always the current flowing to the left of the node. Also, the resistance across the output has a value $1/h_{22}$. Therefore the current flowing in this resistance is $h_{22}E_2$.

The equations are summarized thus:

$$E_1 = h_{11}I_1 + h_{12}E_2, \quad I_2 = h_{21}I_1 + h_{22}E_2 \qquad (5)$$

We see that these are two simultaneous equations, and I_1 and E_2 are the unknowns. These equations may be solved by any of the conventional methods for simultaneous equations.[1] The method of determinants is the most general way, and is recommended; however, elimination of one variable is sometimes simpler. For the illustration here we will use determinants.

The voltage gain is

$$A_e = \frac{E_2}{E_1} \qquad (6)$$

We have then to use Equations (5) to find E_2 and E_1. Using the method of determinants we have

$$E_2 = \frac{\begin{vmatrix} h_{11} & E_1 \\ h_{21} & I_2 \end{vmatrix}}{\Delta h} = \frac{h_{11}I_2 - h_{21}E_1}{\Delta h} \qquad (7)$$

where $\Delta h = h_{11}h_{22} - h_{12}h_{21}$.

But $I_2 = -\dfrac{E_2}{R_L};$ therefore $E_2 = -\dfrac{h_{21}E_1}{\Delta h + h_{11}/R_L} \qquad (8)$

Then $\dfrac{E_2}{E_1} = -\dfrac{h_{21}}{\Delta h + h_{11}/R_L} \qquad (9)$

We have just seen that when an equivalent circuit is substituted for a transistor in a network, we return to the use of the basic network tools to analyze the network. We can now summarize the equivalent circuit method.

The equivalent circuit is an electric network which, at a particular bias point of the transistor, represents the electrical operation of the device. Thus, after the bias point has been determined, one has to determine the values of h_{11}, h_{12}, h_{21}, and h_{22} at that bias point. In practice the manufacturer of the transistor will specify one or more recommended bias points and will also specify the values of the h parameters at these points. If parameters other than the h ones are specified, these parameters may be converted into the h's by using the

[1] The solution of simultaneous algebraic equations is treated in Appendix 1.

table in Appendix II. Because a particular set of h parameters is accurate only within a region of the bias point, it is remembered that the equivalent circuit method is only accurate for small applied signals.

In making use of the equivalent circuit, the essential technique is, whenever analyzing a transistor in a network, to substitute the equivalent circuit at the same terminals. The result is a network which is made up of the familiar electric elements. The next step is to analyze the resulting network by the use of the ordinary network tools, consisting mainly of Kirchhoff's voltage and current laws. The former specifies the writing of mesh equations, and the latter the writing of nodal equations.

Comparison of Methods

The graphical analysis method consists of using the characteristics of the transistor in conjunction with a graph of the associated circuitry. The equivalent circuit method, on the other hand, consists of reducing the transistor to an electric network which, in conjunction with the associated circuitry, results in an analyzable network. As was mentioned, the characteristics of the transistor specify completely the electrical action of the transistor; that is, they are a graphical presentation of the operation of the transistor at any bias point. A particular equivalent circuit with its parameter values, in comparison, represents the transistor only within the region on the bias point where the parameter values hold. The equivalent circuit can depict different bias points by correcting the parameter values.

The characteristic method then is a *graphical* method whereas the equivalent circuit method is an *analytic* one. As with all graphical methods, there are many times when the only effective manner of getting certain information is by trial and error. The network analysis method makes use of the whole series of algebraic equations to enable one to find a direct solution to various circuit requirements.

Because the equivalent circuit is limited to small variations about the bias point, it is generally true that the equivalent circuit method is used for small signal applications and the characteristics method is used for large signal applications. There are many exceptions to this general rule, however. Even for small signals, the characteristics are usually used to find the bias point; the bias point may be determined by writing network equations, but the former is much simpler.

Often, when treating a large signal case, an equivalent circuit can be made to *approximate* the operation over a large swing. This enables the direct solution of many problems which would be cumbersome graphically. This approximation is accomplished by using element values which represent the average of the values over the entire swing.

Although the characteristics give the complete specification of the transistor, one limitation should be mentioned here. A reactive load impedance, when analyzed at a single frequency, will appear as an ellipse when plotted on the characteristics. The elliptical load line may be plotted for a single frequency to obtain the operating conditions. This method gives a first-order approximation when non-linear distortion is present and is usually sufficiently accurate for most applications.

Problems

1. Using the curves of Figure 7-4 and assuming a load resistance of 7500 ohms and a collector battery voltage of 20 v, what are the values of V_{CB} and I_C at the operating point if $I_E = 1$ ma?

2. What are the values of I_E, I_C, and V_{CB} for an operating point that will have approximately equal swings on either side for the same E_{CC}, R_L, and transistor used in Problem 1?

3. What is the maximum power output of each of the amplifiers in Problems 1 and 2? Assume that the signal input does not overdrive either amplifier.

4. What are the units of h_{11}, h_{12}, h_{21}, and h_{22}?

5. When would you normally choose to use a graphical analysis instead of an equivalent circuit analysis?

8

Small-Signal Amplifiers

It was mentioned in the preceding chapter that equivalent circuits are usually used when analyzing electronic circuits for small-signal applications, and a graphical analysis is used for large-signal applications. It will be our purpose here to consider the analysis procedures that are used for small-signal amplifiers; hence we are dealing with an electric network in which the active electronic device is replaced by its equivalent circuit.

Sometimes we meet an electronic circuit that consists of a single stage; however, in most cases the circuit involves a number of connected stages. It will be remembered that the two general means for analyzing electric networks are the mesh and the nodal methods. Therefore the multistage electronic circuit can be analyzed in its entirety by the use of either of these methods. However, such an analysis quickly results in a large number of simultaneous equations and consequently the solution becomes fairly difficult. For this reason it is profitable to consider the multistage circuit not in terms of the entire circuit, but in terms of single stages that are connected together. This breaking up of a complex circuit into its separate stages represents a very powerful tool for the analysis of electronic circuits.

When analyzing one stage of a multistage circuit by the use of this method, the previous stage will become the source and the following stage will become the load. Thus we can effectively analyze any complex electronic circuit by analyzing carefully only a single stage with its source and load and using this single-stage analysis repeatedly in the complex network.

It is for this reason that, in this chapter, we will consider carefully the analysis of single-stage transistor amplifiers. Since the transistor can be connected in three different ways in a circuit—grounded base, grounded emitter, and grounded collector—these three single-stage connections will be analyzed. It is important to stress that the concept of treating a complex circuit by means of the single-stage method is essentially a time- and worksaving device which avoids the large number of simultaneous equations which would result from considering the entire circuit as a whole.

When considering the three types of single-stage circuits in this chapter, the first objective will be to obtain the basic formulas for each connection. The resulting formulas can be applied for any stage within a complex circuit if the proper source and load are determined. While deriving the formulas, an additional objective will be to illustrate the analysis method so that the principles may be extended to a multistage network considered in its entirety.

The Important Quantities

As mentioned previously, the general problem when dealing with amplifying circuits lies in achieving the maximum amplification under the prescribed conditions. When using the single-stage method of analysis, the important quantities that determine the amplifying capabilities of the stage are: (1) the power gain, (2) the current gain, (3) the voltage gain, (4) the input resistance, and (5) the output resistance.

Power gain. For transistors the most basic criterion of performance is the power gain. It is this quantity that determines how much work can be done by the output of a transistor circuit. Thus if the circuit consists of a radio, the power gain considered from the input to the output specifies what power is available for conversion into acoustical energy for a certain input.

The power gain is defined simply as the ratio of the power out to the power in.

$$A_p = \frac{\text{a-c power output}}{\text{a-c power input}} \tag{1}$$

It is interesting to diverge here, for a moment, and compare the transistor to the vacuum tube in the matter of power gain. While considering the physical operation, we saw that the transistor is basically a *current-operated* device. That is, it is the holes and electrons (current-carrying particles) of the input side that control the holes and electrons of the output side. The vacuum tube, on the other hand, is basically a *voltage-operated* device. There a voltage applied to the grid (no input current flows) controls the amount of electrons flowing from the cathode to the plate. For the vacuum tube a voltage is the basic control quantity; for the transistor a current is the basic control quantity.

Since the transistor is a current-operated device and requires input power it is essentially a power amplifier. For this reason it was stated previously that power gain is the basic criterion of performance. The power gain of a vacuum tube operating in a class A circuit, on the other hand, has no meaning since it would generally be almost infinite (input power approximately equals zero). The basic criterion of a vacuum tube is the voltage gain. Many times, however, we do speak of a class A vacuum tube power amplifier. This does not mean that the vacuum tube is other than a voltage amplifier; it means that the voltage amplification is used to convert power efficiently from the plate supply battery to a-c power in the load. The performance criterion of such an application is the *plate efficiency* of the vacuum tube amplifier, and is defined as the ratio of the a-c power out to the total power supplied by the battery.

$$\text{plate efficiency} = \frac{\text{a-c output power}}{\text{d-c input power}} \times 100 \qquad (2)$$

In conclusion, optimum performance of a transistor amplifier is achieved only when maximum power gain is realized. This means that stage-to-stage impedance matching is required for optimum performance of a transistor circuit. If any mismatch occurs in the circuit it means some amplification is lost. The vacuum tube, when used as a voltage amplifier, requires a mismatch between stages (for optimum performance) so that the following stage does not load down the preceding stage. For the vacuum tube the maximum voltage is desired for the next stage, and not the maximum power.

The fact that the transistor accepts input power whereas the vacuum tube does not is a very important difference between these two electronic devices.

Input and output resistances. Since a resistance match is usually desired for the transistor amplifier, it becomes necessary to know the input and the output resistance of a transistor stage. It is remembered from the electrical review that maximum power transfer from one stage to another depends upon the resistance match between the two stages. In general, the input and the output resistance greatly affect the power gain which a transistor stage will exhibit for a given generator and a given load.

The input resistance is defined as the resistance exhibited by the input terminals *when the load is connected*. As such, it may be defined as the ratio of the input voltage to the input current with the load connected.

$$\text{input resistance} = R_i = \frac{V_i}{I_i} \tag{3}$$

The output resistance is defined as the resistance which appears looking back from the output terminals, with the source connected. The source may be an actual generator or a previous stage. Output resistance can be calculated by the relation

$$\text{output resistance} = R_o = \frac{V_o}{I_o} \tag{4}$$

Current and voltage gain. Sometimes the final output of a transistor circuit is not converted to some form of work, but is utilized directly. In these cases we may be interested in the current gain or the voltage gain. The current gain is defined as the ratio of the current through the load to the input current.

$$A_i = \frac{I_{\text{load}}}{I_{\text{input}}} \tag{5}$$

This current gain should not be confused with the α (for the grounded base) or the β (for the grounded emitter). It is remembered that α and β are parameters of the transistor alone and specify the current gain if the a-c load is zero. Their importance is in specifying a parameter of the transistor equivalent circuit.

The voltage gain is defined by the ratio of the output voltage to the input voltage:

$$A_e = \frac{V_{\text{load}}}{V_{\text{input}}} \tag{6}$$

When considering the three single-stage amplifiers in this chapter we shall be interested in finding the equations for the quantities discussed above. Although frequency response is an important factor for amplifiers, we shall restrict the discussion of this chapter to those frequencies where the transistor exhibits resistive parameters only. Frequency response will be considered in a later chapter.

Grounded-Base Amplifier

The h-parameter equivalent circuit of the transistor was developed in the electrical review and treated again in Chapter 7. The equivalent circuit as discussed there applies to the grounded-base connection. Figure 8-1 below shows a grounded-base amplifier and its equivalent circuit; this figure is a repetition of Figure 7-12.

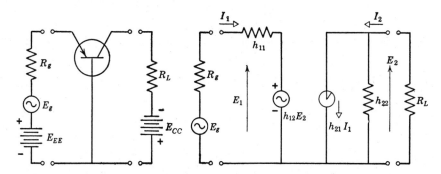

Fig. 8-1. Grounded-base amplifier and its equivalent circuit.

We now wish to calculate the gains and impedances by the use of this equivalent circuit. Let us begin by finding the input resistance at the source terminals. For this calculation the source is removed and the ratio of E_1 to I_1 at the source terminals, with the load attached, is found. Figure 8-2 shows the proper circuit.

Equating the sum of the voltage drops, in the input mesh, to the voltage rises, we have

$$E_1 = h_{11}I_1 + h_{12}E_2 \tag{7}$$

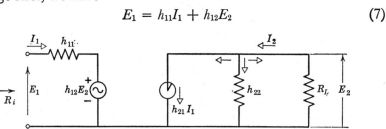

Fig. 8-2. Grounded-base equivalent circuit used for calculating R_i, A_i, A_e, and A_p.

For the output side the sum of the currents (nodal equation) flowing out of node 1 are set equal to zero (see arrows).

$$0 = h_{21}I_1 + h_{22}E_2 + \frac{E_2}{R_L} \tag{8}$$

The two simultaneous equations for Figure 8-2 then, are

$$\begin{aligned} E_1 &= h_{11}I_1 + h_{12}E_2 \\ 0 &= h_{21}I_1 + (h_{22} + 1/R_L)E_2 \end{aligned} \tag{9}$$

We note that I_1 and E_2 are unknowns and E_1 is the constant of these equations. Solving for I_1 by the use of determinants, we find

$$I_1 = \frac{\begin{vmatrix} E_1 & h_{12} \\ 0 & h_{22} + 1/R_L \end{vmatrix}}{\begin{vmatrix} h_{11} & h_{12} \\ h_{21} & h_{22} + 1/R_L \end{vmatrix}} = \frac{E_1(h_{22} + 1/R_L)}{h_{11}(h_{22} + 1/R_L) - h_{12}h_{21}} \tag{10}$$

To find R_i we divide E_1 by I_1 of Equation (10).

$$\begin{aligned} R_i = \frac{E_1}{I_1} &= \frac{h_{11}(h_{22} + 1/R_L) - h_{12}h_{21}}{h_{22} + 1/R_L} \\ &= \frac{h_{11}(h_{22}R_L + 1) - h_{12}h_{21}R_L}{h_{22}R_L + 1} \end{aligned} \tag{11}$$

$$\text{input resistance} = \boxed{R_i = \frac{R_L\Delta^h + h_{11}}{h_{22}R_L + 1}}$$

where $\Delta^h = h_{11}h_{22} - h_{21}h_{12}$.

Given the h parameters of the transistor and the value of the load resistance, we find the input resistance by using Equation (11).

It is necessary to emphasize the fact that the input resistance depends upon the value of R_L. In the vacuum tube (at low frequencies), for example, this is not the case. The R_L dependence means that the input and output side of a transistor are not isolated. That is, what is done to the output side directly affects the input side. This is basically different from the vacuum tube, where a change in load resistance does not change the grid-to-cathode resistance appreciably.

To find the voltage gain (A_e) we can use the same circuit (Figure 8-2), and hence the simultaneous Equations (9) apply. This time we shall solve for the other unknown, E_2.

$$E_2 = \frac{\begin{vmatrix} h_{11} & E_1 \\ h_{21} & 0 \end{vmatrix}}{\begin{vmatrix} h_{11} & h_{12} \\ h_{21} & h_{22} + 1/R_L \end{vmatrix}} = \frac{-h_{21}E_1}{h_{11}(h_{22} + 1/R_L) - h_{12}h_{21}}$$

$$= \frac{-h_{21}E_1R_L}{h_{11}(h_{22}R_L + 1) - h_{12}h_{21}R_L} \tag{12}$$

Taking the ratio of E_2 to E_1, we find

$$\text{voltage gain} = \frac{E_2}{E_1} = \boxed{A_e = \frac{-h_{21}R_L}{R_L\Delta^h + h_{11}}} \tag{13}$$

To find the current gain (A_i) we have merely to note that, from Figure 8-2,

$$E_2 = -I_2R_L \tag{14}$$

If we substitute Equation (14) into Equation (8), we find

$$0 = h_{21}I_1 - h_{22}I_2R_L - I_2 \tag{15}$$

The ratio of I_2/I_1 is then found to be

$$\text{current gain} = \frac{I_2}{I_1} = \boxed{A_i = \frac{h_{21}}{1 + h_{22}R_L}} \tag{16}$$

It was noted in the previous chapter that

$$h_{21} = -\alpha \tag{16a}$$

and that h_{21} and α apply only to the transistor. Equation (16) now shows us the relation between the current gain of the transistor (h_{21} or α) and the circuit current gain when that transistor is used in an amplifier.

To find the power gain (A_p) we have only to use the quantities already calculated. The power gain equals

$$A_p = \frac{I_2}{I_1} \cdot \frac{E_2}{E_1} = \frac{I_2^2}{I_1^2} \cdot \frac{R_L}{R_i} \tag{17}$$

By using either of the two relations shown in Equation (17), the power gain is found to be

$$\text{power gain} = \boxed{A_p = \frac{h_{21}^2 R_L}{(1 + h_{22}R_L)(h_{11} + \Delta^h R_L)}} \tag{18}$$

The remaining quantity to be calculated is the output resistance, R_o. To calculate this we need to find the resistance looking into the

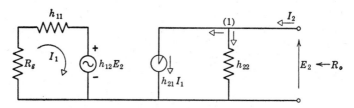

Fig. 8-3. Grounded-base equivalent circuit for calculating R_o.

output terminals with the generator connected. For this calculation the circuit of Figure 8-3 is used, and the two simultaneous equations are

$$0 = (R_g + h_{11})I_1 + h_{12}E_2$$
$$I_2 = h_{21}I_1 + h_{22}E_2 \tag{19}$$

The unknowns are I_1 and E_2. Solving for E_2, we find

$$E_2 = \frac{\begin{vmatrix} R_g + h_{11} & 0 \\ h_{21} & I_2 \end{vmatrix}}{\begin{vmatrix} R_g + h_{11} & h_{12} \\ h_{21} & h_{22} \end{vmatrix}} = \frac{(R_g + h_{11})I_2}{(R_g + h_{11})(h_{22}) - h_{12}h_{21}} \tag{20}$$

To find the output resistance we need to find the ratio of E_2 and I_2.

$$\text{output impedance} = \frac{E_2}{I_2} = \boxed{R_o = \frac{R_g + h_{11}}{R_g h_{22} + \Delta^h}} \tag{21}$$

We note that the R_o is dependent upon R_g. This again tells us that the transistor output is not isolated from the input. This phenomenon was noted before for R_i. Any changes in the generator resistance affect the output resistance of the transistor. Again, this phenomenon does not occur for a vacuum tube.

In the manner shown above, the performance quantities for a single stage amplifier are calculated. Our purpose here was twofold: (1) to provide the equations for the various quantities, and (2) to illustrate the method by which they are calculated.

Before leaving the grounded base amplifier, let us calculate the values of R_i, R_o, A_i, A_e, and A_p for a typical junction transistor. The parameters of the transistor as listed by the manufacturer, are

$$h_{11} = 40 \qquad h_{12} = 4 \times 10^{-4}$$
$$h_{21} = -0.98 \qquad h_{22} = 1 \times 10^{-6}$$

Calculating Δ^h:

$$\Delta^h = h_{11}h_{22} - h_{12}h_{21}$$
$$= 40 \times 10^{-6} + (4 \times 10^{-4})(0.98) = 4.36 \times 10^{-4}$$

The recommended values for the grounded-base connection are a load resistance $R_L = 50,000$ and a source resistance $R_g = 100$ ohms. The following values are then calculated:

$$R_i = \frac{\Delta^h R_L + h_{11}}{1 + h_{22}R_L} = \frac{(4.32 \times 10^{-4})(5 \times 10^4) + 40}{1 + (1 \times 10^{-6})(5 \times 10^4)}$$
$$= 58.6$$

$$R_o = \frac{h_{11} + R_g}{\Delta^h + h_{22}R_g} = \frac{40 + 100}{(4.32 \times 10^{-4}) + (1 \times 10^{-6})(1 \times 10^2)}$$
$$= 263,000$$

$$A_i = \frac{h_{21}}{1 + h_{22}R_L} = \frac{-0.98}{1 + (1 \times 10^{-6})(5 \times 10^4)} \qquad (22)$$
$$= -0.933$$

$$A_e = \frac{-h_{21}R_L}{h_{11} + \Delta^h R_L} = \frac{(+0.98)(5 \times 10^4)}{40 + (4.32 \times 10^{-4})(5 \times 10^4)}$$
$$= 795$$

$$A_p = A_i A_e = -\frac{h_{21}^2 R_L}{(1 + h_{22}R_L)(h_{11} + \Delta^h R_L)}$$
$$= -742$$

The fact that A_i is preceded by a negative sign merely means that the actual output current I_2 is out of phase to the direction assumed as positive in Figure 8-3. Thus the grounded-base connection has no phase shift since the output current flows in the same direction as the input current. The negative sign preceding the power gain is also a result of conventions; the power is actually consumed in the load, whereas a current and voltage as shown in Figure 8-3 would result in power being consumed by the transistor.

The I.R.E. has established standards for the transistor which indicate that either the double number subscripts on the h parameters[1] may be used for the grounded-base configuration or that the subscripts shown on page 154 may be used.

[1] The term h without superscript is used to specify the set of grounded-base parameters, and is also used whenever hybrid parameters in general are referred to. In each instance the context should determine which meaning is meant, and no undue confusion should be encountered.

Grounded base:

$h_{11} = h_{ib}$ input resistance
$h_{12} = h_{rb}$ voltage feedback ratio
$h_{21} = h_{fb}$ forward current ratio
$h_{22} = h_{ob}$ output admittance

It should be noticed that the first letter of the double subscript stands for the type of function and the second for the configuration. The *h* parameters for the grounded-emitter and grounded-collector configurations which will be taken up next are:

Grounded emitter:

h_{ie} = input resistance
h_{re} = voltage feedback ratio
h_{fe} = forward current gain
h_{oe} = output admittance

Grounded collector:

h_{ic} = input resistance
h_{rc} = voltage feedback ratio
h_{fc} = forward current gain
h_{oc} = output admittance

Grounded-Emitter Amplifier

A grounded-emitter amplifier showing the basic biasing conditions is shown in Figure 8-4. In order to find the performance quantities for this connection we have to find the proper equivalent circuit for a grounded-emitter transistor. It is remembered that the conventional *h* parameters, as specified by the manufacturer, apply only to the grounded-base connection.

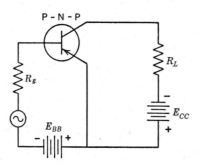

Fig. 8-4. Grounded-emitter transistor amplifier.

Equivalent circuit. One simple way to find the grounded-emitter equivalent circuit is simply to rearrange the grounded-base equivalent circuit. Figure 8-5 shows the grounded-base equivalent circuit and the rearranged circuit which is suitable for the grounded-emitter connections. Note that, in the rearranged circuit, the values for the sources are changed. They are the same quantities as for the circuit of (a), but they must be named differently since the input and output currents and voltages now appear at different places; the input current now appears at the base.

We could proceed to use the circuit of Figure 8-5(b) to calculate the new values of R_i, A_i, etc., using the same parameters as for the grounded base. This would, of course, result in different equations, for the various quantities, than resulted for the grounded-base connection.

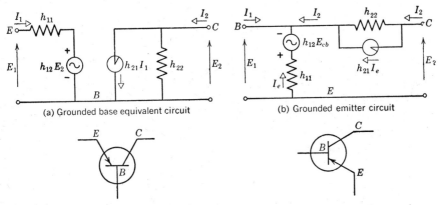

(a) Grounded base equivalent circuit   (b) Grounded emitter circuit

Fig. 8-5. Grounded-emitter equivalent circuit from rearranged grounded-base circuit.

An alternative to proceeding thus is to find a grounded-emitter equivalent circuit which is identical in form to that of the grounded-base circuit. The h parameters of this circuit would be different from the grounded-base h parameters, and could be called the h^e parameters. Using these parameters, we can use the same equations for the R_i, R_o, A_i, A_v, and A_p as were used for the grounded base.

Since there is a definite advantage to using the same equations for all connections of the transistor, we will use the latter method suggested. That is, we will use the circuit of Figure 8-5(b) to find a circuit identical in form to that of (a). The circuit will appear as shown in Figure 8-6, and it is seen that this circuit is identical to that for the grounded base except that the parameters have the proper subscripts to indicate that they are grounded-emitter parameters. We now proceed to find the values of the h^e parameters in terms of the h (grounded-base) parameters.

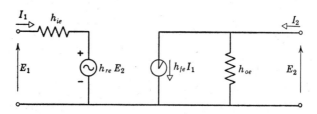

Fig. 8-6. Grounded-emitter h^e parameter equivalent circuit.

We can accomplish this determination of the h^e parameters by using the basic defining equations, as stated before:

$$h_{ie} = \left.\frac{E_1}{I_1}\right|_{E_2=0} \qquad h_{re} = \left.\frac{E_1}{E_2}\right|_{I_1=0}$$

$$h_{fe} = \left.\frac{I_2}{I_1}\right|_{E_2=0} \qquad h_{oe} = \left.\frac{I_2}{E_2}\right|_{I_1=0} \tag{23}$$

By applying these definitions to the circuit of Figure 8-5(b), we can evaluate the h^e parameters in terms of the h parameters.

The definitions of both h_{ie} and h_{fe} specify that $E_2 = 0$. Figure 8-7 shows the circuit of 8-5(b) with the output (E_2) short-circuited. We need to solve this circuit for the ratios of E_1 to I_1 and I_2 to I_1.

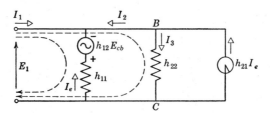

Fig. 8-7. Circuit of Fig. 8-5(b) when output is shorted.

This circuit consists essentially of two meshes, so we write two mesh equations. The two meshes selected are shown by dashed lines. The equation for the first mesh is

$$E_1 = -h_{12}E_{cb} - h_{11}I_E \tag{24}$$

For the second mesh, we first note that I_3, the current through the conductance h_{22}, is

$$I_3 = h_{21}I_E - I_2 \tag{25}$$

The equation for the second mesh is then

$$E_1 = \frac{h_{21}I_E - I_2}{h_{22}} \tag{26}$$

From Figure 8-7 we verify that $I_E = -(I_1 + I_2)$ and $E_1 = -E_{cb}$. Making these substitutions, the two simultaneous equations are

$$E_1 = h_{12}E_1 + h_{11}I_1 + h_{11}I_2$$

$$E_1 = -\frac{h_{21}}{h_{22}} I_1 - \frac{h_{21}}{h_{22}} I_2 - \frac{I_2}{h_{22}} \tag{27}$$

Written more conventionally, they appear

$$E_1 = \frac{h_{11}}{1 - h_{12}} I_1 + \frac{h_{11}}{1 - h_{12}} I_2$$

$$E_1 = -\frac{h_{21}}{h_{22}} I_1 - \left(\frac{h_{21}}{h_{22}} + \frac{1}{h_{22}}\right)I_2 \tag{28}$$

Solving these equations for the unknown I_1:

$$I_1 = \frac{\begin{vmatrix} E_1 & \dfrac{h_{11}}{1 - h_{12}} \\[2ex] E_1 & -\left(\dfrac{h_{21}}{h_{22}} + \dfrac{1}{h_{22}}\right) \end{vmatrix}}{\begin{vmatrix} \dfrac{h_{11}}{1 - h_{12}} & \dfrac{h_{11}}{1 - h_{12}} \\[2ex] -\dfrac{h_{21}}{h_{22}} & -\left(\dfrac{h_{21}}{h_{22}} + \dfrac{1}{h_{22}}\right) \end{vmatrix}} = -\frac{E_1[(h_{21}+1)(1 - h_{12}) + h_{11}h_{22}]}{h_{11}h_{21} - h_{11}(h_{21}+1)} \tag{29}$$

After further simplification, the ratio of E_1 to I_1 is

$$h_{ie} = \frac{E_1}{I_1}\bigg|_{E_2=0} = \frac{h_{11}}{\Delta^h + h_{21} - h_{12} + 1} \tag{30}$$

Equation (30) can be accurately simplified by referring to the h parameters given previously for a typical junction transistor. It is always true that $\Delta^h - h_{12}$ is small with respect to $1 + h_{21}$. Therefore Equation (30) becomes

$$\boxed{h_{ie} \approx \frac{h_{11}}{1 + h_{21}}} \tag{31}$$

To find h_{fe} we need the ratio of I_2 to I_1. Using Equations (28), we solve for the unknown I_2.

$$I_2 = \frac{\begin{vmatrix} \dfrac{h_{11}}{1 - h_{12}} & E_1 \\[2ex] -\dfrac{h_{21}}{h_{22}} & E_1 \end{vmatrix}}{\begin{vmatrix} \dfrac{h_{11}}{1 - h_{12}} & \dfrac{h_{11}}{1 - h_{12}} \\[2ex] -\dfrac{h_{21}}{h_{22}} & -\left(\dfrac{h_{21}}{h_{22}} + \dfrac{1}{h_{22}}\right) \end{vmatrix}} = \frac{E_1 \left[\dfrac{h_{11}h_{22} + h_{21}(1 - h_{12})}{(1 - h_{12})(h_{22})}\right]}{\dfrac{h_{11}h_{21} - h_{11}(h_{21} + 1)}{(1 - h_{12})(h_{22})}} \tag{32}$$

Taking the ratio of I_2 to I_1 given by Equation (29), we have

$$h_{fe} = \frac{I_2}{I_1}\bigg|_{E_2=0} = -\frac{\Delta^h + h_{21}}{\Delta^h + 1 + h_{21} - h_{12}} \qquad (33)$$

Using the same simplification as above, plus the fact that Δ^h is small with respect to h_{21}, we have

$$\boxed{h_{fe} \approx \frac{-h_{21}}{1 + h_{21}}} \qquad (34)$$

Since h_{fe} is the transistor current gain for the grounded-emitter connection, h_{fe} equals β (defined previously):

$$h_{fe} = \beta \qquad (34a)$$

Remembering that h_{21} equals $-\alpha$, we see in Equation (33) the same relation between β and α as was stated in Equation (2b) of Chapter 7.

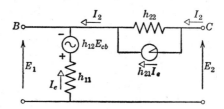

Fig. 8-8. Circuit of Fig. 8-5(b) when the input is open-circuited.

From the defining Equations (23) we see that h_{re} and h_{oe} are calculated for $I_1 = 0$. Therefore we return to Figure 8-5(b) and obtain the equations for the circuit when the input is open-circuited. The circuit is shown in Figure 8-8.

Since only one mesh exists for this circuit, we need write only one mesh equation.

$$E_2 = \frac{I_2 - h_{21}I_E}{h_{22}} - h_{12}E_{cb} - h_{11}I_E \qquad (35)$$

From Figure 8-8 it can be seen that $I_E = -I_2$ and $E_{cb} = \dfrac{I_2 - h_{21}I_E}{h_{22}}$.
Using these substitutions, the equation appears

$$E_2 = \frac{1 + h_{21}}{h_{22}} I_2 - h_{12} \left(\frac{1 + h_{21}}{h_{22}} \right) I_2 + h_{11}I_2 \qquad (36)$$

Taking the ratio of I_2 to E_2, we find h_{oe}:

$$h_{oe} = \frac{I_2}{E_2}\bigg|_{I_1=0} = \frac{h_{22}}{\Delta^h + h_{21} - h_{12} + 1} \qquad (37)$$

Using the same simplifications as for Equations (34) and (31), this simplifies to

$$h_{oe} \approx \frac{h_{22}}{1 + h_{21}} \qquad (38)$$

To find the value of h_{re} we need the ratio of E_1 to E_2. By referring to Figure 8-8, we see that E_1 is equal to

$$E_1 = -h_{12} \frac{(1 + h_{21})I_2}{h_{22}} + h_{11}I_2 \qquad (39)$$

Taking the ratio of this equation to that for E_2 given by Equation (36), it is found that

$$h_{re} = \frac{E_1}{E_2} = \frac{\Delta^h - h_{12}}{1 + h_{21} - h_{12} + \Delta^h} \qquad (40)$$

Using the simplifications as before,

$$h_{re} \approx \frac{\Delta^h - h_{12}}{1 + h_{21}} \qquad (41)$$

The equations we have just found give the grounded emitter h^e parameters in terms of the grounded-base h parameters. They are listed here for easy reference.

$$h_{ie} \approx \frac{h_{11}}{1 + h_{21}} \qquad h_{fe} \approx -\frac{h_{21}}{1 + h_{21}}$$

$$h_{re} \approx \frac{\Delta^h - h_{12}}{1 + h_{21}} \qquad h_{oe} \approx \frac{h_{22}}{1 + h_{21}} \qquad (42)$$

Since the grounded-base parameters are the ones usually given by the manufacturers, the above equations may be used to convert these to the grounded-emitter parameters.

We can now calculate the grounded emitter parameters for the typical junction transistor used before. The given parameters for the 2N43 are

$$h_{11} = 40 \qquad\qquad h_{21} = -0.98$$
$$h_{12} = 4 \times 10^{-4} \qquad h_{22} = 1 \times 10^{-6}$$
$$\Delta^h = 4.32 \times 10^{-4}$$

$$h_{ie} \approx \frac{h_{11}}{1 + h_{21}} = \frac{40}{1 - 0.98} = 2000$$

$$h_{re} \approx \frac{\Delta^h - h_{12}}{1 + h_{21}} = \frac{4.32 \times 10^{-4} - 4 \times 10^{-4}}{1 - 0.98} = 16 \times 10^{-4} \quad (43)$$

$$h_{fe} \approx \frac{-h_{21}}{1 + h_{21}} = \frac{+0.98}{1 - 0.98} = +49$$

$$h_{oe} \approx \frac{h_{22}}{1 + h_{21}} = \frac{10^{-6}}{1 - 0.98} = 5 \times 10^{-5}$$

The important thing to note here is that h_{fe} is much larger than h_{21}. Thus it is reaffirmed that the current gain of a junction transistor is less than 1 for the grounded-base connection, but is in the order of 50 for the grounded-emitter case. This may go as high as 150 in some transistors.

Amplifier. Since we now have the emitter parameters in terms of what may be called the *conventional* equivalent circuit, we can use the performance equations developed for the grounded base connection. Thus the quantities R_i, R_o, A_i, A_e, and A_p can be found by using the equations below. It is noted that these are identical to those of Equation (22) except that h^e parameters replace the h parameters.

$$R_i = \frac{R_L \Delta^{h^e} + h_{ie}}{1 + h_{oe} R_L}, \qquad R_o = \frac{h_{ie} + R_g}{\Delta^{h^e} + h_{oe} R_g}$$

$$A_i = \frac{h_{fe}}{1 + h_{oe} R_L}, \qquad A_e = \frac{-h_{fe} R_L}{\Delta^{h^e} R_L + h_{ie}} \qquad (44)$$

$$A_p = A_i A_e = \frac{(h_{fe})^2 R_L}{(1 + h_{oe} R_L)(\Delta^{h^e} R_L + h_{ie})}$$

As an example of the application of these performance quantities, we shall use the same transistor as before in the amplifier shown in Figure 8-9. For this transistor the recommended values of load re-

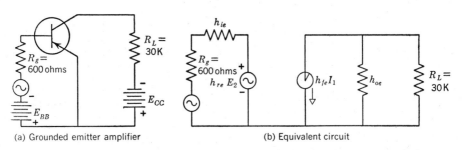

(a) Grounded emitter amplifier　　　　　　(b) Equivalent circuit

Fig. 8-9. Grounded-emitter amplifier and its equivalent circuit.

sistance and source resistance, for the grounded-emitter connection, are 30,000 and 600 ohms, respectively.

$$\Delta^{h^e} = h_{ie} h_{oe} - h_{re} h_{fe}$$

$$= (2 \times 10^3)(5 \times 10^{-5}) - (16 \times 10^{-4})(49) = 0.0216$$

$$R_i = \frac{R_L \Delta^{h^e} + h_{ie}}{1 + h_{oe} R_L} = \frac{(3 \times 10^4)(2.16 \times 10^{-2}) + 2000}{1 + (5 \times 10^{-5})(3 \times 10^4)} = 1060$$

$$R_o = \frac{h_{ie} + R_g}{\Delta^{h^*} + h_{oe}R_g} = \frac{2000 + 600}{(2.16 \times 10^{-2}) + (5 \times 10^{-5})(6 \times 10^2)}$$
$$= 50,400 \tag{45}$$

$$A_i = \frac{h_{fe}}{1 + h_{oe}R_L} = \frac{49}{1 + (5 \times 10^{-5})(3 \times 10^4)} = 19.6$$

$$A_e = \frac{-h_{fe}R_L}{\Delta^{h^*}R_L + h_{ie}} = \frac{-(49)(3 \times 10^4)}{(2.16 \times 10^{-2})(3 \times 10^4) + 2000}$$
$$= -554$$

$$A_p = A_i A_e = (19.6)(-554) = -10,850$$

The important thing to note here is that comparison of Equations (45) with Equations (22) indicates that the *current and power gain of a grounded-emitter amplifier are higher than for the grounded-base amplifier.* It is for this reason that the grounded-emitter connection is the one most used in transistor amplifiers.

The negative sign preceding the voltage gain means that the direction of the actual output voltage E_2 is opposite to that shown in Figure 8-6. This, plus the fact that the current gain is positive, means that the grounded emitter has a phase shift of 180°; i.e., a sine wave input will cause a sine wave output that is shifted 180° from the input wave. This is similar, then, to the conventional vacuum tube stage.

The negative power gain simply means that the output power is consumed in the load.

Grounded-Collector Connection

A grounded-collector amplifier showing the basic biasing conditions is shown in Figure 8-10. For this connection the input signal is placed between the base and the collector and the output appears between the emitter and the collector. As in the

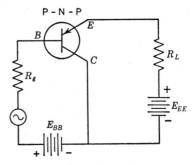

Fig. 8-10. Grounded-collector transistor amplifier.

grounded-emitter connection, we will find an equivalent circuit which is identical in form to that of the grounded-base connection. It is remembered that the advantage to this method is that the R_i, R_o, A_i, A_e, and A_p can be calculated by the use of the same equations as were found previously. Thus, in finding the grounded-collector equivalent circuit, we shall find the h^c parameters in terms of the basic h parameters. Since the derivation for the grounded-emitter case was followed rather closely, we shall here only sketch the derivation.

Figure 8-11(a) shows the grounded-base equivalent circuit rearranged to form the circuit for the grounded-collector connection. Figure 11(b) shows the basic h parameter circuit, and the parameters are suitably labeled h^c.

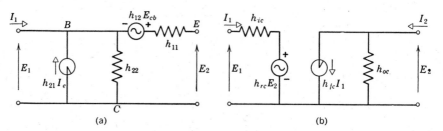

(a)   (b)

Fig. 8-11. Grounded-collector equivalent circuits: (a) circuit obtained from rearranging grounded-base circuit; (b) conventional circuit showing h^c parameters.

The h^c parameters are found by operating suitably upon the circuit of Figure 8-11(a). It is remembered from Equation (23) that, for h_{ic} and h_{fc}, the output is short-circuited to make $E_2 = 0$. For h_{rc} and h_{oc} the input is open-circuited to make $I_1 = 0$.

When the output of Figure 8-11(a) is short-circuited the two mesh equations for the resulting circuit are

$$E_1 = \frac{I_1}{h_{22}} + \frac{h_{21}I_E}{h_{22}} + \frac{I_2}{h_{22}}$$

$$E_1 = I_2 h_{11} + h_{12}E_{cb} \tag{46}$$

Making the substitution, $I_E = I_2$ and $E_{cb} = -E_1$, the equations are

$$E_1 = \frac{1}{h_{22}} I_1 + \frac{1 + h_{21}}{h_{22}} I_2$$

$$E_1 = \frac{h_{11}}{1 - h_{12}} + 0I_2 \tag{47}$$

From these two simultaneous equations, it is found that

$$h_{ic} = \frac{h_{11}}{\Delta^h - h_{12} + 1 + h_{21}} \tag{48}$$

Making use of the fact that $\Delta^h - h_{12}$ is much less than $1 + h_{21}$,

$$h_{ic} \approx \frac{h_{11}}{1 + h_{21}} \qquad\qquad (49)$$

From the same equations h_{fc} is found to be

$$h_{fc} = -\frac{1 - h_{12}}{\Delta^h - h_{12} + 1 + h_{21}} \qquad\qquad (50)$$

Upon simplification,

$$h_{fc} \approx -\frac{1}{1 + h_{21}} \qquad\qquad (51)$$

If the input circuit of Figure 8-11(a) is left open-circuited, and the resulting mesh equations are solved, it is found that

$$h_{oc} = \frac{h_{22}}{\Delta^h - h_{12} + 1 + h_{21}} \approx \boxed{\frac{h_{22}}{1 + h_{21}}} \qquad\qquad (52)$$

and

$$h_{rc} = \frac{1 + h_{21}}{\Delta^h - h_{12} + 1 + h_{21}} \approx \frac{1 + h_{21}}{1 + h_{21}} = \boxed{1} \qquad\qquad (53)$$

Summarizing then, the grounded-collector h^c parameters can be found in terms of the specified h parameters by the following:

$$
\begin{aligned}
h_{ic} &\approx \frac{h_{11}}{1 + h_{21}} & h_{rc} &\approx 1 \\[2mm]
h_{fc} &\approx \frac{-1}{1 + h_{21}} & h_{oc} &\approx \frac{h_{22}}{1 + h_{21}}
\end{aligned}
\qquad\qquad (54)
$$

Taking the same transistor as was used previously, the h^c parameters are

$$h_{11} = 40 \qquad\qquad h_{21} = -0.98$$
$$h_{12} = 4 \times 10^{-4} \qquad h_{22} = 1 \times 10^{-6}$$
$$\Delta^h = 4.32 \times 10^{-4}$$

$$h_{ic} = \frac{h_{11}}{1 + h_{21}} = \frac{40}{1 - 0.98} = 2000$$

$$h_{fc} = -\frac{1}{1 + h_{21}} = -\frac{1}{1 - 0.98} = -50 \qquad\qquad (55)$$

$$h_{rc} = 1$$

$$h_{oc} = \frac{h_{22}}{1 + h_{21}} = \frac{10^{-6}}{1 - 0.98} = 5 \times 10^{-5}$$

These parameters appear to be about the same as for the grounded emitter, except for the value of h_{rc}. It will be found that this difference in h_{rc} causes a major difference between a grounded-emitter connection and a grounded-collector connection.

Using the above values, we can calculate the performance quantities for the grounded collector amplifier. For the typical junction transistor the recommended load resistance is 600 ohms and 30,000 is specified for the source impedance. Using these values in the basic circuit of Figure 8-10, the quantities are

$$\Delta^{hc} = h_{ic}h_{oc} - h_{rc}h_{fc} = (2000)(5 \times 10^{-5}) - (1)(-50) = 50.1$$

$$R_i = \frac{R_L\Delta^{hc} + h_{ic}}{1 + h_{oc}R_L} = \frac{(600)(50.1) + 2000}{1 + (5 \times 10^{-5})(600)} = 31,000$$

$$R_o = \frac{h_{ic} + R_g}{\Delta^{hc} + h_{oc}R_g} = \frac{2000 + 30,000}{50.1 + (5 \times 10^{-5})(3 \times 10^4)} = 620$$

$$A_i = \frac{h_{fc}}{1 + h_{oc}R_L} = \frac{-50}{1 + (5 \times 10^{-5})(6 \times 10^2)} = -48.5 \tag{56}$$

$$A_e = \frac{-h_{fc}R_L}{\Delta^{hc}R_L + h_{ic}} = \frac{-(-50)(600)}{(50.1)(600) + 2000} = 0.938$$

$$A_p = A_i \times A_e = (-48.5)(0.938) = -45.5$$

With the sign of the current gain we see that the grounded collector, like the grounded base, has no phase shift. The negative power gain simply asserts that the power is consumed in the load.

Comparison of Three Connections

Having considered the three types of single-stage connections, we can compare their properties as amplifiers. For this comparison we will refer to Tables 1, 2, and 3. Table 1 summarizes the equations for calculating the h parameters for each of the three connections. The quantities of Table 2 are the values of the h parameters for the 2N43 junction transistor. Table 3 contains the performance values for a typical transistor calculated by using the recommended load and source impedance for each connection (given earlier).

From Table 3 we see that the grounded emitter has the largest power gain of the three connections. Since the output of most electronic circuits is converted to some form of work, the power gain is a basic criterion. It is for this reason that the grounded-emitter connection is the most used connection for transistor amplifiers. Table 3

TABLE 1. THE h PARAMETER EQUATIONS FOR THE
THREE TRANSISTOR CONFIGURATIONS

General parameter	Grounded base	Grounded emitter	Grounded collector
h_{11}	Given by manufacturer as h_{11} or h_{ib}	$h_{ie} \approx \dfrac{h_{11}}{1 + h_{21}}$	$h_{ic} \approx \dfrac{h_{11}}{1 + h_{21}}$
h_{12}	Given by manufacturer as h_{12} or h_{rb}	$h_{re} \approx \dfrac{\Delta^h - h_{12}}{1 + h_{21}}$	$h_{rc} \approx 1$
h_{21}	Given by manufacturer as h_{21} or h_{fb}	$h_{fe} \approx -\dfrac{h_{21}}{1 + h_{21}}$	$h_{fc} \approx -\dfrac{1}{1 + h_{21}}$
h_{22}	Given by manufacturer as h_{22} or h_{ob}	$h_{oe} \approx \dfrac{h_{22}}{1 + h_{21}}$	$h_{oc} \approx \dfrac{h_{22}}{1 + h_{21}}$

shows that the cascading of grounded-emitter circuits does not result in a perfect impedance match, since the output impedance is much greater than the input impedance. Remembering that matched impedances are required for maximum power transfer, some of the power gain will be lost unless transformer impedance matching is used. The reasons for not using grounded-base and grounded-collector circuits in cascade without transformer coupling will be discussed in Chapter 10.

The grounded-base connection has a sizable power gain, but it is considerably smaller than that of the grounded emitter. It is seen that the voltage gain of the grounded base is the greatest of all the three connections. Thus if an application requires only a voltage output (such as to drive an oscilloscope trace where essentially no power is

TABLE 2. VALUES OF THE h PARAMETERS FOR THE THREE CONFIGURATIONS,
USING A TYPICAL JUNCTION TRANSISTOR

Parameters h = grounded base h^e = grounded emitter h^c = grounded collector	Grounded base (h)	Grounded emitter (h^e)	Grounded collector (h^c)
h_{11}	40	2000	2000
h_{12}	4×10^{-4}	16×10^{-4}	1
h_{21}	-0.98	49	-50
h_{22}	10^{-6}	5×10^{-5}	5×10^{-5}

TABLE 3. VALUES OF PERFORMANCE QUANTITIES FOR THE THREE
CONFIGURATIONS, USING A TYPICAL JUNCTION TRANSISTOR WITH
RECOMMENDED LOADS AS USED IN EQUATIONS 22, 45, 56.

Quantity	Performance Equation Use: h = grounded base h^e = grounded emitter h^c = grounded collector	Grounded base (use h parameter)	Grounded emitter (use h^e parameter)	Grounded collector (use h^c parameter)
$R_i =$	$\dfrac{\Delta^h R_L + h_{11}}{h_{22}R_L + 1}$	58.8	1,060	31,000
$R_o =$	$\dfrac{h_{11} + R_g}{\Delta^h + h_{22}R_g}$	261,000	50,400	620
$A_i =$	$\dfrac{h_{21}}{h_{22}R_L + 1}$	−0.933	19.6	−48.5
$A_e =$	$\dfrac{-h_{21}R_L}{h_{11} + \Delta^h R_L}$	793	−554	0.938
$A_p =$	$A_i A_e$	−740	−10,850	−45.5
M.A.G.*	$\dfrac{h_{21}^2}{[(\Delta h)^{\frac12} + (h_{11}h_{22})^{\frac12}]^2}$	1,248	11,100	45.6

* The M.A.G. will be defined and discussed in the following section.

required) the grounded base is the best connection. It is also noted
that the impedance mismatch for cascading stages is the worst for the
grounded-base connection. In fact, if two grounded-base stages are
cascaded, transformers must be used for impedance matching. Otherwise, the gain of two stages will be less than for a single stage. This is
another reason for usually choosing the grounded-emitter connection
for amplifiers.

Table 3 shows that, although the power gain of the grounded
collector is small, the current gain is the highest. This, together with
the fact that the input impedance is high and the output impedance is
low, means that the grounded collector is most profitably used as an
impedance-matching stage. Thus the addition of a grounded-collector stage between two emitter stages would, it is seen, practically
match the input and output impedances. This may be a valuable
alternative to the use of transformers.

In summary then, the grounded emitter is the best power amplifier, the grounded base is the best voltage amplifier, and the grounded

collector is often useful as an impedance-matching connection. This simple comparison is somewhat altered, however, when the properties of bias stability and frequency response are considered. By bias stability we refer to the change in performance with a variation in bias voltages. Although these topics will be considered in detail later, it is useful to summarize the major considerations in this comparison. The grounded emitter has less bias stability and the frequency bandpass is smaller than for the grounded base. Therefore the higher power gain of the grounded emitter is acquired at the sacrifice of both the bias stability and the frequency response. An additional difference between the two connections lies in the fact that the grounded-emitter stage can be biased with a single battery, whereas the grounded base requires a separate battery (or bias circuitry) for both the input and the output. In any design situation, those characteristics which are most important must determine the choice between the two connections.

Point Contact Transistor Amplifiers

Although all the examples of the preceding paragraphs utilized a junction transistor, all the methods illustrated certainly apply to the point contact type. The chief difference between point contact and junction transistors, for the purposes of amplifiers, is that the h_{21} or $-\alpha$ is greater than unity for the point contact type. Because of this the input impedance of point contact transistor amplifiers can become negative. This is especially true of the grounded-emitter and the grounded-collector connections.

Consequently, the grounded-base connection is the only connection appropriate for amplifiers. Here too, however, care must be taken to avoid a negative input resistance.

Because of the relative ease of achieving a negative input resistance with point contact connections, they lend themselves especially to oscillators and multivibrators. We will learn later that one of the conditions necessary to form an oscillator or multivibrator is that an effective negative impedance appear in the circuit.

Until recently the point contact transistor had a higher-frequency response than any of the junction types. Therefore the point contact type was used almost exclusively for oscillators and radio frequency amplifiers. However, with the appearance of the surface-barrier and the diffused-junction (junction type) transistors, the high-frequency response of the junction units has exceeded that of the point contact type.

Transducer and Available Power Gain

When discussing the performance quantities of single-stage amplifiers in this chapter, it was noted that the power gain is the basic criterion of performance. This is true because the transistor is basically a power amplifier. The power gain, as treated thus far, was defined simply as the ratio of the power out to the power in:

$$A_p = \frac{P_{out}}{P_{in}} = \frac{I_2^2 R_L}{I_1^2 R_i} = A_i^2 \frac{R_L}{R_i} \tag{57}$$

Using the value of power gain, we can find the power out if the input power is known.

Many times, when designing electronic circuits, we are given a certain source for the circuit and are not allowed to change its parameters. In other words, we are not allowed to change the internal impedance of the source so that it will match the electronic circuit input impedance; hence maximum power transfer cannot be effected. For this reason it is important to know how efficiently we are using the given source. Note that the power gain, given by Equation (57), gives no measure of how efficiently the source is used.

The transducer gain and the available gain have been defined in order to include the consideration of how efficiently the given source is utilized.

Transducer gain. The transducer gain is defined as the ratio of the actual output power in the load to the power *available* from the generator or source.

$$\text{transducer gain} = \frac{\text{power out}}{\text{power available from generator}} \tag{58}$$

By available power we mean the maximum power that can be drawn from the source. It is remembered from the electrical review that maximum power is achieved when the load impedance (for the source) is equal to the internal resistance of the source. The power achieved, under the matched conditions, for a source whose open-circuit voltage is E_g and whose internal resistance is R_g is

$$P_{\text{avail}} = \frac{E_g^2}{4R_g} \tag{59}$$

The transducer gain can then be written

$$\text{transducer gain} = \frac{P_0}{E_g^2/4R_g} = \frac{E_2^2/R_L}{E_g^2/4R_g}$$

$$= \frac{4I_2^2 R_L R_g}{E_g^2} = \frac{4I_2^2 R_L R_g}{I_1^2 (R_g + R_i)^2} \tag{60}$$

If we now substitute the values for A_i and R_i as given by Table 3, the transducer gain is found to be

$$\text{transducer gain} = \frac{4R_L R_g h_{21}^2}{(R_g R_L h_{22} + R_g + \Delta^h R_L + h_{11})^2} \tag{61}$$

It is noted, of course, that the transducer gain is a function of source resistance R_g, as it must be since it takes into account the efficiency with which the source is utilized.

Equation (61) can be used for either of the three connections if the appropriate h parameters (h^e for grounded emitter, etc.) are used.

For comparing two amplifiers with fixed loads that are to operate from the same source, the transducer gain will specify which circuit provides the higher output power. It is noted that the power gain, defined without respect to the source, would give no information for such a comparison.

Available power gain. The available power gain is defined for a reason similar to that for the transducer gain. It includes the effect of the source, and in addition, concerns the power output if the load resistance were matched to the transistor output resistance. The available power gain is defined as the ratio of the power *available* from the transistor output to the power available from the source:

$$\text{available power gain} = \frac{\text{available power of transistor output}}{\text{available generator power}} \tag{62}$$

As mentioned, the available output power would be achieved if the load resistance were matched to the transistor output resistance. In terms of circuit quantities, then, the available power gain is

$$\text{available power gain} = \frac{V_{oc}^2/4R_o}{E_g^2/4R_g} = \frac{V_{oc}^2 R_g}{E_g^2 R_o} \tag{63}$$

where V_{oc} = output voltage when output is open-circuited.

To find V_{oc} the circuit Equations (9) indicate that, with $R_L = \infty$, the $V_{oc} = \dfrac{h_{21}}{\Delta^h} E_1$; R_i with $R_L = \infty$, is equal to Δ^h/h_{22}, and $E_g =$ $I_1 R_g + \dfrac{h_{12}h_{21}}{h_{22}} I_1 + h_{11}I_1$. Making these substitutions in Equations (63), the available power gain is found to be

$$\text{available power gain} = \frac{h_{21}^2 R_g}{(\Delta^h + R_g h_{22})(R_g + h_{11})} \qquad (64)$$

Note that the available gain is independent of R_L. For any particular transistor amplifier, the available gain is the same, regardless of the actual R_L. This gain figure has to do with what power is available; hence, what power could be realized *if* the R_L were equal to R_o. The available gain is a function of R_g since the available output power depends upon how much of the generator power is inserted into the input. Again Equation (64) applies to all three connections providing the proper h parameters are used.

If we have two amplifiers that are to operate from the same source, and we can adjust the loads, then the available gain will specify which circuit would provide the higher output power. This is dependent upon being able to use the matched load resistance to *obtain* the available power. Even if the matched load is not used the available gain will remain the same; we simply do not achieve all the available power.

Maximum available gain. The maximum available gain (M.A.G.) is the upper bound for the transducer gain, the available gain, and the power gain. If both the input side and the output side of the transistor are matched, maximum available gain will occur. This is, of course, the optimum condition. The value of the M.A.G. is determined solely by the parameters of the transistor. Therefore the M.A.G. can be regarded as a *figure of merit* for comparing various transistors or various connections of the transistors.

The transducer gain and the power gain are not so high as the M.A.G. if both the R_g and the R_L are not matched to the input and output, respectively. The available gain, since it is not dependent on R_L, is less than the M.A.G. if the R_g is not matched to the input. As mentioned, then, all three gains become equal when both input and output are matched, and the resulting gain is called M.A.G.

In order to find the correct value (for M.A.G.) of R_g and R_L

for a certain transistor, we must write the following equations:

$$R_g = R_i, \qquad R_L = R_o \qquad (65)$$

We remember that R_i is a function of R_L (Table 3) and R_o is a function of R_g. Therefore the two Equations (65) must be solved as simultaneous equations. Determinants can be used for this solution, and the results are

$$R_g = \sqrt{\frac{\Delta^h h_{11}}{h_{22}}}, \qquad R_L = \sqrt{\frac{h_{11}}{\Delta^h h_{22}}} \qquad (66)$$

Knowing the h parameters of the transistor, we can find the matched values of R_L and R_g by using Equation (66). If these values are substituted in Equation (61) for transducer gain, or in Equation (64) for available gain, the M.A.G. is found to be

$$\text{M.A.G.} = \frac{h_{21}^2}{[(\Delta^h)^{1/2} + (h_{11}h_{22})^{1/2}]^2} \qquad (67)$$

It is necessary to emphasize that the M.A.G. is a function of the transistor only and does not depend on R_L or R_g. Thus every transistor has its M.A.G.; whether that gain is achieved in an actual circuit is a question of whether the R_L and R_g fulfill Equation (66). If the matched conditions are used, then *the power gain, the transducer gain, and the available gain are all equal to the M.A.G.* The values of M.A.G. for a junction transistor in the three connections are shown in the bottom of Table 3. Again all the above equations can be used for all three connections by using the proper h parameters.

In the design of transistor amplifiers M.A.G. can be achieved only by the use of impedance-matching transformers. Since this is often undesirable, the M.A.G. remains as an optimum value of gain or as a figure of merit for comparison.

Example of Small Signal Analysis

It was noted in the beginning of this chapter that the single-stage analysis we have just considered is useful, not only for single-stage amplifiers, but also for multistage circuits. Here we will illustrate the application of this single-stage method to a two-stage transistor amplifier.

The transistor amplifier is shown in Figure 8-12, and it is seen that two grounded-emitter amplifiers are connected in cascade. At this point we do not wish to discuss the function of the various elements of this circuit, or their values, as this will be considered later. We will regard this as a circuit whose various performance quantities can be found by the tools developed in this chapter. Note that both transistor stages are biased in the conventional manner: a battery for each lead. We will find later that a two-stage amplifier such as this can be entirely biased from a single battery.

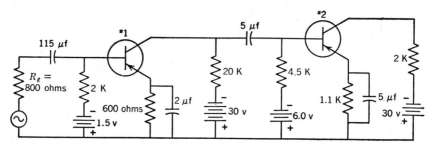

Fig. 8-12

When performing a small-signal analysis, the first step consists of reducing the circuit to its a-c equivalent. This means removing the bias batteries and replacing them by their internal impedance (if any) and removing those resistors which are by-passed by capacitors. Additionally, the coupling capacitors (in Figure 8-12) are removed if their reactance is sufficiently small. The a-c equivalent of Figure 8-12 then, is the circuit of Figure 8-13. Figure 8-13 also shows the values of the h^e parameters for both transistors. These values are typical for junction transistors.

Since we are going to use the single-stage performance equations derived in this chapter, we need not analyze those parts of the circuit shown within the boxes; i.e., the transistor portion has already been analyzed.

Although we will use the single-stage method of analysis, it is necessary to emphasize its relation to that of the general mesh or nodal method. We could analyze the circuit of Figure 8-13 in its entirety by writing either mesh or nodal equations. If we did this, we would have to include the actual equivalent circuit of the transistor, as shown within the boxes. This would result in simultaneous equations, the number of equations being equal to the number of meshes (or nodes), and would be solved by determinants. Since even with only a two-stage amplifier the number of mesh equations is large, the solution of

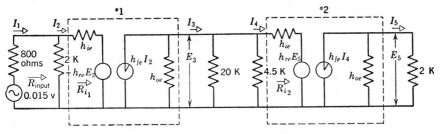

Fig. 8-13. The a-c equivalent of Fig. 8-12.

Parameters of #1	Parameters of #2
$h_{ie} = 890$	$h_{ie} = 2500$
$h_{re} = 5.89 \times 10^{-4}$	$h_{re} = 2 \times 10^{-3}$
$h_{fe} = 21.2$	$h_{fe} = 49$
$h_{oe} = 2.22 \times 10^{-5}$	$h_{oe} = 5 \times 10^{-5}$
$\Delta^{he} = 7.25 \times 10^{-3}$	$\Delta^{he} = 2.7 \times 10^{-2}$

such simultaneous equations is difficult. This difficulty can be avoided by considering the circuit on a stage-by-stage basis, and using the results we have found in this chapter.

We will use the circuit of Figure 8-13, then, to illustrate the use of the single-stage method. We will find the power gain, the actual output power, and the transducer gain for this circuit.

To find the power gain, the relation of Equation (17) will be used:

$$A_p = \frac{I_5^2 R_L}{I_1^2 R_i} = A_i^2 \frac{R_L}{R_i} \qquad (68)$$

The quantities we have to calculate are the A_i and the R_i. To do this one must begin with the last stage and work to the left.

Second stage. For the second stage the calculations are direct. Using the previously found equations,

$$A_{i_2} = \frac{I_5}{I_4} = \frac{h_{fe}}{h_{oe}R_L + 1} = \frac{49}{[(5 \times 10^{-5})(2 \times 10^3) + 1]} = 44.5 \quad (69)$$

$$R_{i_2} = \frac{\Delta^h R_L + h_{ie}}{h_{oe}R_L + 1} = \frac{(2.7 \times 10^{-2})(2 \times 10^3) + 2500}{(5 \times 10^{-5})(2 \times 10^3) + 1} = 2322 \quad (70)$$

Interstage. We need to find the current gain of the interstage because not all of the first-stage output current (I_3) flows into the second-stage input (I_4). Therefore, we need to find the ratio of I_4 to I_3 by using basic circuitry methods. The interstage appears as in

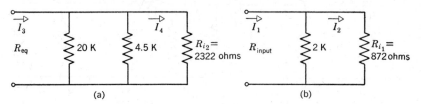

Fig. 8-14. The interstage networks of Fig. 8-13: (a) interstage between stages 1 and 2; (b) interstage between source and stage 1.

Figure 8-14(a). By use of the current division law, the value of I_4 is found to be

$$I_4 = \frac{(20K)(4.5K)/24.5K}{[(20K)(4.5K)/(24.5K] + 2322)} I_3 = 0.6215 \qquad (71)$$

The ratio, or current amplification is then:

$$(A_i)_{\text{interstage}} = \frac{I_4}{I_3} = 0.6125 \qquad (72)$$

By combining the three parallel resistors of Figure 8-14, the equivalent resistance is found to be

$$\frac{1}{R_{\text{eq}}} = \frac{1}{2322} + \frac{1}{4500} + \frac{1}{20,000} \qquad (73)$$
$$R_{\text{eq}} = 1420$$

First stage. It is necessary to know the R_{eq} above because *this forms the load resistance* (R_{L_1}) *of the first stage.* Calculating the current gain and input resistance with this value of R_{L_1}:

$$A_{i_1} = \frac{I_3}{I_2} = \frac{h_{fe}}{h_{oe}R_{L_1} + 1} = \frac{21.2}{(2.22 \times 10^{-5})(1.42 \times 10^3) + 1}$$
$$= 20.5 \qquad (74)$$

$$R_i = \frac{\Delta^h R_{L_1} + h_{ie}}{h_{oe}R_{L_1} + 1} = \frac{(7.25 \times 10^{-3})(1.4 \times 10^3) + 890}{(2.22 \times 10^{-5})(1.42 \times 10^3 + 1)}$$
$$= 872 \qquad (75)$$

Pre-first stage. We have yet to find the current gain and input resistance for the single resistor preceding the first stage. This must be charged to the amplifier since it is a bias resistor. The simple circuit for this appears in Figure 8-14(b).

$$(A_i)_{\text{pre}} = \frac{I_2}{I_1} = \frac{2000}{2000 + 872} = 0.697 \tag{76}$$

$$R_{\text{input}} = \frac{R_1 R_2}{R_1 + R_2} = \frac{(2 \times 10^3)(872)}{(2 \times 10^3) + 872} = 607 \tag{77}$$

Total power gain. We can now find the total current gain by simply multiplying all the individual gains:

$$(A_i)_{\text{total}} = \frac{I_5}{I_1} = (0.697)(20.5)(0.6125)(44.5) = 390 \tag{78}$$

The R_i, of course, is equal to the R input found above:

$$R_{\text{input}} = 607 \tag{79}$$

Thus the total power gain is

$$A_p = A_i^2 \frac{R_L}{R_i} = (390)^2 \frac{2 \times 10^3}{607} = 501,000 = 57.1 \text{ db} \tag{80}$$

Now we see why it is necessary to begin with the last stage and work to the left. The last-stage input resistance depends upon its load resistance; the previous stage's load resistance depends upon the last-stage input, and so on.

Using this stage-by-stage method, any transistor circuit can be analyzed relatively quickly. It is necessary to be careful when finding the a-c equivalent circuit, since this is a critical step in the procedure. Unless great accuracy is required, the reactive elements may usually be eliminated (as was done here) at the frequencies of interest. Following the procedure illustrated above, then, the great number of simultaneous equations otherwise required is avoided.

Output power. Before leaving this example, it is interesting to find the transducer gain and the value of power output. Using the source values as shown in Figure 8-13, the input power supplied by the generator is

$$P_{\text{in}} = \frac{E_g^2 R_i}{(R_g + R_i)^2} = \frac{(1.5 \times 10^{-2})^2}{(800 + 607)^2} 607 = 6.9 \times 10^{-8} \text{ watts} \tag{81}$$

Multiplying this by the power gain found above, the power output is

$$\begin{aligned} P_{\text{out}} &= P_{\text{in}} A_p = (6.9 \times 10^{-8})(5.01 \times 10^5) \\ &= 34.6 \times 10^{-3} \text{ watts} = 34.6 \text{ milliwatts} \end{aligned} \tag{82}$$

Thus if the load of the circuit consisted of a loudspeaker (with a transformer to transform resistance to 2000 ohms) there would be 34.6 milliwatts of power available for conversion into acoustical energy.

For calculating the transducer gain we need the available power from the generator. This is

$$P_{\text{gen. avail.}} = \frac{E_g^2}{4R_g} = \frac{(1.5 \times 10^{-2})^2}{4 \times 800} = 7.04 \times 10^{-8}\,\text{watt} \qquad (83)$$

The transducer gain is then

$$\text{transducer gain} = \frac{P_{\text{out}}}{P_{\text{gen. avail.}}} = \frac{34.6 \times 10^{-3}}{7.04 \times 10^{-8}}$$

$$= 4.92 \times 10^5 = 56.3\,\text{db} \qquad (84)$$

It is noted that the transducer gain is nearly equal to the power gain. Therefore the generator is being utilized efficiently and this is verified by noting the near match between the generator 800 ohms and the input 607 ohms.

In conclusion, then, the single-stage method depicted in this example shows that a multistage network can be analyzed in a straight-forward manner without encountering the set of simultaneous equations resulting from use of the general mesh or nodal method.

It is interesting to compare the situation encountered with vacuum tubes to the analysis method just described. For vacuum tubes, the single-stage method is natural because the input of a vacuum tube is isolated from the output. Thus if the equivalent circuit of a vacuum tube is inserted in a network, the resulting circuit is already broken up due to the isolation between grid and plate. Hence the stage-by-stage method is very appropriate. For the transistor, as we have seen, the output is not isolated from the input. This can be stated in this manner: the transistor has internal feedback. Consequently, any network containing a transistor equivalent circuit is a fully connected network and the general mesh or nodal equations seem applicable. However, a great saving in work can be accomplished by using the stage-by-stage method and thus utilizing the performance equations derived in this chapter.

Problems

1. What is the power gain of each of the transistor amplifiers shown in Figure 8-15? The grounded-base h parameters for the transistor used in these circuits are $h_{ib} = 50$ ohms, $h_{rb} = 5 \times 10^{-4}$, $h_{fb} = -0.97$, and $h_{ob} = 10^{-6}$ mho.

2. What are the transducer gains for the amplifiers of Figure 8-15?
3. Calculate the available gains for the circuits of Figure 8-15.
4. What are the maximum available gains for the circuits of Figure 8-15?
5. How do the stage gains compare with the transducer gains, available gains, and maximum available gains for the amplifiers of Figure 8-15?

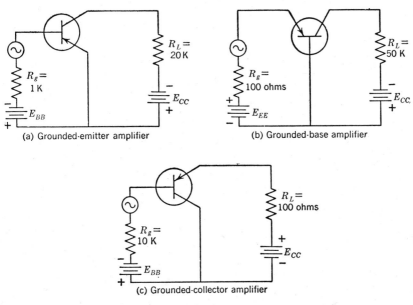

(a) Grounded-emitter amplifier   (b) Grounded-base amplifier

(c) Grounded-collector amplifier

Fig. 8-15. Transistor amplifiers.

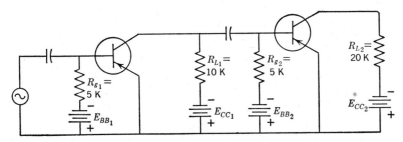

Fig. 8-16. Two-stage grounded-emitter amplifier.

6. Calculate the gain of the two-stage amplifier shown in Figure 8-16. Show the gain of the two individual stages and the interstage losses. Use the same transistor parameters as in Problem 1. The internal resistance of the generator is 1000 ohms.

9

Power Amplifiers

A general situation that occurs in electronic circuits consists of having a series of cascaded amplifiers that amplify a very small signal until sufficient power is available to perform some useful work (such as drive a radio speaker). In such a situation the signal level grows with each stage until the final stage is reached.

For analyzing such a series of cascaded amplifiers, the first few stages may usually be treated as small-signal amplifiers and the methods of the previous chapter are applicable. The stages following these small-signal amplifiers, however, will be operating at a higher signal level so that the equivalent circuit method is no longer accurate. It is remembered from Chapter 7 that the parameters of an equivalent circuit are applicable only within a small region of a specified operating point. If the transistor operation swings over a region greater than this, the method of graphical analysis must be used for accurate results. Many times, of course, a large-signal, single-stage amplifier will be encountered, and again the graphical procedure must be used.

In general, the last stage of a series of cascaded stages is called the *power stage*. The power amplifier is distinguished from all the stages that precede it in that here a concentrated effort is made *to obtain a maximum output power*. In this chapter it will be seen that, because of physical limitations, this criterion conflicts with the criterion of maximum power gain. Also the problem of distortion appears. A transistor that is suitable for a power amplifier is usually called a *power transistor*. This differs from other transistors mostly in its size; it is considerably larger to provide for handling the greater amount of power.

Although specifically treating power amplifiers, *this chapter should be also construed as dealing with the methods of large-signal amplifiers in general*. In other words, the method of graphical analysis used for power amplifiers is identical with the graphical method used for large-signal amplifiers in general. The difference is that for a large-signal circuit that is not a power amplifier, the performance criterion is the same as for the small-signal amplifiers—maximum *power gain*. For example, the stage (or stages) immediately preceding the power amplifier usually require a large-signal analysis, and are called *driver* stages. For these driver stages, *maximum* power gain is generally the basic criterion.

Power amplifiers are classified according to their mode of operation as Class A, B, C, or a combination of Class A and B referred to as Class A-B. For transistors, the important types are Class A and Class B.

It will be the object of this chapter to describe and analyze the Class A and Class B power amplifiers. Graphical analysis, of course, will be used to accomplish this. Although the design of electronic circuits can never be reduced to a set procedure, a design example will be given for each type of power amplifier to illustrate the general approach.

Performance Quantities

As stated, the prime objective for a power amplifier is to obtain the maximum output power. Since the transistor, like every electronic device, has voltage, current, and power dissipation limits, the criteria for a power amplifier are: (1) collector efficiency; (2) distortion; and (3) power dissipation capability. An additional criterion is frequency response, but we shall here restrict the analysis to those frequencies where the characteristics are accurate.

Physical limitations. Before considering the actual performance quantities it is necessary to consider the current, voltage, and power limitations of the transistor.

The voltage limitation applies mainly to the collector junction since this is the junction that experiences the high bias voltage in both the grounded-base and the grounded-emitter connections. It was noted in Chapter 5 that the Zener effect may be induced if an excessive voltage is applied to a semiconductor junction. If the Zener effect occurs, a high current will flow and transistor action will cease. Two other effects of an excessive voltage are (1) the widening of the depletion region so that the emitter may be ohmically connected to the collector; and (2) the back current that flows because of thermal generation may become high enough so that the junction temperature will rise—this causes a greater current and the action may become self-sustaining. For either of the above three reasons, then, every transistor has a maximum allowable collector voltage that is specified by the manufacturer.[1]

The allowable power dissipation of the transistor is a very important item for power transistors. Since the transistor possesses resistances, as evidenced by h_{11} and h_{22} of the equivalent circuit, the usual I^2R power losses occur within the transistor. Since any temperature changes influence the semiconductor operation of the transistor (Chapter 4), the heat generated by these power losses must be dissipated to the surroundings. The amount of heat that can be dissipated depends almost entirely upon the physical construction of the transistor and the temperature of the surroundings (ambient temperature). Sometimes provision is made to fasten the transistor on a heat-conducting body, such as a chassis, so that additional heat can be dissipated in this manner. Therefore every transistor will have a specified value of power which it can dissipate under specified conditions and this value is always stated by the manufacturer. If the design conditions specify a temperature higher than that quoted by the manufacturer, the given dissipation value must be decreased accordingly. Again, information provided by the manufacturer will allow calculation of the proper decrease.

The most direct effect of this power limitation upon the design of power amplifiers is that the product of the voltage and current of the operating point should never exceed the maximum power dissipation. We shall see the reason for this in a later section. For any transistor, then, we can draw a curve of constant power dissipation; that is, a curve on which the product of current and voltage at any

[1]The current is limited by hot spots produced by high current density across the collector junction and in some transistors (such as the grown junction) by size of contacts in the base region.

point is equal to the allowable power dissipation. We shall see such a curve in the next section.

Power efficiency. At first the problem of obtaining a maximum output power may seem identical with the problem of obtaining an optimum power gain, as for the small-signal amplifiers. However, the voltage and current limitations specify that power gain be sacrificed for a maximum power output. A simple example will serve to illustrate this.

Figure 9-1 shows the characteristics of a power transistor. On these characteristics the curved line is the power dissipation curve mentioned in the preceding section. The operating point should never be placed in the region to the right of this curve. Figure 9-1(a) also shows the maximum allowable current and voltage values on the respective axes.

Referring to Chapter 7 for the construction of load lines, we see that if an operating point on the dissipation curve is used, the loads (1) and (2) can be used without exceeding the maximum values of current and voltage. These load lines correspond to the operating points Q_1 and Q_2 (for equal swings) and load resistances of 40 ohms and 7 ohms, respectively.

From the previous chapter we remember that maximum power gain is realized if the load is matched to the output resistance. The transistor of Figure 9-1(a) has an output resistance of approximately 2500 ohms; the load line for a load resistance of 2500 ohms is shown in Figure 9-1(b).

By comparing Figures 9-1(a) and 9-1(b) we can see why power gain is sacrificed to obtain a maximum power output. Although the power gain of Figure 9-1(b) is high, only an extremely small input is allowed before the maximum voltage value is exceeded. Therefore the power output of Figure 9-1(b) is much less than for either of the loads shown in Figure 9-1(a).

It is for this reason, then, that the power gain is not suitable as a criterion for power amplifier performance. The criterion that is suitable is the *collector efficiency*, which is defined as the ratio of the output power to the d-c input power supplied by the battery.

$$\text{collector eff.} = \frac{\text{a-c output power}}{\text{battery input power}} \qquad (1)$$

The conclusion, then, is that for small-signal amplifiers and driver

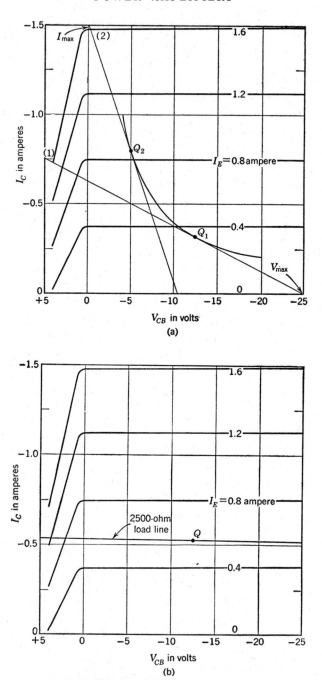

Fig. 9-1. Characteristics showing permissible load lines with current and voltage limitations.

stages a maximum power gain is the desirable goal, while for power amplifiers a maximum collector efficiency is the optimum case. This is the design difference between the small-signal and power amplifiers.

Distortion. Whenever large signals are applied to electronic devices such as the transistor and the vacuum tube the problem of distortion immediately appears. This is true because each of these devices is essentially nonlinear. We noted this in Chapter 7, when it was learned that the equivalent circuit parameters change for different points on the set of characteristics. If the transistor were perfectly linear one set of parameters would be suitable for all regions on the characteristics.

The result of distortion is that the output signal is not exactly like the input signal. Thus the amount of distortion present can be regarded as determining the "accuracy" of the electronic circuit. It is clear that distortion is not a problem for the small-signal circuits since the transistor is linear for small variations about an operating point.

A common measure of distortion is the amount of *second harmonic distortion.* If a pure sine wave is applied to a power amplifier the distortion can be measured by noting the variation from the sine wave in the output. Since a nonsine wave can be considered the sum of a series of sine waves of different frequencies (Fourier analysis), the nonsine wave output can be analyzed in this manner. The value of the second harmonic distortion (alone) is a close approximation to the total distortion. For the comparison of two power amplifiers, that amplifier which has the lower second harmonic distortion is the better.

We shall briefly analyze the distortion values for the amplifiers considered in this chapter. The equations and methods will be considered there.

Class A Power Amplifiers

Amplifiers are defined as Class A, Class B, or Class A-B depending upon where the bias point is placed with respect to the total swing of the signal. Class A operation occurs when the bias point is placed so that the signal swing does not carry the operation out of the region of normal transistor action. The small-signal amplifiers discussed in the preceding chapter were implicitly regarded as Class A.

Since the power amplifier is a large-signal situation we shall use the method of graphical analysis to describe it. For this the concepts discussed in Chapter 7 will be relied upon. It is remembered that the essential concept consists of superimposing the graph of the attached circuit on the graph of the transistor characteristics. Although both the grounded-base and the grounded-emitter connections are suitable for Class A amplifiers, we will begin by considering the grounded-base case.

Figure 9-2 shows the conventional grounded-base circuit and the graphical operation. It is remembered from Chapter 7 that the load line is determined by the collector battery and the value of the load resistance. The operating point occurs, on the load line, at the proper value of input (emitter) current. The total swing is then determined by the variation in input current produced by the signal.

Another circuit that is useful for power amplifiers is shown in Figure 9-3(a), and is called the *shunt-fed* circuit. The essential feature of this circuit is that, for the output side, separate paths are provided for the a-c signal and the d-c bias currents. The inductor provides practically a zero resistance path for the biasing direct current. This eliminates the d-c power losses in the load resistance and allows the use of a lower bias battery. For the a-c signal output the inductor presents a high impedance so that the alternating current flows through the load resistance. The capacitor prevents the biasing direct current from flowing through the load.

The action of separating the d-c and a-c paths is also accomplished by using an output transformer, as in Figure 9-3(b). An additional feature here is that any value of R_L^1 can be transformed to a suitable R_L by varying the turns-ratio of the transformer. The graphical analysis of this circuit is identical to that of (a), and we can regard the transformer circuit as a type of shunt-fed circuit. Note that R_L, and not R_L^1, is the load resistance used for the load line.

Since the a-c and the d-c loads of the shunt-fed circuits are not the same, we have to construct two separate load lines; one to find the d-c operating point and the other to depict the operation when an a-c signal is present. One begins by constructing the d-c load line in the manner described above; if the d-c resistance is practically zero, the d-c load line appears vertical as shown in Figure 9-3. After the operating point is determined the a-c load line is constructed to pass through this point. This a-c load line may be constructed by momentarily assuming that the a-c load is the only one present. The

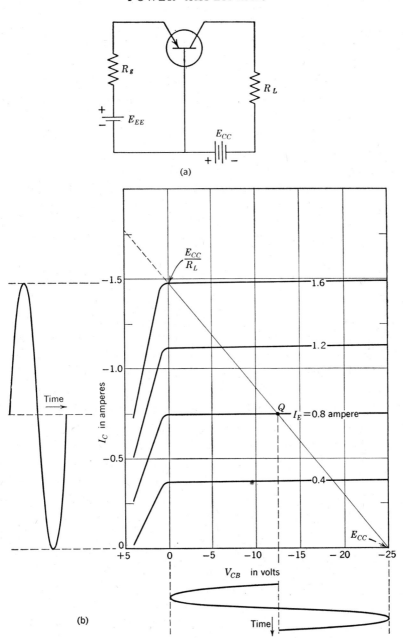

Fig. 9-2. (a) Conventional grounded-base circuit with its (b) graphical operation.

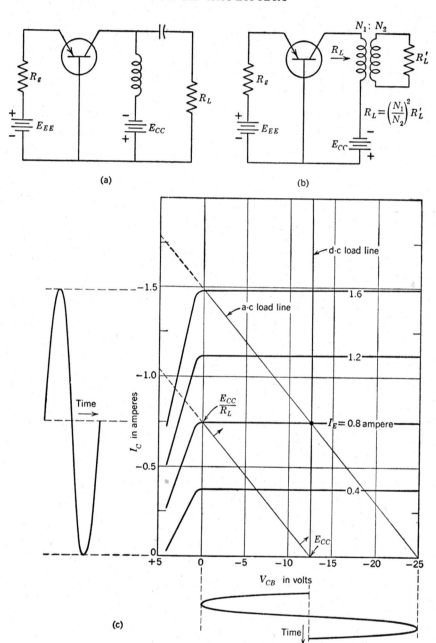

Fig. 9-3. (a) Conventional shunt-fed circuit; (b) separation of d-c and a-c paths using an output transformer; (c) graphical analysis of these circuits.

resulting line must then be moved parallel to itself until it intercepts the operating point. This process is shown on the graph of Figure 9-3. This a-c load line, then, must be used to depict the a-c operation of the circuit.

It is important to stress that, for *any* circuit in which the a-c and the d-c load values are not the same, the two separate load lines must be constructed—the d-c load line to determine the operating point and the a-c load line to find the a-c operation. This situation is very

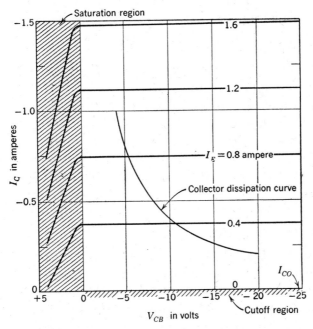

Fig. 9-4. Characteristics showing the saturation and the cutoff regions.

common and occurs whenever amplifiers are coupled by capacitors or when inductors are used for biasing circuits. Therefore, *for any large-signal analysis, the two load lines must be constantly kept in mind.*

In Figure 9-3 it is noted that, since the same value of load resistance is used, the a-c operation is identical to that of Figure 9-2. The difference is that the circuit of Figure 9-3 needs a smaller battery to achieve the same operating point and its power efficiency is higher.

It is useful to define two regions on the set of transistor characteristics: the *saturation region* and the *cutoff region*. These regions are shown on the characteristics of Figure 9-4. It is seen that the saturation region begins where the spacing between the constant-emitter-current curves becomes irregular, and that the cutoff region starts at the $I_e = 0$ curve. Although the $I_e = 0$ curve appears along the voltage axis on Figure 9-4 (as is usually the case for large power transistors), it should be noted that this curve corresponds to the back current flowing across a reversed bias diode, and was formerly labeled I_{co}.

Operating point. For Class A amplifiers the choice of operating point depends upon the total swing of the signal and the allowable power dissipation of the transistor. In general, the operating point may be placed at any point to the left of the *constant dissipation curve*. Usually it is placed about midway between the saturation and the cutoff region so that equal swings on either side of the bias point can occur without clipping.

The constant dissipation curve, mentioned previously, is also shown on the graph of Figure 9-4 above. This curve is calculated in the following manner: select a value of voltage on the V_{cb} axis; divide this voltage into the value of maximum power dissipation stated by the manufacturer—the result is the allowable collector current for the chosen value of voltage; finally, plot the resulting point on the graph. The above procedure can be defined by the equation

$$P_{diss} = V_c I_c = \text{constant} \tag{2}$$

If this equation is used for the whole range of voltage values, the curve shown in Figure 9-4 will result.

The value of dissipation stated by the manufacturer holds only for room temperature (25°C). If the transistor is used in surroundings that are at a higher temperature than this, the allowable dissipation must be calculated by the relation

$$P_{diss} = K(T_{max} - T_{ambient}) \tag{3}$$

where K = degradation factor in watts per degree centigrade,
    T_{max} = maximum allowable temperature for the transistor,
    $T_{ambient}$ = temperature of surroundings.

The various manufacturers are presently not consistent in the manner of giving the dissipation-versus-temperature information. Sometimes the factors of Equation (3) are given directly so that the allowable power for any given temperature can be calculated directly. At other times only the room temperature dissipation and the maximum temperature of the transistor are given. In this case, the following relation can be used to calculate K:

$$K = \frac{P_{\text{diss}} \text{ at } 25°\text{C}}{T_{\text{max}} - 25°\text{C}} \qquad (4)$$

By use of Equations (3) and (4), then, the proper dissipation curve can be drawn, similar to the curve of Figure 9-4.

If the maximum possible output of the transistor is required, the operating point should be placed on or near the dissipation curve. If less power output is required, any suitable point in the region to the left of the dissipation curve is permissible.

Load. With the operating point set, the next step is to decide upon the load resistance. The general idea is to select a load line that allows equal swings on either side of the operating point. This can be approximated graphically by placing a ruler on the bias point and rotating it.

Within the restriction of equal swings, it is generally best to use the higher values of load resistance that are suitable. Even though this may result in the same power output it will increase the power gain somewhat. Consequently less power will be needed to drive the power amplifier to its full output.

Performance equations. We are interested here in calculating the power output, the collector efficiency, and the amount of distortion. Figure 9-5 shows the graphical operation obtained with either the circuit (a) or (b) provided that the same R_L is used for both. Note that circuit (b) is meant to include also the output transformer circuit.

Since the load is resistive we can calculate the a-c power output by multiplying the alternating voltage by the alternating current. This a-c power is independent of the bias conditions and depends only on the maximum and minimum values of output waves. Referring to Figure 9-5, the maximum value of the sine-wave output voltage is

$$E_m = \frac{E_{\text{max}} - E_{\text{min}}}{2} \qquad (5)$$

Remembering that the rms value of a sine wave is determined by dividing E_m by $\sqrt{2}$:

$$E_{\text{rms}} = \frac{E_{\text{max}} - E_{\text{min}}}{2\sqrt{2}} \qquad (6)$$

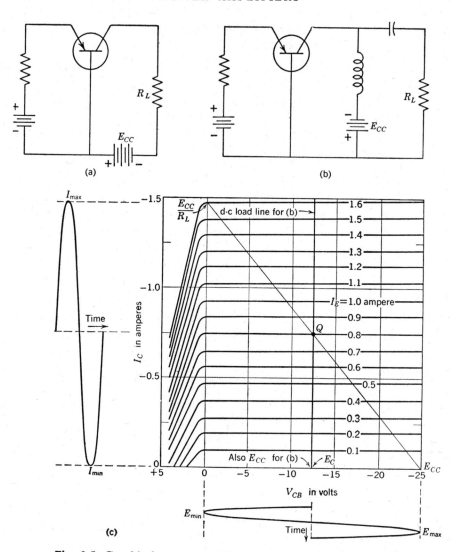

Fig. 9-5. Graphical operation of both conventional and shunt-fed Class A, grounded-base operation.

Performing the same operation for the current,

$$I_{rms} = \frac{I_{max} - I_{min}}{2\sqrt{2}} \tag{6a}$$

The a-c power output, consequently, is

$$P_{out} = E_{rms}I_{rms} = \frac{(E_{max} - E_{min})(I_{max} - I_{min})}{8} \tag{7}$$

To find the collector efficiency, we need to know the power supplied by the battery. Since the battery can supply only d-c power, the power must be the product of E_{cc} and I_c:

$$P_{\text{battery}} = E_{cc}I_c \qquad (8)$$

Although the output alternating current may flow through the battery, as in (a) of Figure 9-5, the battery itself supplies only I_c. It is useful to think of the total output current as an a-c sine wave superimposed on the d-c component I_c.

The collector efficiency, then, is given by the ratio of Equation (7) to Equation (8).

$$\text{collector eff.} = \frac{P_{\text{output}}}{P_{\text{input}}} = \frac{(E_{\max} - E_{\min})(I_{\max} - I_{\min})}{8E_{cc}I_c} \qquad (9)$$

Equation (9) tells us how much of the input battery power is converted to useful a-c output power. In this sense the transistor acts as a *convertor;* it converts d-c input power to a-c output power.

It is useful to find the "ideal" collector efficiencies for the circuits of (a) and (b); that is, the collector efficiencies if the transistor were ideal. An ideal transistor would have perfectly linear characteristics, for our purposes we may say that the characteristics of 9-5(c) are ideal. The value of I_{co} causes a reduction in the efficiency derived in the following material. For the conventional circuit of (a), the maximum possible voltage swing for an ideal transistor would be

$$E_{\max} - E_{\min} = E_{cc} \qquad (10)$$

For this condition, the current swing would be

$$I_{\max} - I_{\min} = 2I_c \qquad (11)$$

Substituting these two relations into Equation (9),

$$\text{ideal coll. eff.} = \frac{E_{cc}2I_c}{8E_{cc}I_c} = 25\% \qquad (12)$$

Therefore the ideal collector efficiency for the circuit of Figure 9-5(a) is 25%.

For the shunt-fed circuit of (b), the fact that E_{cc} equals E_c results in maximum possible swings (for an ideal transistor) of

$$E_{\max} - E_{\min} = 2E_{cc}$$
$$I_{\max} - I_{\min} = 2I_c \qquad (13)$$

The ideal collector efficiency then is

$$\text{ideal coll. eff.} = \frac{(2E_{cc})(2I_c)}{8E_{cc}I_c} = 50\% \tag{14}$$

Consequently the ideal collector efficiency for the shunt-fed circuit is 50%. It is now clear why the shunt-fed circuit may be desirable for Class A power amplifiers.

Although an ideal efficiency can never be reached since the transistor itself is never ideal, it can be closely approximated by a good design. Ideal efficiencies are useful for comparing the various connections and for making preliminary approximate calculations.

Making use of the above power relations, we may now find the dissipation power for the transistor. We have simply to write a power equation:

$$P_{in} = P_{output} - P_{losses} \tag{15}$$

Since any input power on the emitter (input) side is negligible compared with the powers on the collector side, the only essential input power is supplied by the collector battery. Then

$$P_{battery} = P_{output} + \text{d-c losses in load resistance} + P_{diss. of transistor} \tag{16}$$

This equation applies to both circuits (a) and (b) if it is remembered that, for any shunt-fed circuit, the d-c load resistance losses are zero. We may write then

$$E_{cc}I_c = P_{output} + I_c^2 R_{L_{dc}} + P_{diss} \tag{17}$$

Solving for the P_{diss},

$$\begin{aligned} P_{diss} &= E_{cc}I_c - I_c^2 R_L - P_{output} \\ &= I_c(E_{cc} - I_c R_L) - P_{output} \end{aligned} \tag{18}$$

From the circuit of Figure 9-5(a), a simple d-c mesh equation will verify that $E_c = E_{cc} - I_c R_L$; for the circuit (b), $E_{cc} \cong E_c$ and $R_{L_{d-c}} = 0$. Therefore, for either case,

$$P_{diss} = E_c I_c - P_{output} \tag{19}$$

Since $E_c I_c$ is the operating point, *we now see why the operating point is restricted by the dissipation curve mentioned earlier.*

If there is no a-c power output, momentarily, Equation (19) tells us the transistor must dissipate a power equal to the product of E_c

and I_c. This is why it is necessary to calculate the power dissipation curve and keep the operating point to the left of this curve. Since an operating amplifier does not always have a signal present, the design must be based on the worst condition; i.e., when no signal is present. Note that the above applies to both conventional and shunt-fed circuits.

We can now find the relation between the required transistor power dissipation and the desired output power. For the shunt-fed circuit the E_{cc} is practically equal to E_c (see Figure 9-5). Then the dissipation, for the worst condition of no signal, must be

$$P_{\text{diss}} = E_{cc}I_c = P_{\text{battery}} \tag{20}$$

Since the ideal collector efficiency, for the shunt-fed case, is 50%, the ideal power out is

$$(P_{\text{out}})_{\text{ideal}} = 0.50P_{\text{battery}} \tag{21}$$

Then, using Equation (20), the dissipation capability required is

$$(P_{\text{diss}})_{\text{ideal}} = \frac{(P_{\text{out}})_{\text{ideal}}}{0.50} = 2(P_{\text{out}})_{\text{ideal}} \tag{22}$$

For the conventional circuit with a series load resistance, the E_c is approximately $E_{cc}/2$ if an ideal full swing is used. Using the 25% ideal efficiency of this circuit and performing the same operations as above, Equation (22) is found to hold for this circuit also.

Since an ideal efficiency is never achieved, the required dissipation will always be somewhat greater than that specified by Equation (22). Therefore, for any required output power in Class A operation, *the transistor must be capable of dissipating greater than twice the amount of output power.* This criterion is very useful for the initial selection of a transistor.

Distortion. The sources of distortion in Class A amplifiers are (1) nonequal spacing between constant-current curves along the load line, (2) the nonlinear input resistance, (3) too large a signal so that clipping occurs from saturation or cutoff, and (4) movement of the bias point with variation in temperature.

In the grounded-base connection the constant-emitter-current curves are usually equally spaced so that little distortion is introduced from this source. This quality may be checked, for any transistor and a proper load line, by making a plot of I_C versus I_E. If the result is a straight line up to the saturation region, there is no distortion from nonequal spacing.

The nonlinear input resistance is probably the chief source of distortion for transistor power amplifiers. By nonlinear we mean that the input resistance changes for different values of input current. Thus the input resistance may be 50 ohms for an I_E of 1 ma, and might change to 10 ohms at 5 ma. Figure 9-6 shows the general effect

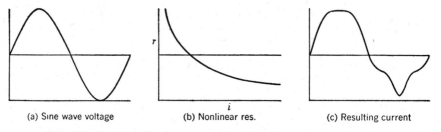

(a) Sine wave voltage   (b) Nonlinear res.   (c) Resulting current

Fig. 9-6. Sketches showing current resulting from sine-wave voltage applied to a nonlinear resistance.

of applying a sine-wave voltage to a nonlinear resistance. Part (b) shows that the nonlinear resistance decreases with increase in current. Part (a) shows the applied sine-wave voltage and (c) indicates the resulting current. It is seen that the current is flattened on the top and exhibits a peak at the bottom.

If the current sketch shown in Figure 9-6(c) were the input current of a transistor amplifier, the output current would be an amplified version of the same wave, since the basic phenomenon of a transistor consists of operating upon the input current. Consequently, if a sine-wave *voltage* is applied to a transistor power amplifier, the output signal will be distorted similarly to (c) of Figure 9-6.

The remedy for this *consists of using a current generator to drive the transistor power amplifier*. That is, a generator that has a high impedance compared with the range of values of the transistor input resistance must be used. If this is the case, the changing input resistance will hardly affect the total resistance, so that a nondistorted sine-wave input *current*, and consequently output current, will result. Remember that the source may be either an actual generator or the Thevenin's equivalent of the preceding circuit.

The price paid for this remedy, however, is that the power gain of generator plus amplifier is reduced. The presence of a high series resistance means that signal power is being lost. Therefore the amount of distortion must always be weighed against the loss of signal power in any particular design. For grounded-base amplifiers, a source resistance of about twice the normal input resistance is usually used.

Distortion caused by clipping occurs when the signal swings into the saturation or the cutoff regions (defined in Figure 9-4). Both saturation and cutoff would cause the output sine wave to be flat-topped. If the allowable power dissipation permits, the clipping may be remedied by moving the operating point farther from the origin (of the graph). If the operating point is already on the dissipation curve, the only remedy is either to change the load or to decrease the output signal.

If the signal operates close to the saturation and the cutoff region, distortion may be induced if the bias point is shifted because of a change in ambient temperature. The shift would allow the signal to move into either the saturation or the cutoff region. We remember, from the physics chapter, that the properties of the transistor are temperature dependent. The most drastic effect, when temperature changes occur, is the shift in operating point. This can be remedied only by bias stabilization. This topic will be considered in detail in Chapter 11. The methods described there can be used to eliminate this source of distortion.

Many times it is convenient to measure the distortion of an amplifier by the use of a harmonic analyzer. If we wish to calculate the amount of distortion, techniques making use of the graphical analysis are available. These techniques consist essentially of finding the coefficients of the various harmonics (in the Fourier series) that are present in the output signal. Although we shall not describe these methods here, one common measure of distortion is the amount of second harmonic present. Referring to the quantities of Figure 9-5, the second harmonic component can be shown to be

$$\text{second harmonic} = \frac{1}{\sqrt{2}}\left(\frac{I_{max} + I_{min}}{4} - \frac{1}{2}I_c\right) \qquad (23)$$

The per cent distortion is then found by dividing this value by the fundamental component of Equation 6(a):

$$\% \text{ second harmonic distortion} = \frac{\frac{1}{4}(I_{max} + I_{min}) - \frac{1}{2}I_c}{\frac{1}{2}(I_{max} - I_{min})} \times 100 \qquad (24)$$

Using Equation (24), then, the per cent of second harmonic distortion can be used as a measure of the total distortion.

Grounded emitter class A amplifier. All the methods and equations of the previous sections, illustrated for the grounded-base connection, apply equally well to the grounded-emitter case. The difference lies in using the grounded-emitter characteristics; i.e., the constant-current curves are for the base current I_B and the collector voltage is the voltage from collector to emitter V_{CE}. Also it may be noted that the characteristic $I_E = 0$ is the cutoff current for grounded-emitter connection; this curve I_{CEO} is related to the I_{CO} curve (for the

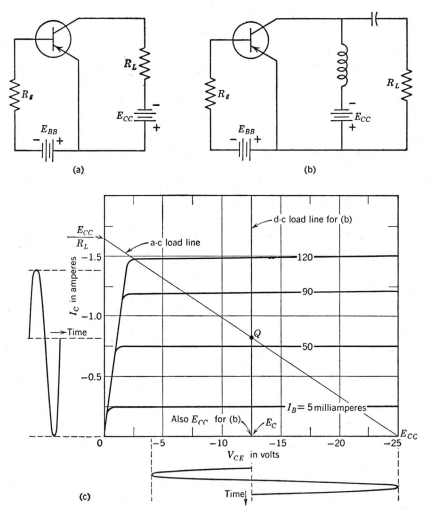

Fig. 9-7. Graphical operation of both conventional and shunt-fed Class A grounded-emitter operation.

grounded base) by the relation,

$$I_{CEO} = \frac{I_{CO}}{1 + h_{21}} \qquad (24a)$$

These characteristics are shown in Figure 9-7. Again the choice of a conventional or a shunt-fed circuit is available. The graphical procedure, applied to Figure 9-7, is identical to the procedure shown before for the grounded base.

Concerning distortion, it is remembered that the four sources are: (1) nonequal spacing of current curves, (2) nonlinear input resistance, (3) clipping, and (4) movement of bias point.

By comparing Figure 9-7 with Figure 9-5 it can be seen that the constant-current curves for the grounded emitter are more nonuniformly spaced than for the grounded base. *Thus the grounded emitter has inherently more distortion than the base connection.* This may be remedied, somewhat, by choosing a proper source resistance.

Since the grounded-emitter input resistance is nonlinear, as in the grounded-base case, the source resistance is chosen on the basis of compensating for this nonlinearity and also for correcting the inherent distortion mentioned above. Since these two considerations are opposing, there is usually an optimum value of source resistance for providing minimum distortion. Typical values of source resistance vary from one to three times the normal input resistance.

The clipping and bias stabilization aspects of the grounded emitter are identical to those of the grounded base.

Although the grounded-emitter amplifier will provide more *power gain* than the grounded-base amplifier (like the small-signal case), the power output for a given value of distortion will be usually less than that for the grounded-base amplifier, because of the sources of distortion considered above.

Design example. Although each designer follows his own peculiar methods, and each design is different, the following is given as an example of the design of a Class A power amplifier.

Problem. It is desired to design a single-stage, grounded-base transistor power amplifier that will supply 1.5 watts of audio power to a loudspeaker with a voice coil impedance of 4.0 ohms.

Solution. The first step is to select a transistor, and the most essential criterion is the power-dissipating capability. From Equation (22) we know that the transistor must be able to dissipate at least

twice the output power, or 3.0 watts. Another immediate consideration is that the transistor have sufficient frequency response, in this
case the entire audio spectrum of 0 to 20,000 c.

The Sylvania 2N68 germanium P-N-P power transistor is selected
because it will supply the required power (capable of 4.0 watts dissipation) and has a sufficient frequency response. The characteristic
curves for this transistor are shown in Figure 9-8(a) (for complete
characteristics see Appendix III). In order to assure that the operating

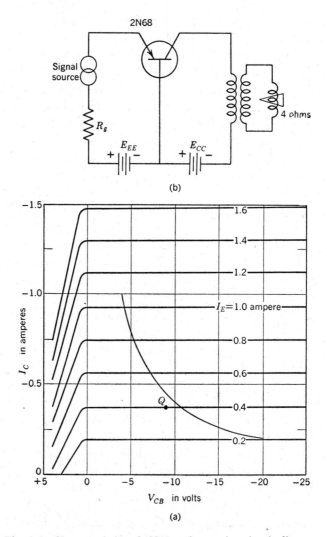

Fig. 9-8. Characteristics of 2N68 and tentative circuit diagram.

point will be placed within the dissipation limits, the dissipation curve
is drawn for these characteristics.

For this design, the voice coil cannot be connected directly in the
collector circuit for two reasons: (1) its resistance is too low to act as a
suitable load for the transistor, and (2) the voice coil will not operate
properly if the bias direct current flows through it. Therefore a transformer will be used on the output side. Note that the transformer also
permits operating close to an ideal 50% efficiency, which would not

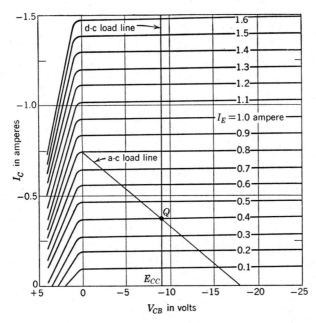

Fig. 9-9. A-c and d-c load lines for Class A, transformer-coupled amplifier of Fig. 9-8.

be possible for the directly connected case. The tentative circuit diagram, then, is shown in Figure 9-8(b).

The next step consists of selecting the operating point. Knowing
that the transistor can dissipate 4.0 watts and that nearly 50% efficiency is possible with the transformer coupling, we note that the
transistor could supply almost 2.0 watts. Since we need only 1.5 watts
we do not have to operate directly on the maximum dissipation curve,
but can operate at a point having slightly greater than 3.0 watts
dissipation.

The available power supply should also be considered when de-
ciding upon the operating point. The maximum transistor collector

voltage is 25 volts, and we remember that the collector voltage has a maximum swing of twice the supply voltage in a Class A transformer connected circuit. Therefore the battery must be less than 12.5 volts. We will select a 9.0 volt battery, although a 12.0 volt battery would be satisfactory. If an emitter current of 0.4 amp is selected, the power dissipation at the operating point is

$$P_{diss} = V_C I_C = 9 \times 0.38 = 3.42 \text{ watts} \qquad (25)$$

This operating point Q is shown on Figure 9-8(a). By placing a ruler through this operating point and rotating it, an a-c load line is selected that has approximately equal swings on both sides of the operating point. A load of 25 ohms will result in a proper load line. The resulting d-c and a-c load lines through the operating point are shown in Figure 9-9. The resulting maximum swings in collector current and voltage can be obtained from this figure:

$$E_{max} \cong 18 \text{ volts} \qquad I_{max} \cong 0.73 \text{ amp}$$
$$E_{min} \cong 0 \text{ volt} \qquad I_{min} \cong 0.02 \text{ amp} \qquad (26)$$

These values correspond to an emitter current peak-to-peak swing of 0.78 amp, or 0.39 amp on either side of the operating point. The output power and collector efficiency under these maximum conditions are

$$P_o = \left(\frac{18}{2\sqrt{2}}\right)\left(\frac{0.71}{2\sqrt{2}}\right) = 1.6 \text{ watts}$$
$$\text{eff.} = \frac{1.6}{3.42} \times 100 = 46.8\% \qquad (27)$$

Therefore the operating point and load resistance are satisfactory. The amplifier has a slightly higher output power available than required and is operating close to the maximum possible efficiency.

The remainder of the design consists of providing the correct emitter bias current, setting the transformer turns ratio, and checking the collector circuit distortion.

The emitter battery and series resistor can be found by writing a d-c equation for the input side. For this equation the emitter-to-base voltage may be neglected if the emitter battery is larger than a few volts. If, in addition, the signal source consists of the secondary of an input transformer, the d-c resistance of the source is essentially zero. Then, selecting a 4.0 volt battery,

$$R_g = \frac{E_{EE}}{I_E} = \frac{4}{0.4} = 10 \text{ ohms} \qquad (28)$$

The final circuit will then be as shown in Figure 9-10. The capacitor across R_g is used to by-pass this resistance for alternating currents. The transformer must exhibit an impedance transformation of 25 to 4, so that the turns ratio is 2.5 to 1.

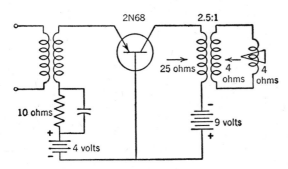

Fig. 9-10. Final grounded-base, Class A transistor power amplifier.

The second harmonic distortion of this circuit may be found by using Equation (24).

$$\left.\begin{array}{c}\text{second harmonic}\\ \text{distortion}\end{array}\right\} = \frac{\frac{1}{4}(I_{max} + I_{min}) - \frac{1}{2}I_C}{\frac{1}{2}(I_{max} - I_{min})} \times 100$$

$$= \frac{\frac{1}{4}(0.73 + 0.02) - \frac{1}{2}(0.38)}{\frac{1}{2}(0.73 + 0.02)} \times 100 = 1.41\% \quad (29)$$

If we wish to know the power gain of this circuit, the approximate input power may be calculated by using the 2 ohm input resistance stated by the manufacturer (Appendix III). The input power for a peak emitter current of 0.39 amp is then

$$P_{in} = I_{rms}^2 R_{in} = \left(\frac{0.39}{\sqrt{2}}\right)^2 2 = 0.152 \text{ watt} \quad (30)$$

Thus 0.152 watt is required to drive the power amplifier for a 1.6 watt output. The resulting power gain is

$$A_p = 10 \log_{10} \frac{P_{out}}{P_{in}} = 10 \log_{10} \frac{1.6}{0.152} = 10 \text{ db} \quad (31)$$

Class B Power Amplifiers

If Class B operation is used in a power amplifier, two transistors placed back to back are required and the two transistors work alternately. That is, if a sine-wave signal is applied, one transistor amplifies the upper half of the wave and the other transistor amplifies the lower half. Class B operation occurs when the bias point is located at cutoff; any signal swing above the bias point will be amplified normally by the transistor, and any signal below cutoff will not be operated on by the transistor. Thus, by placing two transistors back to back, operating Class B, one transistor can be made to amplify the positive signals and the other to amplify the negative signals. The use of this scheme (commonly called push-pull) permits a greater collector efficiency than is possible for the Class A type, although the distortion is usually greater. Consequently the Class B power amplifier is very appropriate if a large power is required and the distortion limits are not too stringent.

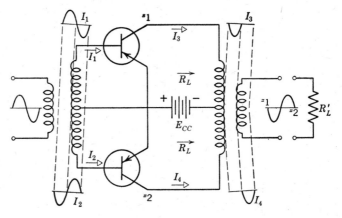

Fig. 9-11. Circuit diagram and waveforms showing basic operation of Class B power amplifiers.

The basic circuit of a Class B power amplifier, using the grounded-emitter connection, is shown in Figure 9-11. The essential operation of this circuit is described in the following. Considering a sine-wave applied to the input terminals, a sine wave of like phase occurs in the upper half of the transformer secondary. Thus the input to transistor #1 is a sine wave whose phase is equal to that of the input. The lower half of the transformer secondary exhibits a current whose phase is opposite to that of the input; therefore transistor #2 receives a sine wave of opposite phase from that of transistor #1. It is seen that the center-tapped transformer acts as a phase inverter for the transistor input. Although other phase inverting circuits are available, the center-tapped transformer is the most convenient.

If both transistors are operating Class B, they are biased at cutoff and will amplify only positive voltages. Referring to Figure 9-11, then, transistor #1 amplifies the first half of the input sine wave and stays in the cutoff condition for the other half. The half cycle amplified by this transistor is inverted in the collector lead because of the 180° phase shift of the grounded-emitter connection. Transistor #2, also amplifying only positive voltages, amplifies the second half of the input wave because its input phase is 180° from that of transistor #1. The currents appearing in the two collector leads are as shown in the figure.

The center-tapped output transformer now combines the two collector currents to form the sine-wave output in the secondary.

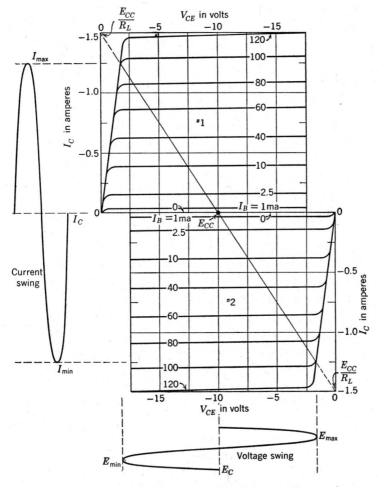

Fig. 9-12. Graphical illustration of Class B, push-pull operation.

It is the phase inversion property of the center-tapped transformer that causes the output of transistor #2 to be inverted in the secondary.

We can illustrate graphically the operation of the amplifier by joining the characteristics of the two transistors in the proper manner. In a push-pull circuit transistors of the same type (and as nearly identical as possible) are used; therefore the two sets of characteristics will be the same. Figure 9-12 shows the back-to-back joining of the characteristics. It is seen that the characteristics of transistor #2 are inverted and joined to those of #1, much in the same manner that the transistors are actually electrically connected. *The two sets of characteristics are aligned at the value of E_{CC},* 10 volts in this case. In order for both transistors to be biased at cutoff, the operating point for each must be on the $I_B = 0$ line and appears as shown in the figure.

A proper load line is shown on the characteristics of Figure 9-12, and the resulting operation is depicted by the current and voltage waves shown. Now it is seen how transistor #1 deals with the upper half of the sine wave, and #2 deals with the lower half.

The important things to note on Figure 9-12, for the present, are: (1) the characteristics are aligned at the value of E_{CC}, since the collector battery is common to both transistors; (2) the load line is drawn for the a-c load resistance, that is, the R'_L transformed through one-half the output transformer; (3) the load line is obtained, for the R_L on both transistors, by the conventional method of noting E_{CC} and E_{CC}/R_L; and finally (4) the d-c load line would be a vertical line at the point $E_{CC} = 10$ since the output side is shunt-fed.

From the above comments it is clear that we could graphically analyze the push-pull circuit by considering only one stage and doubling the proper values. However, by using the total graph of Figure 9-12 we can easily visualize the basic operation.

Performance calculations. We shall refer to Figure 9-12 for finding the performance equations. Many of the calculations are similar to those for the Class A amplifier discussed earlier; therefore we shall treat in detail only that which is new.

The power output is

$$P_{out} = E_{rms}I_{rms} = \frac{(E_{max} - E_{min})}{2\sqrt{2}} \cdot \frac{(I_{max} - I_{min})}{2\sqrt{2}}$$
$$= \frac{(E_{max} - E_{min})(I_{max} - I_{min})}{8} \tag{32}$$

Care must be used in reading the values of E_{max}, E_{min}, I_{max}, and I_{min}. It is noted in Figure 9-12 that the total current and voltage swings move from one set of characteristics to the other. Therefore we *add* the swing on the one characteristic to that of the other: i.e., $E_{max} - E_{min} = (17.5 + 1) - 1.5$ and $I_{max} - I_{min} = 1.25 - (-1.25) = 2.5$.

To find the collector efficiency we need to know the d-c power supplied by the battery. The battery power calculation is quite different from the Class A situation since here the one battery supplies both transistors, and each transistor operates fully over only one-half a cycle. Consequently, the only resort is to calculate the d-c power required by one stage and then multiply it by two.

The direct voltage, of course, for either stage is simply the battery voltage E_{CC}. We have, then, to find the direct current supplied to

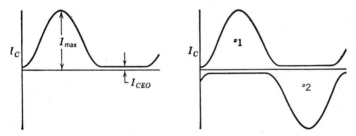

Fig. 9-13. Current waves for two transistors operating Class B.

each transistor. Remembering that the transistor is conducting a sine-wave current for one-half cycle and is cut off for the other half cycle, the current for one transistor will appear as in Figure 9-13. The current during the cutoff portion, although very small, is never quite zero; this current is exactly the back-current of a reversed biased diode in the grounded-emitter connection and is given by Equation (24a). Part (b) of Figure 9-13 shows the currents of both transistors and exhibits how the total sine wave is preserved.

The *average value* or d-c component of the wave of Figure 9-13(a) can be shown to be

$$I_{d\text{-}c} = \frac{I_{max} - I_{CEO}}{\pi} + I_{CEO} \qquad (33)$$

Equation (33) is obtained by finding the d-c component of a sine wave over half a cycle, and then adding the I_{CEO} (a d-c value) of the remaining half cycle.

The total battery input power is then found by multiplying Equation (33) by E_{CC} and then doubling to account for both transistors:

$$P_{\text{battery}} = 2E_{CC} \left(\frac{I_{\max} - I_{CEO}}{\pi} + I_{CEO} \right) \tag{34}$$

The collector efficiency is found by dividing this quantity into Equation (32):

$$\text{collector eff.} = \frac{P_{\text{out}}}{P_{\text{battery}}} = \frac{(E_{\max} - E_{\min})(I_{\max} - I_{\min})}{16E_{CC} \left(\dfrac{I_{\max} - I_{CEO}}{\pi} + I_{CEO} \right)} \tag{35}$$

Since, for any reasonable current swing, the I_{CEO} is negligible with respect to $I_{\max}$, this can be written

$$\text{coll. eff.} = \frac{\pi(E_{\max} - E_{\min})(I_{\max} - I_{\min})}{16E_{CC}I_{\max}} \tag{36}$$

As in the Class A case, it is useful to find the ideal collector efficiency, where ideal refers to conditions for an ideal transistor. If the transistor were thus ideal, the operation could swing out to the current axis (along the dashed lines of Figure 9-12). For such ideal conditions the following relations would be true (Figure 9-12):

$$E_{\max} - E_{\min} = 2E_{CC}$$
$$I_{\max} - I_{\min} = 2I_{\max} = 2\frac{E_{CC}}{R_L} \tag{37}$$

Substituting these relations into Equation (36), the result is found to be

$$\text{ideal coll. eff.} = \frac{\pi(2E_{CC})(2I_{\max})}{16E_{CC}I_{\max}} = \frac{\pi}{4} = 78\% \tag{38}$$

Remembering that the ideal Class A efficiency is 50%, it is seen that the Class B push-pull amplifier is considerably better in this respect.

Using the relations of Equation (37), the *ideal* power output may be found by substituting into Equation (32):

$$P_{\text{out ideal}} = \frac{(2E_{CC})(2E_{CC}/R_L)}{8} = \frac{E_{CC}^2}{2R_L} \tag{38a}$$

We can now deal with the matter of dissipation required of a Class B operated transistor. Since there are no d-c losses in the load resistor, the power equation for the collector side is

$$P_{in} = P_{output} + P_{losses}$$
$$P_{battery} = P_{output} + P_{diss}$$

(39)

The P_{diss} of Equation (39) pertains to the pair of transistors; if the dissipation per transistor is desired, this result is divided by two. Also, in calculating the dissipation the assumption is made that I_{CEO} is small in comparison to any I_{max}, so that Equation (36) would hold.

$$P_{diss} = P_{battery} - P_{out}$$
$$= \frac{2E_{CC}I_{max}}{\pi} - \frac{(E_{max} - E_{min})(I_{max} - I_{min})}{8}$$

(40)

It is useful to rewrite this by recognizing that, from Figure 9-12,

$$I_{max} - I_{min} = 2I_{max}$$

(41)

$$E_{max} - E_{min} = 2(E_{CC} - E_{min}) = 2I_{max}R_L$$

(42)

The R_L here is the load corresponding to the load line, and consequently is the R_L' transformed through one-half of the output transformer.

Equation (40) then is

$$P_{diss} = \frac{2E_{CC}I_{max}}{\pi} - \frac{I_{max}^2 R_L}{2}$$

(43)

The two important results of Equation (43) are: (1) *the permissible R_L is restricted by the transistor dissipation capability for a fixed E_{CC};* and (2) *the maximum dissipation, for a particular E_{CC} and R_L varies with signal swing.*

Figure 9-14 shows a curve of required transistor dissipation versus I_{max}. Both the I_{max} and the dissipation power are referred to ideal conditions; that is, the I_{max} is expressed as the portion of $I_{max\ ideal} = E_{CC}/R_L$ and the dissipation is expressed as the portion of total battery power under ideal conditions $= 2E_{CC}^2/R_L$. The use of this procedure allows this curve to be used for any value of E_{CC} and R_L, and can thus be applied to any design situation.

Figure 9-14 also shows the battery power and the a-c power output versus I_{max}. Both of these curves are referred to the ideal quantities stated above. Note that the maximum dissipation occurs where the difference between the battery power and the output power is greatest.

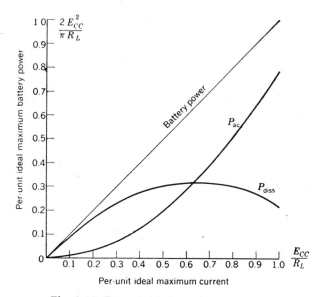

Fig. 9-14. Per-unit ideal maximum current.

From the dissipation curve we see that maximum transistor dissipation is required when the signal causes an I_{max} of

$$I_{max} = 0.637 I_{max\ ideal} = 0.637 \frac{E_{cc}}{R_L} \qquad (44)$$

Since, in any design application, the signal may be of this value for a period of time, the transistor must be capable of dissipating the power required for this worst condition. As seen on the curve, the dissipation needed is

$$(P_{diss})_{max} = 0.315 \frac{2E_{cc}^2}{\pi R_L} \qquad (45)$$

Let us illustrate the foregoing by applying Equation (45) to the situation of Figure 9-12 where the $E_{cc} = 10$ and $R_L = 6.66$ ohms:

$$(P_{diss})_{max} = 0.315 \frac{2 \times 100}{\pi 6.66} \cong 3 \text{ watts} \qquad (46)$$

Since this includes the two transistors, each transistor must be able to dissipate 1.5 watts with the given E_{cc} and R_L. If the manufacturer's specification allows at least this amount, the transistor is suitable. Note that the degradation of capable power dissipation with increase in ambient temperature given in Equation (3) applies here also.

Given the value of $E_{CC} = 10$ and a dissipation capability, we could also use Equation (45) to find the *minimum* value of R_L that would assure that the dissipation is not exceeded.

Since the a-c power output also depends upon R_L and E_{CC}, we can find the relationship between a desired P_{out} and the required dissipation capability. From Figure 9-14 we see the maximum (ideal) P_{out} is $0.78 \times$ ideal battery drain; since the maximum dissipation is $0.315 \times$ ideal battery drain it is found that

$$\frac{\text{dissipation}}{P_{out}} = \frac{0.315 \times \text{battery drain}}{0.78 \times \text{battery drain}} = 0.404 \qquad (47)$$

Therefore for any desired power output, *the combined dissipation of the two transistors must be equal to greater than 0.404 times the desired power.*

$$P_{diss} > 0.404 \, P_{out} \qquad (48)$$

The value of 0.404 applies only in the case of ideal efficiency. Since this never occurs, the actual dissipation will be greater by an amount proportional to the decrease in efficiency (below 78%). It is clear, then, that Equation (48) is useful only in approximating the dissipation for purposes of selecting a transistor.

Load line. We have just seen in the previous section that the choice of a load line for Class B operation is affected by the transistor dissipation capability. The dissipation defines the minimum value of R_L that is allowed for a certain E_{CC}.

The maximum value of R_L, on the other hand, is limited by the required output. If the R_L is increased, the load line of Figure 9-12 becomes more horizontal and less signal swing is available. Although the bias battery could be increased to compensate, this is limited also by the voltage maximum of the transistor.

As with the Class A amplifier, the best procedure is to study the characteristics carefully and then try tentative load lines with approximate calculations. Many times the availability of transformers and power supplies fixes the load line.

Distortion. The Class B power amplifier has the same sources of distortion as the Class A plus another source known as *crossover* distortion. It is remembered that the distortion sources for Class A are: (1) nonequal spacing of constant current curves, (2) nonlinear input resistance, (3) signal clipping, and (4) shift of bias point with temperature.

The most important distortion source for Class B power amplifiers is the crossover point. This stems from the fact that the worst nonlinearity in input resistance occurs near the cutoff region of a transistor. Consequently, when two transistors are placed back to back as in the push-pull circuit, a serious distortion occurs when the operation moves from the cutoff region of one transistor to the cutoff region of the other. An exaggerated picture of the resulting distorted sine wave is shown in Figure 9-15.

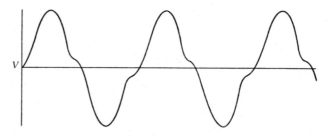

Fig. 9-15. Typical distortion that results from "cross-over" nonlinearity.

Since this is essentially a nonlinear effect, one remedy is again the use of increased source resistance (at the expense of power gain) where the source is either an actual generator or the Thevenin's equivalent of the preceding circuit. Another possible remedy is the use of a small bias on the input side. Feedback may be used to reduce distortion also, see Chapter 12.

Because the serious distortion occurs at crossover, the second harmonic distortion is not a good measure of the total distortion. Hence Equation (24) is not very useful for Class B operation. Probably the best means of evaluating the distortion is to measure it.

Grounded-base Class B amplifier. Although a grounded-emitter connection was used for the above Class B analysis, all the equations and graphical procedures apply also to the grounded-base connection. The characteristics, of course, would be I_C versus V_{CB} with emitter current as the variable.

The power gain for the grounded base will be less than that of the grounded emitter; however, the power output for a certain distortion will probably be higher for the grounded base.

Design example

Problem. Design a 6 watt push-pull grounded-emitter amplifier to drive a 4 ohm voice coil. The driving stage has an output resistance of 5000 ohms.

Solution. From the use of Equation (48) we see the total dissipation required is at least

$$P_{diss} = 0.404P_{out} = (0.404)(6 \text{ watts}) = 2.42 \text{ watts} \qquad (49)$$

Each transistor, then, must dissipate at least 1.21 watts; the actual dissipation will be higher since the ideal efficiency of 78% can never

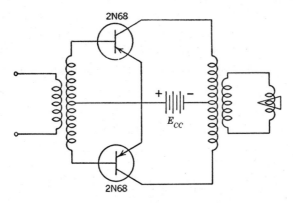

Fig. 9-16. Tentative grounded-emitter push-pull amplifier.

be reached. Since the Sylvania 2N68 has a dissipating capability of 4.0 watts, this transistor is suitable. The tentative circuit diagram is shown in Figure 9-16.

Since the maximum allowable voltage for the 2N68 is 25 volts, the maximum bias point is 12.5 volts due to the double swing incurred in Class B operation. A 12.5 volt battery is chosen.

Knowing the value of E_{cc}, we can now use Equation (45) to find the minimum value of load resistance with the 4.0 watts dissipation of the 2N68. Since the pair of transistors will give 8.0 watts, the equation is

$$P_{diss} = 0.315 \frac{2E_{cc}^2}{\pi R_L} = 8 \text{ watts} \qquad (50)$$

Solving for R_L gives

$$(R_L)_{min} = \frac{0.315 \times 2E_{cc}^2}{8\pi} = \frac{0.630(12)^2}{8\pi} = 3.6 \text{ ohms} \qquad (51)$$

This is the minimum load resistance, then, that can be used with 8.0 watts dissipation and an E_{CC} of 12 volts.

Since the required power output specifies the maximum value of load resistance, we can use the relation of Equation (38a):

$$(P_{out})_{ideal} = \frac{E_{CC}^2}{2R_L}$$

$$(R_L)_{max} = \frac{E_{CC}^2}{2(P_{out})_{ideal}} = \frac{(12)^2}{(2)(6)} = 12 \text{ ohms} \tag{52}$$

Consequently the load resistance that we must use lies between 3 and 12 ohms. These values give only an approximation since they are based on the ideal case. In order to obtain 6 watts output we must use a resistor somewhat less than 12 ohms. Based upon the limiting values just calculated, and upon trying various loads on the graph, a load resistance of 8 ohms is selected.

The combined characteristics and the load line corresponding to 8 ohms is shown in Figure 9-17. From this graph the following values are read for a maximum swing:

$$E_{max} \cong 23.2 \text{ v} \qquad I_{max} \cong 1.32 \text{ amp}$$
$$E_{min} \cong 1.8 \text{ v} \qquad I_{min} \cong -1.32 \text{ amp} \tag{53}$$

Using these values, the actual power output is

$$P_{out} = \frac{(23.2 - 1.8)(1.32 + 1.32)}{8} = 7.05 \text{ watts} \tag{54}$$

For the battery drain, Equation (34) specifies that

$$P_{battery} = 2E_{CC}\left(\frac{I_{max} - I_{CEO}}{\pi} + I_{CEO}\right) \tag{55}$$

The value of I_{CEO}, too small to be read from the graph, is obtained from the manufacturer's specifications and is 0.004. Then

$$P_{battery} = (2)(12.5)\left(\frac{1.32 - 0.004}{\pi} + 0.004\right) = 10.55 \tag{56}$$

Using the above results,

$$\text{collector eff.} = \frac{P_{out}}{P_{battery}} = \frac{7.05}{10.55} \times 100 = 66.8\% \tag{57}$$

The total dissipation is

$$P_{diss} = P_{battery} - P_{output} = 10.55 - 7.05 = 3.50 \text{ watts} \tag{58}$$

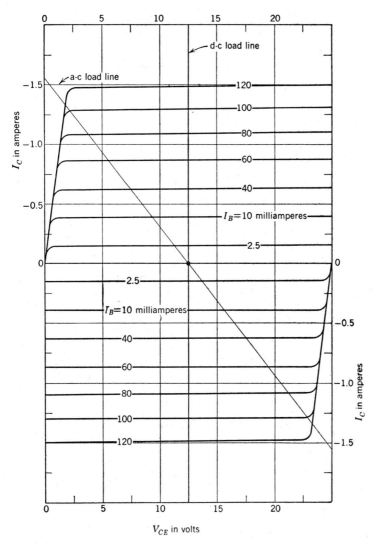

Fig. 9-17. Class B amplifier load line.

This means that each transistor must dissipate 1.75 watts, and therefore this operation is suitable with the 2N68.

Since each transistor is to see a load of 8 ohms, and the actual load (R_L') is 4 ohms, each *half* of the center-tapped output transformer must have an impedance transformation of 8 to 4. We can consider each half of the center-tapped transformer as a separate unit, since only one transistor operates at a time. Therefore the turns ratio across one-half of the transformer must be

$$\left(\frac{N_1}{N_2}\right)^{1/2} = \sqrt{\frac{8}{4}} = \sqrt{2} \tag{59}$$

Since each half must have this ratio, considered one at a time, the total turns ratio must be

$$\frac{N_1}{N_2} = \sqrt{2} + \sqrt{2} = 2.83 \tag{60}$$

The impedances will then appear as in Figure 9-18. When either half is considered alone, 8 ohms will appear as desired. If the entire transformer is considered, it is seen that 4 times the single-side impedance (4 × 8 = 32 ohms) appears from collector to collector. This is characteristic of all push-pull Class B operation.

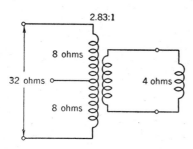

Fig. 9-18. Impedance relations for the center-tapped transformer.

The same procedure as above can be applied to the input transformer. From the characteristics (Appendix III) it is learned that the average input impedance for the grounded emitter 2N68 is about 50 ohms. Since the driver impedance is 5000 ohms, the total transformer ratio is

$$\frac{N_1}{N_2} = \sqrt{\frac{5000}{4 \times 50}} \cong 5 \tag{61}$$

The total circuit for this amplifier is then shown in Figure 9-19. This amplifier provides the required power output and its efficiency is good, 66.8% compared with the ideal 78%.

For finding the power gain, the power input is

$$(P_{\text{a-c}})_{\text{input}} = \left[\frac{(I_B)_{\text{pk-to-pk}}}{2\sqrt{2}}\right]^2 R_{\text{in}} = \left(\frac{0.210}{2\sqrt{2}}\right)^2 \times 50 = 0.276 \text{ watts}$$

The power gain is then

$$A_p = 10 \log_{10} \frac{P_{\text{out}}}{P_{\text{in}}} = 10 \log_{10} \frac{6.75}{0.276} = 13.9 \text{ db}$$

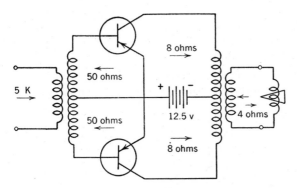

Fig. 9-19. Final circuit for Class B, grounded-emitter power amplifier.

Other Power Circuits

Although Class A and Class B are the basic modes of operation for transistor power amplifiers, there are other types which are worthy of mention here. These types are Class A push-pull, Class A-B, complementary symmetry, and Class C. It is our purpose here only to describe these various types briefly; the basic analysis procedures used in the preceding sections can be used, with modifications, for these other types.

Class A push-pull. The Class A push-pull amplifier consists essentially of two transistors connected back to back, with both transistors biased so as to operate Class A. The circuit connection for this amplifier is identical to that of the Class B except that here a bias battery is necessary in the input side to provide the Class A bias conditions. The chief advantage of this amplifier is that it exhibits an extremely low distortion compared with the other power amplifiers.

The circuit diagram of the Class A push-pull amplifier is shown in Figure 9-20. As in the case of the Class B amplifier, the input transformer acts as a phase inverter for the input signal. If a sine wave is applied to the input, transistor #1 receives a current wave that is in phase with the input wave, while transistor #2 receives a sine wave whose phase is 180° from that of the input. Since both transistors are operating Class A, the entire wave in each case is amplified by the respective transistor. With the 180° phase shift of the grounded-emitter connection, the entire sine wave for each transistor will appear in the collector lead. The phase of these two waves, however, will be opposing (180° apart) as shown in Figure 9-20. The center-tapped output transformer then combines the two waves by acting as a phase inverter for the one wave. Consequently the amplified output appears in the secondary of the output transformer.

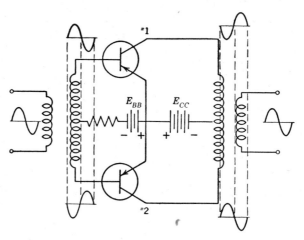

Fig. 9-20. Circuit diagram and waveforms showing basic operation of Class A, push-pull amplifier.

Because of the action of the output transformer, all the even-order harmonics of the output sine wave will be eliminated in the output if the transistors used are well balanced. Since the second harmonic distortion is often the chief source, the distortion of this circuit can be made very low. Also, this circuit does not suffer from crossover distortion as does the Class B type. Compared with Class B, however, the power output is less and it operates less efficiently.

The power output from this circuit would, of course, be twice that obtainable from a single-transistor Class A amplifier.

If it is desired to analyze graphically the push-pull amplifier, the two transistor characteristics must be joined in the same manner as shown in Figure 9-12 for the Class B amplifier. The analysis differs somewhat from that of the Class B, however, since here both transistors are conducting at the same time. This can be handled by combining the characteristic curves for the two transistors to form a set of composite characteristics. This can be accomplished by subtracting the entire curve for x ma below the current bias value of transistor #2 from the entire curve of x ma above the bias value of transistor #1.

For example, referring to Figure 9-12, let us assume that the I_B bias current is 40 ma for each transistor. One composite curve would be found by subtracting the $40 - 20 = 20$ ma curve of #2 from the $40 + 20 = 60$ ma curve of #1. This subtraction is performed by subtracting the I_C current values along any vertical line.

Since the characteristics of the junction transistor are essentially linear, the resulting composite characteristics will be linear lines displaced from the original characteristics. By the use of these characteristics and the load line, the graphical picture of push-pull operation can be depicted.

Class A-B. Class A-B operation is exhibited when, in the push-pull circuit of Figure 9-20, the two transistors are biased so that each conducts for more than half a cycle but less than the entire cycle. Thus it is a combination of Class A and Class B operation.

The basic circuit diagram would be identical to that of Figure 9-20; the difference lies in that here the input bias conditions would cause an operating point that does not permit conduction over the entire cycle. ·Since current is flowing in both transistors at the same time, composite characteristics as described above would have to be used to depict the graphical operation.

The advantage of this circuit is that more power output and greater collector efficiency can be achieved than for the Class A push-pull. More distortion, however, will occur since the complete wave in each transistor is not amplified.

Complementary symmetry. Complementary symmetry refers to a method of constructing Class B amplifiers without requiring the phase-inverting center-tapped transformers on the input and output. To do this, two transistors with similar characteristics are used, but one is an N-P-N type and the other a P-N-P. It was noted in Chapter 4 that these two types differ, electrically, in that the bias polarities are reversed; hence the grounded-emitter P-N-P transistor requires a negative base current drive and the N-P-N grounded-emitter transistor requires a positive drive. Therefore, if an N-P-N and a P-N-P are connected back-to-back and biased at cutoff in a push-pull circuit, the N-P-N unit will amplify the positive half signals and the P-N-P will operate on the negative signals. It is seen that the need for phase inversion has been eliminated.

Figure 9-21 shows the basic connection of a complementary symmetry circuit. It is noted that a single battery will no longer suffice, since the two transistors require opposite polarities. Since there is no phase inversion here, the input sine wave feeds both transistors. The N-P-N unit operates only on the positive portion since it is biased at cutoff; the 180° phase shift of the grounded-emitter connection will cause the positive wave to be inverted in the output. The P-N-P unit amplifies the negative portion of the input wave, and with 180° phase shift a positive half cycle appears in its output. We now have a negative and a positive half-cycle, so they may be added directly in the load; no output phase-inversion transformer is needed.

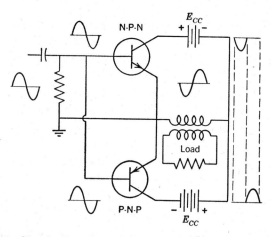

Fig. 9-21. Circuit diagram and waveforms of amplifier using complementary symmetry.

Figure 9-21 shows an output transformer (not center-tapped) that is usually required to transform the impedance of the load to a suitable transistor load.

If this circuit is to be illustrated graphically, the characteristics and load line of each transistor must be considered separately; the characteristics cannot be combined as they were in Figure 9-12. It is noted that the load line for each transistor would consist of the actual load transformed by the complete turns ratio of the output transformer.

A stage of grounded-collector complementary symmetry may be added to the previous circuit to transform the impedance down so as to permit driving a low load resistance directly. This is advantageous from the viewpoint of obtaining some additional gain from the grounded-collector stage and also eliminating the output transformer. A circuit diagram is shown in Figure 9-22.

It is seen that a P-N-P follows the N-P-N transistor and an N-P-N follows the P-N-P. This is required since the grounded-emitter connection inverts the signal wave because of its phase shift. It is noted that the grounded-collector stage does not shift the phase of the signal. Since the output impedance of the collector stages are low, a low load resistance may be driven directly with this connection.

It should also be noted, in Figure 9-22, that the grounded-emitter stages are *biased through the grounded-collector ones.* That is, the first

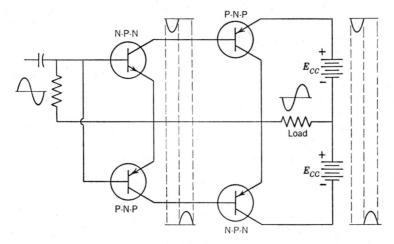

Fig. 9-22. Circuit diagram and waveforms of two-stage complementary symmetry amplifiers.

N-P-N transistor obtains its collector-to-emitter bias through the emitter-to-base path of the P-N-P transistor. Since the emitter-to-base voltage is always small, the collector of the N-P-N receives practically the entire voltage of E_{cc}.

This method of biasing through another transistor is always a possibility in transistor circuits, and should be kept in mind when designing circuits. Here again we see a basic difference from the vacuum tube, where this method of biasing is not possible.

Class C amplifiers. Class C operation is defined as that combination of bias and signal where the transistor operates for less than one-half of a cycle. For the rest of the cycle, the transistor remains in cutoff condition and the very small value of cutoff current flows.

Although an amplifier using Class C operation is of no use for audio signals because of the great distortion resulting from the intermittent current flow, it has application. If we have an application where a sinusoidal output voltage is required at a single frequency, then we can use a parallel-resonant circuit as the load, instead of a resistor. This parallel circuit, at the resonant frequency, will cause the output voltage to be sinusoidal in spite of the fact that the transistor conducts only in bursts. The reason for this is that, in the physical operation of the parallel circuit, energy oscillates from the inductor to the capacitor at the resonant frequency. This oscillation can be sustained if sufficient power is supplied to the circuit to supply the losses which occur in inductor resistance. It is this power that the transistor supplies during its conducting intervals. Thus the Class

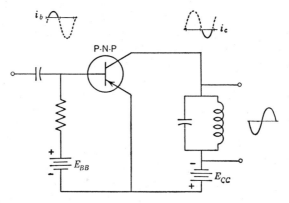

Fig. 9-23. Basic circuit and waveforms for a Class C amplifier.

C amplifier with a tuned load can be regarded as a resonating oscillator whose losses are supplied by the bursts of transistor conduction. It should be noted that the output sine wave will be greater than the input wave by the factor of the voltage gain.

Figure 9-23 shows a schematic of a basic Class C amplifier. It should be noted that, in order to achieve a bias point considerably below cutoff, the emitter bias battery has to be reversed from what is normal. As seen, then, current flows only during the top peak of the input current, but the output is sinusoidal because of the resonating circuit. It should be emphasized that this circuit is useful only for a single frequency (the resonant frequency) and only for sine wave output; thus a general audio signal is not permissible.

If the resonant output circuit is tuned to a multiple of the frequency of the input sine wave, the above circuit can be used as a frequency multiplier. It usually does not provide gain in this application since the power available in a multiple of the input frequency is not as great as for the fundamental itself.

Problems

1. Using the characteristics of the 2N68 shown in Figures 9-8 and 9-9, calculate the maximum obtainable power output from a Class A transformer-coupled circuit for a load of 20 ohms when the collector battery is 7.5 v. The emitter current at the operating point is 0.4 amp.
2. Calculate the collector efficiency and the per cent of second harmonic distortion for the amplifier of Problem 1.
3. If a 25 ohm load resistor is used in Problem 1, what would the power output, collector efficiency, and second harmonic distortion be?
4. Using the example of the grounded-base Class B push-pull amplifier, change the load to 10 ohms and recalculate the output power and collector efficiency.
5. What is the maximum possible power that may be dissipated in the transistor for the example used in Problem 4? Use the curves of Figure 9-14.
6. What implications are manifest in Figure 9-14 concerning the design of a Class B push-pull amplifier?
7. What are the advantages and disadvantages of using a Class A push-pull stage?
8. What are the advantages and disadvantages of complementary symmetry power amplifiers?

10

Cascade Amplifiers

In Chapter 8 we considered the single-stage small-signal amplifier. The concentration there was upon finding the equations for the performance quantities of the transistor in small signal applications. The equivalent circuit was used for the analysis and it was emphasized that any complex transistor network can be analyzed by considering the entire circuit on a stage-by-stage basis and using the performance equations derived there and listed in Tables 1 and 3.

Chapter 9 was devoted to the study of single-stage large-signal amplifiers; specifically power amplifiers. The method of graphical analysis was used for these power amplifiers, and it was noted that the techniques applied to the power amplifiers apply to large-signal amplifiers in general.

Thus we can consider the two previous chapters as dealing with the two fundamental methods of analyzing and designing transistor amplifier circuits: the equivalent circuit method for small-signal applications, and the graphical analysis for large-signal conditions.

It is our purpose now to add to these two basic tools the additional factors that are encountered when transistor amplifiers are connected in cascade. These additional factors center around the interstage networks that are required for cascaded transistor stages.

The interstage networks between any electronic circuit devices are required for three reasons: (1) to provide the proper biases to the circuit device, (2) to separate the bias currents (or voltages) of one stage from that of another and (3) to give better impedance match in the case of transformers only. Concerning (2), it is usually true that the desired bias conditions in the output of one stage are not the same as those desired for the input of the next stage; therefore the bias currents must be separated. This amounts to providing separate paths for the alternating and direct currents between the electronic devices. As in the case of vacuum tubes, the two common means of accomplishing this separation is by the use of RC coupling or transformer coupling. Both of these separate the output of one stage, d-c wise, from the input of the next stage.

As would be expected, any type of interstage network affects the a-c operation of the cascaded amplifiers. The bias circuits tend to shunt out the a-c signal, and the coupling of the interstage introduces frequency response. Even if the transistor were completely frequency-independent, the interstage network would introduce a frequency dependency. We shall find that, for cascaded transistor amplifiers with RC coupling (and usually for transformer coupling), the low-frequency response is determined by the interstage and the high-frequency action is specified by the transistor.

In this chapter, then, we will first consider the various schemes available for providing proper transistor bias. Following this, the effect of the complete interstage on the gain and the frequency response will be investigated. Since the transistor itself usually limits the high-frequency action, the frequency dependence of the transistor and the resulting effect will be considered. Finally, the concepts of gain and frequency response for cascaded amplifiers will be illustrated by a design example.

Biasing Circuits

Thus far, when exhibiting the bias of a transistor, the simple method of inserting a suitable battery in each lead was used; this procedure was used to allow concentration to be placed on the a-c analysis tools being considered. We wish here to consider the various available biasing schemes with approximate calculations to find a desired operating point.

It should be emphasized that when dealing with biasing circuits we are concerned with the d-c conditions of the circuit. It will be remembered from Chapter 7 that one of the basic tools for analyzing and designing electronic circuits consists of treating the a-c and the d-c conditions separately. In Chapter 8, when working with the h parameters, we were dealing with the a-c properties. The values of these h parameters *are not* valid for d-c conditions. It is interesting to note that we could solve the d-c problem by substituting an equivalent circuit for the transistor and treating the resulting network. This equivalent circuit would appear similar to the a-c one, but the values of the parameters *would have to be the d-c values*. Although not given specifically by the manufacturer, these d-c parameters could be obtained from the characteristics. The equivalent-circuit method of solution, however, would be a complicated way to solve a relatively simple problem, and hence is undesirable. The method generally used to find the d-c operating point consists of placing the d-c load line on the output characteristics and then writing an equation to find the value of input direct current.

The basic biasing conditions for a P-N-P transistor in the three possible connections are shown in Figure 10-1. For each of the connections, both an RC coupling and a transformer coupling are shown on the input side. The capacitor in the transformer-coupled circuits provides an a-c shunt across the bias resistor; if this were not present, the a-c signal would be decreased by the bias resistor. It should be noted that in all following circuits, the main bias resistor will be denoted by R_B.

It is remembered that the biasing conditions of a transistor are that the emitter junction be biased in the forward direction and the collector junction be biased in the reverse direction. For a P-N-P transistor this means that the emitter voltage will be slightly positive with respect to the base, and the collector is negative with respect to the base. With this criterion, it can be verified that the battery polarities of Figure 10-1 are correct. For an N-P-N transistor, the basic conditions would be reversed and hence all the battery polarities of this figure would be reversed.

As noted before, the best procedure when dealing with the d-c operating point is to use the characteristics with the d-c load line for the output side, and a d-c equation for the input side. It is remembered that the operating point will always lie along the d-c load line of the output characteristics. In an analysis situation, then, where we are given the E_{CC}, the R_L, and the R_B, it remains to find the input current to establish the operating point; in a design situation, the proper operating point is determined (as considered in the preceding chapters) and it remains to select the proper E_{CC}, R_L, and R_B to give the desired input current, and hence operating point. Since we

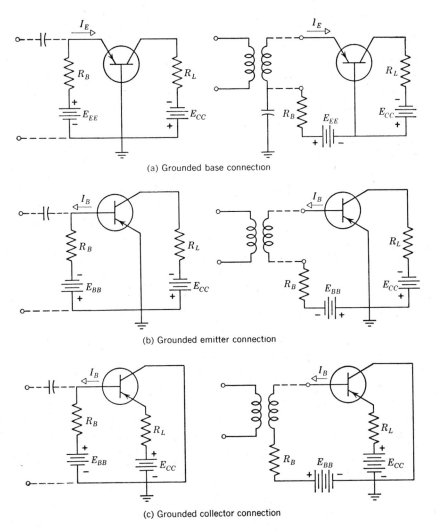

(a) Grounded base connection

(b) Grounded emitter connection

(c) Grounded collector connection

Fig. 10-1. Basic battery polarities for the three connections using a P-N-P transistor and showing two types of coupling.

treated the topic of d-c load lines previously, we have now to determine, for either design or analysis, the input direct current.

This input current can usually be reasonably approximated by writing a d-c equation for the input loop. Another method would be to use the input characteristics along with an input load line. The manufacturer, however, rarely gives the input characteristics so that the d-c equation method is recommended.

In Figure 10-1 the d-c equation for the input loop, for the grounded-base connection, can be seen to be

$$E_{EE} = I_E R_B + V_{EB} \tag{1}$$

where V_{EB} = emitter-to-base direct voltage. Note that this equation applies to both the capacitor-coupled and the transformer-coupled case, since it is assumed that the d-c resistance of the transformer is zero.

Since the emitter junction is biased in the forward direction, the V_{EB} is always small. Consequently, for a good approximation *we can neglect V_{EB} with respect to the other quantities.* We shall make this approximation for all the d-c calculations hereafter.

Solving for I_E, then,

$$\text{(grounded base)} \qquad \boxed{I_E = \frac{E_{EE}}{R_B}} \tag{2}$$

The d-c equation for the grounded-emitter case, for both capacitor- and transformer-coupled, is

$$E_{BB} = I_B R_B + V_{EB} \tag{3}$$

Neglecting V_{EB}, the result is

$$\text{(grounded emitter)} \qquad \boxed{I_B = \frac{E_{BB}}{R_B}} \tag{4}$$

For the grounded-collector case of Figure 10-1, the collector direct current must also be considered, since the R_L appears in the input loop. The equation is found to be

$$E_{BB} - E_{CC} = I_B(R_B + R_L) - I_C R_L - V_{EB} \tag{5}$$

Then, solving for I_B,

$$\text{(grounded collector)} \qquad \boxed{I_B = \frac{E_{BB} - E_{CC} + I_C R_L}{R_B + R_L}} \tag{6}$$

By using Equations (2), (4), or (6) in conjunction with the d-c load line on the output characteristics, then, the operating point can be established. It should be noted here that, in the transformer-coupled circuits of Figure 10-1, the bias direct current through the transformer may be undesirable; if that is the case, the transformer can be connected to the left of the capacitor in the *RC* coupled circuits. None of the above equations will be changed.

For the grounded base and the grounded collector connection there are no appropriate biasing schemes other than those of Figure 10-1. For the grounded emitter, however, *it is possible to provide both input and output bias with only one battery.* It was mentioned in an earlier chapter that this is one of the reasons for usually choosing the grounded-emitter connection for amplifier circuits. Since the grounded-emitter connection is the most popular type, the cascading aspects of this chapter will be mainly concerned with this connection; however, the methods can be applied to any connection.

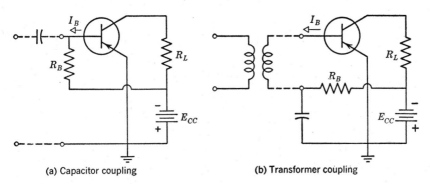

(a) Capacitor coupling   (b) Transformer coupling

Fig. 10-2. One possibility for single-battery grounded-emitter bias.

Figure 10-2 shows a grounded-emitter connection that is biased with only one battery. The circuit is shown for both capacitor and transformer coupling. By comparison with (b) of Figure 10-1, it may be seen that the right polarities are provided. The value of R_B must be high for two reasons: (1) to prevent loading down the a-c signal, and (2) to lower the emitter bias sufficiently from the value of E_{CC}. The d-c equation for the input current is, neglecting V_{EB},

$$I_B = \frac{E_{CC}}{R_B} \tag{7}$$

Although this biasing arrangement is the simplest possible for transistor circuits, it has the disadvantage that the operating point may vary with different transistors and with ambient temperature changes.

Another possibility for single-battery bias with the grounded emitter connection is shown in Figure 10-3. Again the two types of coupling are exhibited. Here the set of resistors R_1 and R_2 acts as a voltage divider to provide the base-to-emitter voltage.

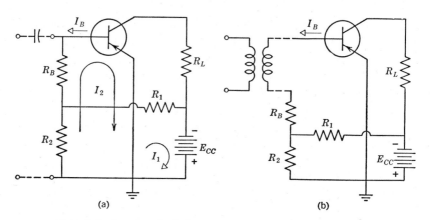

Fig. 10-3. Another single-battery, grounded-emitter connection.

Since two loops are involved for the d-c input circuit, two mesh equations are required. Using the current loops as shown in (a), where $I_2 = -I_B$, the two equations are

$$E_{CC} = I_1(R_1 + R_2) + R_2I_2$$
$$0 = I_1R_2 + (R_2 + R_B)I_2 - V_{EB} \tag{8}$$

Neglecting V_{EB} and solving for I_2, the result is

$$I_B = -I_2 = \frac{E_{CC}R_2}{R_1R_2 + R_BR_2 + R_1R_B} = \frac{E_{CC}R_2}{R_1(R_2 + R_B) + R_BR_2} \tag{9}$$

The value of R_B in Figure 10-3 is usually much higher than R_2, since the R_2 must be kept low to provide only a small V_{EB}. Using this fact, we can simplify the calculation of the bias circuit. We can first find the voltage across R_2 by momentarily assuming that R_1 and R_2 are the only resistors present:

$$V_{R_2} = \frac{E_{CC}}{R_1 + R_2} R_2 \quad \text{if} \quad R_2 \ll R_B \tag{10}$$

The bias current I_B, then, is

$$I_B = \frac{V_{R_2}}{R_B} = \frac{E_{CC}R_2}{(R_1 + R_2)R_B} \quad \text{if} \quad R_2 \ll R_B \tag{11}$$

We can check this result by substituting the condition $R_2 \ll R_B$ into Equation (9). Approximations such as these are necessary when many stages are connected in cascade. If they were not used, the total circuit would require a great many simultaneous equations and the solution would be vastly complex.

Although the circuit of Figure 10-3 will consume more d-c power than that of Figure 10-2, it has an advantage in that the input bias is more stable. In other words, any transistor variations will not affect the value of input current so greatly as in the previous circuit.

Figure 10-4 shows a circuit similar to that of Figure 10-3, but now the emitter lead contains a bias resistor. Note that a capacitor is used to by-pass the alternating current; otherwise the resistor R_3 would

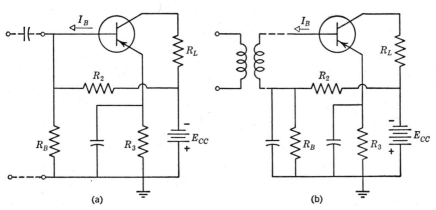

Fig. 10-4. A single-battery, grounded-emitter bias circuit.

provide negative feedback. It is seen that three loop equations are required to solve the d-c input conditions. Without showing the equations, the result is

$$I_B = \frac{E_{cc}R_B - I_C[R_2R_3 + R_BR_3]}{R_2R_B + R_2R_3 + R_3R_B} \tag{12}$$

This equation is quite complex and is of little use to us as it stands. A very rough approximation may be used if the condition $R_B \ll R_2$ is imposed. Then

$$I_B \cong \frac{E_{cc}R_B - I_CR_2R_3}{R_2R_B + R_2R_3} \tag{13}$$

We will find, when considering bias stability, that the circuit of Figure 10-4 is the most stable of the three single-battery circuits.

The biasing of cascaded stages can now be illustrated. For this, we will use RC coupling; transformer coupling can be inserted by referring, for each type, to the previous figures. Three cascaded stages, using the single-battery emitter connection, are shown in Figure 10-5; each stage is biased according to the method of Figure 10-2.

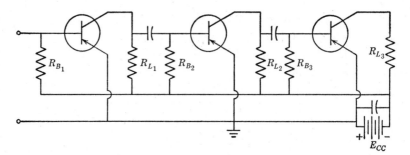

Fig. 10-5. Bias circuit for cascaded emitter stages using the method of Fig. 10-2.

This circuit represents the simplest type of cascaded transistor circuit. The operating point, for each stage, is determined by the d-c load line on the output characteristics, and the use of Equation (7). The capacitor across the battery in this circuit is used to prevent any a-c feedback that would result from the internal resistance of the battery.

Another emitter cascaded circuit is shown in Figure 10-5(a). Each stage here is similar to that of Figure 10-3. Since all the values of R_B are kept high to prevent shunting the a-c signal, the sum of the alternating currents in all the R_B's is usually much less than the current through the bleeder (path $R_1 - R_2 - R_3$). Therefore the input direct current of each stage may be found by first calculating the voltage at the top point and then dividing by the R_B of that stage. The alternative to using this simplified method would be to write simultaneous

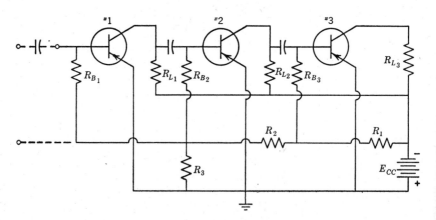

Fig. 10-5(a). Bias circuit for cascaded emitter stages using the method of Fig. 10-3.

equations for the four separate meshes. This, because of its complexity, is usually undesirable. Using the simplified method, then, the following equations can be verified:

$$I_{B_1} = \frac{E_{CC}R_3}{(R_1 + R_2 + R_3)R_{B_1}}$$

$$I_{B_2} = \frac{E_{CC}R_3}{(R_1 + R_2 + R_3)R_{B_2}} \qquad \text{if } R_B \gg R_1 + R_2 + R_3 \qquad (14)$$

$$I_{B_3} = \frac{E_{CC}(R_2 + R_3)}{(R_1 + R_2 + R_3)R_{B_3}}$$

These equations, in conjunction with the load line of each stage, can be used to determine the operating point.

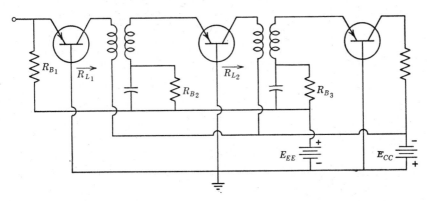

Fig. 10-6. Bias circuit for grounded-base, cascaded stages.

It is useful to illustrate a grounded-base cascaded circuit. Since no single-battery connections are available, two batteries or a tapped battery must be used. Figure 10-6 shows three grounded-base cascaded stages using transformer coupling. It is remembered that for the grounded-base stages, transformer coupling is required for impedance matching; if *RC* coupling were used, the power gain of the cascaded circuit would be less than that for a single stage. The cascaded circuit is made up of the basic circuits of Figure 10-1(a). Assuming that the internal resistance of the battery (or the power supply) is small, Equation (2) can be used to find the input direct current for each stage.

The above, then, are the major types of bias circuits suitable for transistors. We shall find, when considering bias stability, that a series resistor in the emitter lead is desirable from the standpoint of retaining the same operating point with temperature variation or transistor replacement. Since this topic is more complex than the material presented here, it is covered in the next chapter.

Frequency Response

In addition to calculating the gain of electronic circuits for a nominal frequency (as was done in Chapter 8), it is usually necessary to find the range of frequencies over which that value of gain is valid. The signals used in electronic circuits are usually nonsinusoidal, as opposed to the signals of power distribution systems for example. By the use of the Fourier series concept, these nonsinusoidal signals can be treated as the sum of a series of sine-wave components of various frequencies. Because of this, the gain versus frequency is very important for electronic circuits. If the electronic circuit does not amplify equally all frequency components of importance in the signal, the output signal will be distorted.

The frequency response of any electronic circuit depends upon both the electronic device itself and the attached circuitry. As evidenced by the coupling circuits shown in the previous section, a low-frequency limit is provided by either capacitive or transformer coupling. We shall find that the transistor itself provides a high-frequency limit to any transistor circuit (unless a circuit element provides a lower limit).

As stated in the electrical review, the problem of frequency response is solved by dividing the circuit into three frequency areas: low-frequency, mid-frequency, and high-frequency. The low-frequency circuit is controlled by any series capacitors or parallel inductors (see electrical review) and the high-frequency circuit is controlled by parallel capacitors and series inductors. The mid-frequency circuit applies to the range of frequencies between the low and the high regions, and this circuit contains no reactances since it is independent of frequency.

. When dealing with the three frequency areas, the usual procedure is to calculate first the gain for the mid-frequency case, and then find the *change in gain* (from the mid-value) that occurs in the low and the high regions. This is the procedure that will be followed in this chapter.

The central question, then, is: What factors cause the gain, in the low and high regions, to fall off from the mid-band value? As stated above, the capacitive or inductive coupling between stages causes the low-frequency decrease in gain. This is logical since the coupling elements are designed to block the bias direct current; hence the closer the signal frequency approaches direct current, the more the gain will be decreased by the coupling element.

In the high-frequency regions the transistor itself is usually the limiting factor. As in the case of vacuum tubes where the interelectrode capacitances become effective, the transistor exhibits reactances at the high frequencies. The situation for the transistor, however, is vastly more complicated than for the vacuum tube. For the transistor, practically all the parameters show a complex form, in addition to the normal capacitances. In addition, the current gain h_{21} of the transistor decreases for the high frequencies. Still another feature is that most of the reactances of the high-frequency transistor vary with the operating point and with the temperature. Consequently, in order to conduct an exact analysis of the high-frequency operation of the transistor, it would be necessary to make many measurements under different conditions, and the resulting equivalent circuit of the transistor would contain in the order of ten elements.

Consequently, from the design point of view, we shall make no attempt to find an exact analysis of the high-frequency operation. Rather, we shall use the more important phenomenon and achieve a good approximation to the high-frequency problem. For the general purpose transistor, the manufacturer supplies two items of frequency information: the frequency at which the short-circuit current gain of the transistor drops off by 6 db from its low-frequency value; and the value of the collector capacitance for a given operating point. Since these two items are the most important factors in determining the high-frequency response, we shall achieve an approximation based on these two factors.

As stated, then, we will begin by calculating the mid-frequency gain and then find the *change in gain* brought about by the high- and the low-frequency regions.

Mid-frequency gain calculations. Although we have attached the name mid-frequency here to distinguish from the low- and the high-frequency regions, we are dealing with the same quantities as were treated in Chapter 8 for the single stage. Consequently, we use the equivalent circuit and the methods treated in that chapter. It was emphasized there that the most profitable procedure when cascaded stages are encountered is to analyze the circuit on a stage-by-stage basis. The other alternative would be to solve the entire circuit as an entity by the use of many simultaneous equations. Since this latter method involves great work in solving the equations, the stage-by-stage method is recommended. It is remembered that an example at the end of Chapter 8 was used to illustrate the technique of the stage-by-stage analysis.

It will be our purpose here to concentrate upon this analysis method and make one change from the former example; that is, to express the gain in terms of decibels rather than by number ratios. We will see here how the interstage networks influence the gain of the circuit.

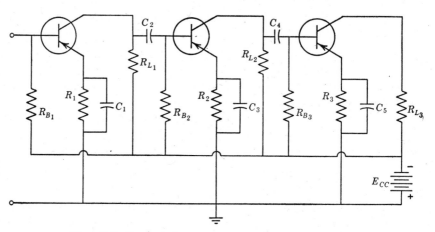

Fig. 10-7. Grounded-emitter transistor cascade amplifier.

Figure 10-7 shows a typical three-stage grounded-emitter circuit. This circuit is basically of the type shown in Figure 10-5; in addition, a by-passed resistor has been added in each emitter lead. These resistors, as we shall find in the next chapter, serve to stabilize the bias point and hence will be frequently encountered in practice.

The first step, when analyzing any electronic circuit, is to find the a-c mid-frequency circuit. This amounts to the following alterations of the original circuit: (1) all batteries (or d-c power supplies) are removed and replaced by their internal impedance; (2) all coupling capacitors are removed for the mid-frequency region; and (3) all by-passed resistors are short-circuited, since the by-pass capacitors are assumed to short-circuit the resistance in the mid-frequency range.

Performing these steps on the circuit of Figure 10-7, the resulting a-c equivalent is shown in Figure 10-8.

Since the power gain is usually of chief interest for a transistor circuit, we will find the power gain of this circuit by using the stage-by-stage procedure. In the example of Chapter 8, we found the current gain of each transistor stage and each interstage, and then

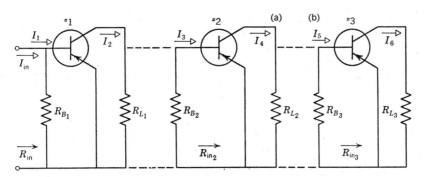

Fig. 10-8. Mid-frequency a-c equivalent of Fig. 10-7.

multiplied them to find the total current gain. This value was then used to find the total power gain by use of the equation

$$A_p = \frac{P_{\text{out}}}{P_{\text{in}}} = (A_i^2)_{\text{total}} \frac{R_L}{R_{\text{in}}} \tag{15}$$

In order to illustrate the effect of each stage, however, *we will here calculate the power gain of each transistor stage and each interstage.* We can then multiply all the power gains to find the total power gain, or we can change each gain value to db and then *add* the various gains to find the total power gain in decibels.

For the gain between the output and the input of the transistor, we use the equations derived in Chapter 8. The gain of the interstages is calculated by elementary circuit rules. It is also necessary to know the input resistance of each transistor input since this acts as part of the load for the previous stage.

It is remembered that we must begin with the last stage and proceed to the left since each stage acts as a load on the preceding one. For the various transistor stages we can use the equations developed in Chapter 8 and listed in Tables 1 to 3. Basic electrical laws will be used for the interstages. We will find the power gain in each case by applying equation (15) to the individual stage.

Third stage. For the third stage the load is R_{L_3}. Using the relation in Table 3 for the current gain, we have

$$A_{i_3} = \frac{I_6}{I_5} = \frac{h_{fe}}{h_{oe}R_{L_3} + 1} \tag{16}$$

The h parameters in this equation are the grounded-emitter parameters for the third-stage transistor.

We need to know the input resistance both for calculating the power gain and for finding the load of the preceding stage. From Table 3,

$$R_{i_3} = \frac{\Delta^h R_{L_3} + h_{ie}}{h_{oe}R_{L_3} + 1} \tag{17}$$

The power gain for the third stage, then, is

$$A_{p_3} = \left(\frac{I_6}{I_5}\right)^2 \frac{R_{L_3}}{R_{i_3}} = (A_{i_3})^2 \frac{R_{L_3}}{R_{i_3}} \tag{18}$$

We can find the decibel value of Equation (18) by the following:

$$\mathrm{Db}_3 = 10 \log_{10} \frac{P_{\text{out}}}{P_{\text{in}}} = 10 \log_{10} A_{p_3} \tag{19}$$

For denoting decibel power gain the symbol db will be used. Capital letters will be used for actual transistor gains, and lower-case letters will denote interstage gains.

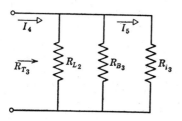

Fig. 10-9. Interstage circuit.

Preceding interstage. It is very important to remember that the relations developed in Chapter 8 and used above specify only the gain from the input to the output of the transistor. Since, in cascaded circuits, not all the output power reaches the next stage, we must find this interstage loss. We have merely to find the power gain of the interstage, and this can again be found by using Equation (15). The interstage appears as in Figure 10-9. The current gain, by the basic current-division law is

$$\begin{aligned}
a_{i_3} = \frac{I_5}{I_4} &= \frac{R_{L_2}R_{B_3}/(R_{L_2} + R_{B_3})}{R_{L_2}R_{B_3}/(R_{L_2} + R_{B_3}) + R_{i_3}} \\
&= \frac{R_{L_2}R_{B_3}}{R_{L_2}R_{B_3} + R_{i_3}(R_{L_2} + R_{B_3})} \tag{20}
\end{aligned}$$

The load for the interstage is R_{i_2}, and the input resistance R_T is given by the three parallel resistors.

$$R_{T_2} = \frac{R_{L_2}R_{B_2}R_{i_3}}{R_{L_2}R_{B_2} + (R_{L_2} + R_{B_2})R_{i_3}} \tag{21}$$

The power gain (a_p) is then given by

$$a_{p_2} = \left(\frac{I_5}{I_4}\right)^2 \frac{R_{i_3}}{R_{T_2}} \tag{22}$$

Again the decibel value may be found by the equation

$$db_3 = 10 \log_{10} a_{p_2} \tag{23}$$

Although the above method is suitable, we can simplify this interstage calculation. If Equation (22) is written out and simplified, it will be found that the a_p can be written directly as

$$a_{p_2} = \frac{R_{T_2}}{R_{i_2}} \tag{24}$$

The decibel value, then, for an interstage is given by

$$db_3 = 10 \log_{10} \frac{R_{T_2}}{R_{i_2}} \tag{25}$$

where R_T = parallel combination of all resistors of the interstage,
R_i = load resistance of interstage, or input resistance to next stage

The value of the interstage decibels will always be negative, since it is really a loss rather than a gain.

Second stage. The load for the second stage consists of the three parallel resistors of Figure 10-9; its value, therefore, is given by Equation (21). The current gain is then

$$A_{i_2} = \frac{I_4}{I_3} = \frac{h_{fe}}{h_{oe}R_{T_2} + 1} \tag{26}$$

The input resistance of the second stage is

$$R_{i_2} = \frac{\Delta^h R_{T_2} + h_{ie}}{h_{oe}R_{T_2} + 1} \tag{27}$$

The power gain in decibels is then

$$Db_2 = 10 \log_{10}\left(A_{i_2}^2 \frac{R_{T_2}}{R_{i_2}} \right) \tag{28}$$

Using the principles exhibited above, the remaining equations for the various power gains can be written. The procedure in each case consists of first finding the current gain, and then determining the load and the input resistance. Remember that all interstages must be accounted for; the equations of Table 3 deal only with the gain from the input to the output of the transistor. The interstage calculation above illustrates the procedure that may be used for any interstage.

After the power gain of each part of the circuit is calculated, and the decibel value is found, we have merely to add the separate decibel values to obtain the total power gain. Remembering that db represents the interstages and Db refers to the transistor portion, the equation for the above circuit may be written

$$\left. \begin{array}{l} \text{total decibel} \\ \text{power gain} \end{array} \right\} = Db_{total} = db_1 + Db_1 + db_2 + Db_2 + db_3 + Db_3 \quad (29)$$

Since the values of interstage decibels are negative, they will actually be subtracted from the transistor gains.

Although there are a number of advantages in using decibels for electronic calculations, we see here one of the main advantages: it allows us to add directly quantities that would otherwise require multiplication. In the next section we will see further how the use of decibels simplifies matters.

For any cascaded circuit, then, we can find the a-c gain by using the stage-by-stage method illustrated above.

Low-frequency gain calculations. We now wish to find how the gain changes from the above calculations when the low-frequency range is encountered; that is, the frequency range where the coupling capacitors begin to decrease the gain. If we wish to find an exact solution for the frequency dependence, we are again faced with the prospect of writing simultaneous equations for the entire network and solving them simultaneously. Since the objectives of a designer rarely warrant such effort, we will exhibit an approximate solution for the low-frequency response.

The procedure to be used consists of, with the proper approximations, finding *the change in gain from the mid-band value*. Thus for any frequency in the low region, we will find the decibel value that must be subtracted from the mid-band gain. The derivation will result in a chart from which the proper loss can be read.

Since the low-frequency calculations are based on the mid-band

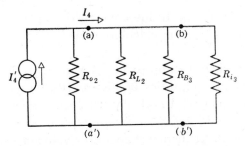

Fig. 10-10. One stage of Fig. 10-8.

values, the first step is to redraw the mid-band interstage circuit. The third interstage circuit of Figure 10-8 is redrawn in slightly different form in Figure 10-10. This circuit is achieved by substituting equivalent circuits for the parts on either side of a-a' and b-b'. The value of the current generator must be of such a value that the I_4' of Figure 10-10 is identical to the I_4 of Figure 10-8. Although it is not important for our purpose, the value of I_4' is

$$I_4' = \frac{h_{fe}(R_{T_3}/R_{o_2} + 1)}{h_{oe}R_{T_3} + 1} I_3 \tag{30}$$

where R_{T_3} = parallel resistance of all resistors in Figure 10-10,
  h^e = parameters for preceding transistor.

With this value of I_4', then, the above circuit correctly represents the chosen portion of Figure 10-9 *for the mid-band conditions*. Note that the values of I_4', R_o, and R_i depend upon other circuit values; hence a given circuit of the type in Figure 10-10 applies only to a *particular* circuit and cannot be regarded as a general equivalent circuit.

If we now put the coupling capacitor between R_o and R_B, we can calculate the ratio of low-frequency gain to mid-band gain. This circuit is shown in Figure 10-11. Since all interstages appear similar to the one we are considering, we will drop the subscripts in order to

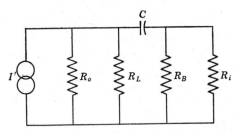

Fig. 10-11. Interstage circuit for low-frequency range.

make the results general. If any concerned interstage does not have either an R_L or an R_B, the calculations will simply neglect this resistor.

We can now view the approximations made in this analysis since we shall regard all quantities of Figure 10-11 except X_c as being constant with frequency. In other words, *we are using the mid-frequency values of I', R_o, and R_i to find the low-frequency response.* In reality, the variation of X_c with frequency changes the value of Z_L and hence the values of I_4 and R_o. Likewise, the varying Z_L of the following stage actually varies R_i. Nevertheless, the stated approximations are necessary if a practical solution is to be effected. These approximations are

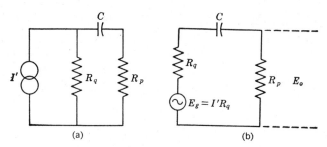

Fig. 10-12. Simplified circuits of Fig. 10-11.

quite good for RC coupled stages; if transformer coupling is used and matched conditions are achieved, only rough approximations result.

The object now is to find the frequency response of the circuit of Figure 10-11. We know that the series capacitor will act to decrease the gain as the frequency decreases. For convenience, the circuit of Figure 10-11 is redrawn in Figure 10-12(a); the only change is that the parallel resistors have been combined. It is noted that R_g and R_p are given by

$$R_g = \frac{R_o R_L}{R_o + R_L}, \qquad R_p = \frac{R_B R_i}{R_B + R_i} \qquad (31)$$

Figure 10-12(b) shows the same circuit except that the current generator has been converted to a voltage source.

We can find the change in gain from the mid-band value by writing the equation for E_o/E_g for both low-frequency and mid-band cases. Referring to Chapter 6, the ratio of E_o/E_g for Figure 10-12(b) is

$$\left(\frac{E_o}{E_g}\right)_{\text{low}} = \frac{R_P}{\sqrt{(R_g + R_p)^2 + (1/\omega C)^2}} \qquad (32)$$

For the mid-band ratio, the capacitor is neglected and the ratio is simply

$$\left(\frac{E_o}{E_g}\right)_{\text{mid}} = \frac{R_p}{R_g + R_p} \tag{33}$$

Since we want the *change* from the mid-band case, we take the ratio of Equation (32) to (33):

$$\frac{(E_o/E_g)_{\text{low}}}{(E_o/E_g)_{\text{mid}}} = \frac{(E_o)_{\text{low}}}{(E_o)_{\text{mid}}} = \frac{1}{\sqrt{1 + 1/[(R_g + R_p)C]^2 \omega^2}} \tag{34}$$

If for any given frequency we convert this voltage gain to power gain, and then find the decibel value, we can add the result to the mid-band decibel value of interstage gain. The final result will be the decibel gain of the interstage at any frequency. The power ratio of Equation (34) is found by squaring the voltage ratio, since the same R_i is assumed for both mid-band and low-frequency ranges.

$$\frac{(a_p)_{\text{low}}}{(a_p)_{\text{mid}}} = \frac{(E_o^2)_{\text{low}}/R_i}{(E_o^2)_{\text{mid}}/R_i} = \left[\frac{(E_o)_{\text{low}}}{(E_o)_{\text{mid}}}\right]^2 \tag{35}$$

The change in decibels, then, from the mid-band value is given by

$$\text{change} = \text{db}_{\text{low}} = 10 \log_{10} \left[\frac{(E_o)_{\text{low}}}{(E_o)_{\text{mid}}}\right]^2 \tag{36}$$

It is noted that the db_{low} is a function of frequency and would have to be calculated for each frequency of interest.

The gain for an interstage in the low-frequency range is now

$$\text{low-frequency db} = \text{db}_{\text{mid}} + \text{db}_{\text{low}} \tag{37}$$

Since the signs of both quantities in this equation are negative, the equation says that the mid-band interstage loss plus the additional loss due to the coupling capacitor will be subtracted from the total gain of the transistor stages.

We can now note how Equation (29), the mid-band total gain, is altered by the low-frequency drop-off. The total gain now appears as

$$\begin{aligned}
\text{total decibel} \atop \text{power gain} \Big\} &= (\text{db}_1 + \text{db}_{\text{low}_1}) + \text{Db}_1 + (\text{db}_2 + \text{db}_{\text{low}_2}) \\
&\qquad + \text{Db}_2 + (\text{db}_3 + \text{db}_{\text{low}_3}) + \text{Db}_3 \\
&= \text{mid-band gain} + (\text{db}_{\text{low}_1} + \text{db}_{\text{low}_2} + \text{db}_{\text{low}_3}) \tag{38}
\end{aligned}$$

Hence, after having calculated the mid-band gain, we need merely add the loss given by each coupling capacitor. This equation may be used at any frequency in the low region.

Rather than calculating the loss at each frequency, it is more profitable to organize the information of Equation (34) so that a chart can be used to directly read the decrease in gain. This may be done by selecting a reference frequency for the gain decrease. *The most convenient reference is that frequency where the power gain is down 3 db.* From Chapter 6 it is remembered that this is also the half-power point, i.e., the power delivered to the following R_i is one-half that delivered at the mid-frequency. This occurs when the denominator of Equation (34) becomes $\sqrt{2}$. Therefore the following equation can be used to find the half-power frequency.

$$\frac{1}{[(R_g + R_p)C]^2 (2\pi f_L)^2} = 1, \qquad f_L = \frac{1}{2\pi(R_g + R_p)C} \tag{39}$$

Each interstage network, then, has a half-power frequency in the low end given by Equation (39).

Substituting Equation (39) back into Equation (34), we find

$$\boxed{\frac{(E_o)_{\text{low}}}{(E_o)_{\text{mid}}} = \frac{1}{\sqrt{1 + (f_L/f)^2}}} \tag{40}$$

Since we wish to work with decibel values, as in (38) above, we can find the power decibel ratio of Equation (40). Remembering that the power ratio is determined by squaring the voltage ratio, it is found that

$$\text{db}_{\text{low}} = 10 \log_{10} \frac{1}{[1 + (f_L/f)^2]} \tag{41}$$

A chart showing the variation of Equation (41) versus the ratio f/f_L is given in Figure 10-13. Using the ratio f/f_L as the independent variable allows us to use this chart for any f_L *and hence for any design situation.* The decibel value read from this curve tells us the decibel loss from the mid-band decibel value. Hence for each interstage that contains a coupling capacitor, the decibel loss for any frequency, as shown on the chart, must be added to the total mid-band gain. (When using the chart, it is convenient to regard the process as subtraction since all losses are negative gains.)

As an example of the use of the chart, let us assume that by Equation (39) we have an f_L of 500 cycles. Then the point 1 on the frequency scale corresponds to 500 cycles. At a frequency of 1000 cycles it is seen that the *additional loss* of the interstage is 1 db. Thus if three identical interstages occurred in a cascaded circuit under the above

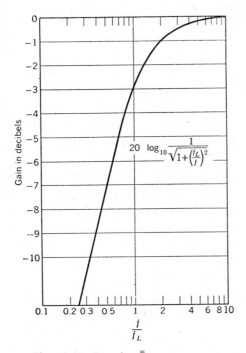

Fig. 10-13. Low frequency response.

conditions, the total circuit would be down 3 db at 1000 cycles from the mid-band gain.

We can now summarize the procedure for calculating the gain in the low-frequency range:

1. Find the mid-band power gain in decibels for the total circuit, including the interstage networks (Equation 29).

2. Find the necessary values of R_o and R_i for the circuit of Figure 10-11. These R_o and R_i values are based on mid-band conditions and the equations appear in Table 3.

3. Find the f_L of each interstage by use of Equation (39) and Equations (31).

4. For any given frequency, read the value of decibel loss associated with each interstage and based upon the f_L of that interstage from the chart.

5. Subtract the loss of each interstage from the total mid-band gain as found in (1).

The use of the chart will be further illustrated in the design example of this chapter. It is necessary to remember that the above procedure is not an exact analysis. The important approximations consist of assuming that the current gain and the output impedance of the preceding stage remain at their mid-band values, and also the input impedance of the following stage remains fixed. These approximations are rather close for the *RC* coupled cases where the permissible combinations are emitter-and-emitter, emitter-and-base, emitter-and-collector, or base-and-collector. The base-and-base, and the collector-and-collector combinations are never used with *RC* coupling since the resulting gain would always be less than that for a single stage.

For transformer coupling, the low-frequency response is determined almost solely by the frequency response of the transformer. If, in addition to the transformer, a capacitor is used to isolate the bias direct current, the above analysis will yield only a rough approximation since the assumptions are not so good when matched conditions are used.

High-frequency gain calculations. As mentioned in the section on frequency response, the action of the transistor at high frequencies

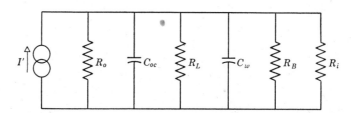

Fig. 10-14. Interstage circuit with collector capacity for high-frequency range.

is extremely complex. Because of this, the extreme difficulty of obtaining an exact solution is not profitable from the designer's point of view. We will here calculate the effects of the two most important high-frequency limitations: the collector capacitance and the decrease of h_{21} at high frequencies. For the general-purpose transistor, the manufacturer always states the value of collector capacitance and the frequency at which the current gain decreases 3 db from its mid-band value.

For these calculations a procedure similar to that used in the previous section will be used. The *change in gain* from the mid-band value will be sought. The same approximations as before will be made. They are: (1) the current gain and R_o of the preceding stage *do not vary with* Z_L; and (2), the input resistance of the next stage remains at its mid-band value. A distinct difference from the previous case is that here we have two effects to consider. This will be handled by again *separating the two effects.* The effect of the collector capacitor will first be considered, assuming that the current gain does not vary with frequency; then the effect of the frequency variation of the current gain will be found with the capacitance removed.

Referring to Figure 10-8, the high-frequency equivalent circuit for the interstage a-a' and b-b' is shown in Figure 10-14. The capacitor C_{oe} is the collector capacitance for the transistor preceding a-a'. The collector capacitance C_{ob} quoted by the manufacturer is usually given for the grounded-base connection. In the emitter connection the value of capacitance becomes

$$C_{oe} = \frac{C_{ob}}{1 + h_{21}} \tag{42}$$

The value of h_{21} is the grounded-base value of short-circuit current gain. It is noted that an additional shunt capacitor C_W is inserted to account for the small value of wiring capacity found in each design.

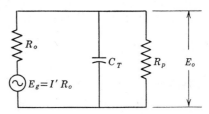

Since all the elements are in parallel, the circuit of Figure 10-14 can be simplified by combining elements. In addition, for ease of calculation, the current generator may be changed to a voltage generator. The result is the circuit of Figure 10-15. In this circuit the following relations hold:

Fig. 10-15. Simplified circuit of Fig. 10-14.

$$C_T = C_{oe} + C_W, \qquad R_p = \frac{R_L R_B R_i}{R_L R_B + R_i(R_L + R_B)} \tag{43}$$

As seen, R_p consists of the parallel combination of the load resistance, the bias resistance, and the input resistance. *If the stage were transformer coupled, R_p would consist only of the R_i transformed by the square of the turns ratio.*

As in the previous section, we need the ratio of E_o/E_g in the above circuit. That is, we are finding *how much the gain changes from the mid-band* value. From Chapter 6, the ratio of E_o/E_g is given by

$$\left(\frac{E_o}{E_g}\right)_{high} = \frac{R_p}{\sqrt{(R_o R_p \omega C_T)^2 + (R_o + R_p)^2}} \tag{44}$$

For the mid-band gain, the result is identical to the previous case, given in Equation (33) as

$$\left(\frac{E_o}{E_g}\right)_{\text{mid}} = \frac{R_p}{R_o + R_p} \tag{45}$$

The ratio then is

$$\frac{(E_o/E_g)_{\text{high}}}{(E_o/E_g)_{\text{mid}}} = \frac{(E_o)_{\text{high}}}{(E_o)_{\text{mid}}} = \frac{1}{\sqrt{1 + \left(\dfrac{R_o R_p w C_T}{R_o + R_p}\right)^2}} \tag{46}$$

For the reference frequency at the 3-db point, we find

$$f_H = \frac{1}{2\pi\left(\dfrac{R_o R_p C_T}{R_o + R_p}\right)} = \frac{1}{2\pi R_T C_T} \tag{47}$$

It may be seen that R_T is the parallel resistance of R_o and R_p, and hence equals the total parallel resistance of all the interstage resistors. From this equation we note a very important fact; *the cutoff frequency decreases with increase in R_p.* Therefore it is best, if mismatch is encountered, to mismatch on the low side. We see here that the criteria of power gain and frequency response conflict; for maximum power gain R_p should equal R_o. However, *the frequency response is improved as R_p is made smaller.* Consequently, in any design situation, the two factors must be weighed against each other.

Substituting Equation (47) back into Equation (46), it is found that

$$\boxed{\frac{(E_o)_{\text{high}}}{(E_o)_{\text{mid}}} = \frac{1}{\sqrt{1 + (f/f_H)^2}}} \tag{48}$$

Although we could use this result directly, similar to the method of Equation (37), it is more profitable again to use a chart. The chart is drawn in terms of decibel loss from the mid-band value, and is plotted versus f/f_H. To find the decibel value of Equation (48) we can write

$$\text{decibel change} = 10 \log_{10} \frac{1}{1 + (f/f_H)^2} \tag{49}$$

The chart is shown in Figure 10-16 and we use it as we do the chart for low-frequency response. That is, the first step is to find the f_H at each interstage by the use of Equation (47). This f_H corresponds to the point 1 on the frequency axis of the chart. For each interstage, then, *the value of additional loss due to collector capacitance* may be read directly from the chart at any frequency. The total losses from all the interstages must be subtracted from the total mid-band decibel gain of the circuit. This, then, is one part of the approximate solution to the high-frequency response.

The remaining problem is to find the loss incurred from the frequency dependence of the current gain (h_{21}) at the high frequencies. We are treating this as a separate problem, and hence the equivalent circuit will not contain the C_{oe}. If one measures the variation of h_{21}

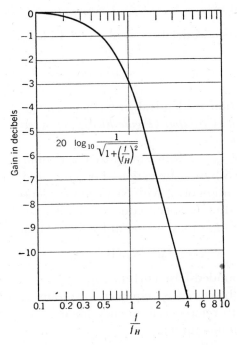

Fig. 10-16. High frequency response.

with frequency, it is found that the resulting curve closely approximates the equation

$$(h_{21})_{\text{high}} = \frac{h_{21}}{\sqrt{1 + (f/f_{\alpha 0})^2}} \tag{50}$$

where $f_{\alpha 0}$ = frequency where the decrease in h_{21} causes a 3-db decrease in power to the load (given by manufacturer),

h_{21} = grounded-base short-circuit current gain at mid-frequencies.

This equation may be used for the parameters of any connection, if the appropriate h parameters and the proper cutoff frequency are used.

Comparing this with Equation (48), it is seen that the approximate variation in current gain with frequency is the same as the variation in voltage gain caused by a shunt capacitor. Although the variation in Equation (48) is for a voltage ratio, and that of Equation (50) is for a current ratio, their effects will be the same since the input resistance to the next stage is assumed to remain at its mid-band value. Since power is given by I^2R, the decibel change in power caused by the h_{21} variation is

$$\text{change in decibels} = \text{db}_{\text{high}} = 10 \log_{10} \frac{I^2_{\text{high}}R_i}{I^2_{\text{mid}}R_i}$$

$$= 10 \log_{10} \frac{1}{1 + (f//f_{\alpha0})^2} \qquad (51)$$

Since this equation is identical in form to that of Equation (49) *we can use the same chart as before (Figure 10-16) to find the decibel loss caused by the $h_{21_{\text{high}}}$ variation.*

The value of $f_{\alpha0}$ is always stated by the manufacturer and applies to the grounded-base connection. For the grounded-emitter connection, the variation of h_{fe} with frequency is identical in form to that of h_{21}, but the 3 db reference frequency is different. The reference for the emitter case ($f_{\beta0}$) may be found by the relation

$$f_{\beta0} = f_{\alpha0}(1 + h_{21}) \qquad (52)$$

where h_{21} = grounded-base current gain,
$f_{\beta0}$ = 3 db reference frequency for grounded emitter,
$f_{\alpha0}$ = 3 db reference frequency for grounded base (stated by manufacturer).

From this equation it is evident *that the cutoff frequency for the grounded emitter is less than that for the grounded base.*

The use of the chart, then, for the grounded-emitter situation is as follows: calculate the $f_{\beta0}$ by use of Equation (52) and then read the decibel power loss due to h_{fe} variation directly from the chart for any given frequency. The resulting decibel loss must then be subtracted, along with the loss due to the C_T found earlier, from the total mid-band decibel gain.

Although the grounded-emitter connection has been used throughout this section, it must be remembered that the same methods can be used for the other connections. One must be careful, of course, to use the proper parameters and capacitance values.

We can now summarize the procedure for finding the approximate high-frequency response, taking account of both the collector capacitance and the h_{21} variation. The steps are as follows:

1. After finding C_{oe} (or C_{ob}), use Equation (43) to find the quantities necessary for determining the f_H of Equation (47).

2. Referring this f_H to the chart, for each interstage, the decibel loss for each interstage may be determined for any frequency.

3. Add the losses of each interstage to determine the total loss due to collector capacitance.

4. Determine the value of $f_{\beta 0}$ (or $f_{\alpha 0}$) from transistor data, and refer to chart.

5. Determine the loss due to decrease in h_{21}, for each interstage, from the chart.

6. Add the decibel loss of each interstage to determine the total loss.

7. Add the loss in (3) to that in (6) and subtract this total from the mid-band decibel gain.

As in the low-frequency case, the approximations used in the above analysis are usually valid for *RC* coupled stages. If matched conditions are achieved with the use of transformers, the above solution will yield only a rough approximation.

Comparing the grounded-emitter and the grounded-base connections, we have seen in this section that the grounded emitter has a lower f_H than the grounded base because of both an increased collector capacitance and a decreased current gain cutoff. (This comparison is valid only if both connections have approximately equal matched or unmatched conditions at input and output.) Therefore a required frequency response may demand the use of the base connection (with transformers) in spite of the higher gain available with the emitter connection.

Design Considerations

The first problem, when designing a cascaded transistor amplifier, consists of determining the number of required stages. The gain will probably be the criterion for the number of stages, although the subsequent frequency response may change this later. Consequently it is useful, after selecting a transistor based upon the general requirements, to find the maximum available gain for a single stage. It is remembered that the M.A.G. is a function of the transistor alone, and hence no consideration of load and source is needed for this preliminary calculation. Based upon this M.A.G. and the total gain needed, the amount of required stages can be estimated. If transformer coupling is to be used, the M.A.G. for each stage can be realized so that the minimum of stages is required; if RC coupling is used, the number of stages is greater since M.A.G. cannot be achieved.

The next logical step is to estimate the high-frequency response; this will be fixed by the transistor, as shown in the previous section. The loss due to h_{21} cutoff can be immediately found by using the chart and the manufacturer's data. The loss due to collector capacitance may be estimated by first performing the calculation for M.A.G. conditions. If the response of the two factors is not sufficient, an estimate of the amount of mismatch necessary is afforded by these calculations. Also, at this point it may be seen whether the chosen transistor is suitable.

After these preliminary calculations the various circuit elements can be fixed. For this, one must always begin with the last stage and proceed to the left since each stage acts as part of the load of the preceding stage. The design example of the following section will illustrate many design factors.

Regarding bias conditions, it is generally true that the operating point will be set at succeedingly higher values for the cascaded stages, since the signal level increases stage by stage from the input to the output. All stages may be set at the same operating point, however, if the point is high enough for the last stage. This is less efficient, d-c powerwise, than the former since more d-c power is consumed by the higher operating points.

Design Examples

The purpose of this design example, in addition to illustrating a design procedure, is to portray the method of treating the frequency response and biasing considerations treated in this chapter.

Problem. It is desired to design a preamplifier that will amplify a signal of -75 dbm to a 0 dbm power level. The source has an impedance of 150 ohms and the impedance of the load is 600 ohms. For frequency response, the amplification is allowed to be down 3 db at 100 and 5000 c. The power level of -75 dbm is sufficiently above the noise level of a transistor so that we will not consider noise here.

Solution. The power level of the signal throughout the amplifier is of such a magnitude that all the stages can be regarded as small-signal amplifiers. Hence the design can be carried out from the equivalent circuit techniques considered in this chapter.

The two criteria, in selecting a transistor for this design, are the power gain and the frequency response. For comparing the various available transistors, we may use the M.A.G. value and the frequency at which the h_{21} is down 3 db. The General Electric 2N43 transistor is recommended for "high-gain, low-to-medium power applications," which fits our category. We note (see characteristics in Appendix III) that the M.A.G. of this transistor in the emitter connection is 40 db, and the h_{21} cutoff frequency ($f_{\alpha 0}$) is 1.0 megacycle. This transistor, then, is selected for this design.

Because of the greater power gain and the simpler bias circuitry, the grounded-emitter connection is chosen for all stages. We have next to choose whether RC or transformer coupling is to be used. It is clear from the above figure of M.A.G. that, for transformer coupling and matching conditions, only two stages are required. For the RC coupling the inevitable mismatch between stages will necessitate at least three stages. In order to show the various methods of design, we shall investigate both the transformer coupled and the RC coupled.

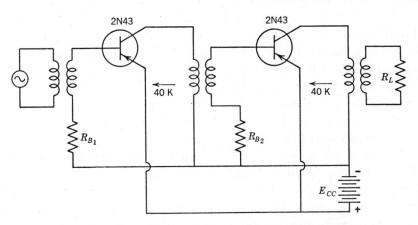

Fig. 10-17. Tentative circuit for transformed coupled design.

Transformer coupled. As noted above, it should be possible to obtain the required 75 db gain from only two stages with transformer coupling. Note that this could be altered later if the resulting frequency response were not sufficient. Using two stages, then, and the simplest biasing circuit, the tentative circuit diagram is shown in Figure 10-17. If the transformer ratios are adjusted properly, we can obtain the full 40 db (the M.A.G.) from each of these stages, and hence can obtain 80 db. It is quite likely, however, that matched conditions will be undesirable in terms of frequency response. In dealing with the frequency response, let us begin by finding the response under the M.A.G. conditions.

Remembering that the two high-frequency factors are current gain cutoff and collector capacity, let us begin with the former. According to the specifications, the $f_{\alpha 0}$ is 1.0 megacycle; the cutoff value for the grounded emitter connection is therefore

$$f_{\beta 0} = f_{\alpha 0}(1 + h_{21}) = (1 \times 10^6)(1 - 0.98) = 20,000 \text{ c} \qquad (53)$$

Using this value and referring to Figure 10-16, we can find the decibel loss, at each interstage, due to the current gain cutoff. Since the response may be down 3 db at 5000 c, we are always interested in the losses at this frequency. Using the chart, we find that the gain loss is 0.28 db at 5 kc. For the two stages, then, the loss due to gain cutoff will be 0.56 db. This means that at 5 kc we can afford $3.0 - 0.56 = 2.44$ db loss from the collector capacitance. It is remembered that we can control the capacitance loss, somewhat, by altering the match conditions between stages.

Let us first find the capacitor loss at 5 kc if the stages are matched. From Equation (47) we see that the f_H due to collector capacitance depends upon the R_o for the transistor and the load facing this R_o; for matched conditions we want R_p equal to R_o. We can calculate the matched load by use of Equation (66) of Chapter 8. (The values are also given in Table 2 of that chapter.) We find that the matched load of the 2N43 in the emitter connection is approximately 40,000 ohms. It is noted that for the transformer coupled case the R_p consists only of the a-c resistance presented by the output transformer. Thus for the moment we will consider that the R_p of Equation (47) is equal to 40,000, which in turn is equal to the R_o; consequently, R_T equals 20,000 ohms. We need yet to find C_{oe}. Using Equation (42) and the manufacturer's value for C_{ob}, we find

$$C_{oe} = \frac{C_{ob}}{1 + h_{21}} = \frac{40}{1 - 0.98} = 2000 \ \mu\mu f \qquad (54)$$

We can now solve for the f_H:

$$f_H = \frac{1}{2\pi R_T C_T}$$

$$= \frac{1}{(2\pi)(2000 \times 10^{-12})(2 \times 10^4)} = 3980 \text{ c} \qquad (55)$$

Thus under matched conditions there is a 3 db loss from each stage due to collector capacitance at 3980 c. This means that we cannot use matched conditions since we can afford only 2.44 db (or 1.22 db per stage) from the collector capacitance at 5000 c.

Knowing that we cannot use matched conditions, let us find what degree of mismatch is needed. Referring to the chart and setting the frequency where the loss is down 1.22 db at 5.0 kc, it is found that the f_H must be 9.0 kc; then the loss will be the allowable 1.22 db at 5.0 kc. We can now calculate what the R_p should be to result in this f_H. Using Equation (47) again,

$$9000 = \frac{4 \times 10^4 + R_p}{2\pi(4 \times 10^4 R_p)(2000 \times 10^{-12})} \tag{56}$$

The resulting value of R_p would be the maximum value of R_p. Although the result is slightly greater than 10,000, we shall use the round figure of

$$R_p = 10,000 \tag{57}$$

This means then, that although the R_o of the transistor is about 40,000 ohms, we shall adjust the transformer ratio so that the transformer presents an impedance of 10,000 ohms to the transistor. Thus there will be a mismatch of about 4 to 1. (Note that the R_o of the final design will be different from 40,000 since it depends upon the source resistance.)

We now need a hasty check to determine whether with this mismatch the two stages will still provide sufficient gain. Using the equation from Chapter 8, the power gain, per stage, is found to be

$$
\begin{aligned}
A_p &= \frac{h_{fe}^2 R_L}{(1 + h_{oe}R_L)(h_{ie} + \Delta^{h'}R_L)} \\
&= \frac{(49)^2(1 \times 10^4)}{[1 + (5 \times 10^{-5})(1 \times 10^4)][2 \times 10^3 + (2.16 \times 10^{-2})(1 \times 10^4)]} \\
&= 7240 = 38.6 \text{ db} \tag{58}
\end{aligned}
$$

Consequently we see that the two stages will still provide sufficient gain with the mismatch necessary to give the desired frequency response. The transformer ratios will be adjusted to provide a load impedance of 10,000 ohms for each stage; although this decreases the excess gain this makes it possible to achieve the desired frequency response.

Having assured ourselves that there are sufficient frequency response and gain available, we can now calculate the a-c operation more thoroughly. We may note that, since we do not now have a matched load, the R_i for each transistor will change; consequently if we change the source resistance accordingly, the R_o for the transistor will change and its value will no longer be exactly 40,000 ohms as stated earlier. Using a load resistance of 10,000 ohms and the h^e parameters for this transistor, the equations of Table 3 can be used to find

$$R_i = \frac{\Delta^{h\cdot} R_L + h_{ie}}{h_{oe} R_L + 1} = 1470, \qquad A_p = 7240 = 38.6 \text{ db} \qquad (59)$$

This will apply to both stages since we are making the conditions the same. If we adjust the transformer turns ratio so that the source resistance equals the R_i, or 1470, it is found that the new R_o for either stage is

$$R_o = \frac{h_{ie} + R_g}{\Delta^{h\cdot} + h_{oe} R_g} = 36,500 \qquad (60)$$

We can now recalculate the frequency response, using the values stated above. For the total capacitance, a value of 100 $\mu\mu$f is added to the transistor collector capacitance to account for the wiring capacitance. The actual f_H is then found to be

$$f_H = \frac{1}{2\pi C_T R_T}$$

$$= \frac{1}{(2\pi)(2000 \times 10^{-12} + 100 \times 10^{-12})(7850)}$$

$$= 9660 \qquad (61)$$

where $R_T = R_o R_L / (R_o + R_L) = 7850$. Referring to the chart again, we see that with this f_H the response is down 1.22 db at the frequency of 5.52 kc. Since this is above the required 5.0 kc, the calculations specify that the design is all right. It must be remembered, however, that the frequency response calculations are only an analysis based on certain approximations. Therefore for any design, the frequency response calculations must be treated with some caution.

The transformer ratios, in each case, can be found by taking the square root of the desired impedance ratios, as shown in Chapter 6.

We have yet to determine the operating points, and the value of bias resistor to result in the chosen operating points.

The power level of 0 dbm at the output stage corresponds to a power of 1 mw, and we can use the graphical relationships of the previous chapter to find a suitable operating point. The chief criterion is that the signal should not swing in to either the cutoff or the saturation region. From the previous chapter, then, it can quickly be shown that the peak-to-peak current and voltage are

$$I_{pp} = \sqrt{\frac{8P_{out}}{R_L}} = \sqrt{\frac{8 \times 10^{-3}}{10,000}} = 0.894 \text{ ma} \tag{62}$$

$$E_{pp} = \sqrt{8P_{out}R_L} = \sqrt{8 \times 10^{-3} \times 10,000} = 8.94 \text{ v}$$

Due to the transformer, the d-c load line will appear as a vertical line and the battery voltage must be at least one-half the peak-to-peak swing. Hence the collector battery must be at least 4.47 volts; we will select a 6.0 volt battery. The collector current, at the operating point, must be at least equal to one-half of the maximum swing plus the value of I_{CEO}. The current may then be found by

$$I_C = \frac{I_{pp}}{2} + I_{CEO} = 0.447 \text{ ma} + 0.500 \text{ ma} = 0.947 \text{ ma} \tag{63}$$

where $I_{CEO} = I_{co}/(1 + h_{21})$. In order to provide some margin, the I_C will be set at 1.5 ma. From the characteristics it may be seen that this corresponds to an I_B of about 15 μa. Therefore, the biasing resistor for the second stage, in conjunction with the 6.0 volt battery, must provide a current of 15 μa. The value of R_{B_2} may be found to be

$$R_{B_2} = \frac{E_{bb}}{I_B} = \frac{6.0}{15 \times 10^{-6}} = 400,000 \text{ ohms} \tag{64}$$

The value of C_2, the shunting capacitance for R_{B_2}, should be adjusted so that at 100 c the capacitor provides a low shunt impedance. We shall use the criterion that the capacitor impedance should be equal to or less than one-tenth the a-c impedance of the input circuit. Remembering that the a-c source impedance is 1500 ohms and the a-c input resistance of the transistor is also about 1500 ohms, the C may be found by

$$X_C = 0.1(R_i + R_g) = \frac{1}{2\pi f_L C}$$

$$C = \frac{1}{(0.1)(2940)(2\pi \times 100)} = 5.4 \times 10^{-6} \text{ f} \tag{65}$$

A capacitor of 10 μf will be selected.

For the first stage, an identical operating point as above may be used. If it is desired, the same procedure can be used to find a lower

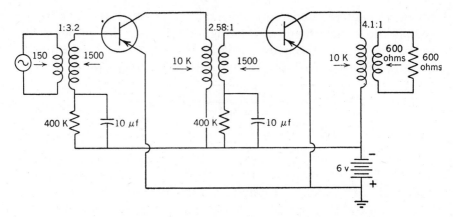

Fig. 10-18. Final transformer coupled design.

operating point, since the power level of the first stage is smaller. This would result in a slightly better d-c power efficiency.

The final design, then, is shown in Figure 10-18.

RC coupled amplifier. We will now design an *RC* coupled amplifier to provide the required 75 db gain and the low and high 3 db points of 100 and 5000 c. Because of the inherent mismatch of *RC* coupled stages, it was estimated earlier that at least three stages would be required. Although this will be checked after proper loads are assumed, we shall for the present assume that three stages are required. In order to exhibit the bleeder type bias circuit (see Figure 10-5) we will use this biasing arrangement. The tentative circuit diagram, then, is shown in Figure 10-19.

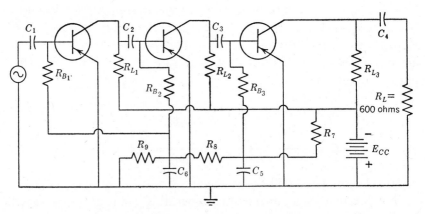

Fig. 10-19. Tentative *RC* coupled design using bleeder type biasing.

In the RC coupled case we cannot adjust the gain readily by altering the matching, since the load of any stage is mainly determined by the input resistance to the next stage. We can make a preliminary gain calculation by considering only the R_i of the next stage as the load on the transistor, and assuming the R_i has the nominal value given by the manufacturer (1000 ohms in this case),

$$A_p = \frac{(h_{fe})^2 R_L}{(1 + h_{oe}R_L)(\Delta^h R_L + h_{ie})} = 1130 \cong 30 \text{ db} \qquad (66)$$

Based upon this preliminary calculation, it is seen that three stages is the correct number.

We can now estimate the frequency response for the three stages. First, it is remembered that the h_{fe} cutoff decreases the gain by 0.28 db at 5 kc for each stage. For three stages the loss due to this is then 0.84 db. This means that we can afford a total of $3 - 0.84$ db = 2.16 db, or 0.72 db per stage from the collector capacitance effect. Referring to the frequency chart of Figure 10-16, this results in requiring an f_H of at least 12.5 kc. This means that if the gain is down 3 db at 12.5 kc, the gain will be down 0.72 db at 5 kc, which is the allowable amount per stage.

Using Equation (47), then, we can find what the maximum value of R_T, the total parallel resistance at the interstage, may be.

$$f_H = \frac{1}{2\pi R_T C_T} = 12.5 \text{ kc}, \qquad R_p = 6.36 \times 10^3 \qquad (67)$$

where $C_T = 2000 \ \mu\mu\text{f}$ = collector capacitance in grounded emitter connection.

Equation (67) says that the parallel combination of R_o, R_L, R_B, and the R_i of the following stage may not be above 6360 ohms. Since the total resistance of a parallel combination is always less than the *lowest* resistance, the value of R_p will never be more than R_i. Furthermore, since the R_i is always of the order of 1000 to 2000 ohms for a grounded-emitter stage without feedback, Equation (67) tells us that *the collector capacitance will not limit the frequency response.* The mismatch is enough to cause the h_{21} cutoff to affect the frequency response before the collector capacitance effect. Consequently, we need consider only the h_{21} cutoff for the rest of this design.

We can now begin assigning proper values to the various resistors, based on the a-c operation. As in the case of analysis, we must start with the last stage. Referring to Figures 10-19, R_{L_3} should be much greater than R_L so that R_{L_3} does not shunt the a-c signal appreciably. However, a very large R_{L_3} would necessitate a large collector battery in order to obtain a suitable operating point. From considerations of the d-c load line, then, 10,000 ohms is selected for the value of R_{L_3}. The total load on the last stage then is 10,000 ohms in parallel with 600 ohms.

$$R_{T_3} = \frac{R_L R_{L_3}}{R_{L_3} + R_L} = 566 \tag{68}$$

Using the equations of Table 3 (Chapter 8), we can find the following values:

$$R_{i_3} = 1960, \qquad A_{p_3} = 655 = 28.14 \text{ db} \tag{69}$$

Since not all the power in the output of the transistor reaches the load resistor, we calculate the interstage loss by use of Equation (25).

$$\text{loss} = 10 \log_{10} \frac{R_{T_3}}{R_L} = 10 \log_{10} \frac{566}{600} = -0.25 \text{ db} \tag{70}$$

The negative sign merely means that a loss is involved. The total power gain so far, then, is

$$\text{Db}_3 + \text{loss} = 28.14 \text{ db} + (-0.25) = 27.89 \text{ db} \tag{71}$$

For the resistors preceding stage three, R_{L_2} and R_{B_3}, we again wish to keep them much higher than the R_{i_3} so that they do not shunt the a-c signal appreciably. The R_{L_2} determines the d-c load line of the second stage, and hence the battery and operating point must be considered. Since the signal swing for the second stage is less than for the third, we can make R_{L_2} larger than R_{L_3} (for the same battery). Consequently, the value of 30,000 ohms is chosen. For the R_{B_3}, we would desire to keep its value as high as 30,000 ohms. However, the bias stability is affected by this resistor (treated in next chapter), and therefore a value of 15,000 ohms is selected. The total a-c load on the second stage then is

$$R_{T_2} = \frac{1}{1/30,000 + 1/15,000 + 1/1960} = 1640 \text{ ohms} \tag{72}$$

Using this load resistance, the gain and R_{i_2} for the second stage are

$$R_{i_2} = 1880, \qquad A_{p_2} = 1795 = 32.54 \text{ db} \tag{73}$$

Subtracting the interstage loss, which is found by

$$\text{db}_3 = 10 \log_{10} \frac{1640}{1960} = -0.78 \text{ db} \tag{74}$$

the net gain is

$$Db_2 + db_3 = 32.54 \text{ db} - 0.78 \text{ db} = 31.76 \text{ db} \qquad (75)$$

The same value of resistors for R_{L_1} and R_{B_2} will be selected as for R_{L_2} and R_{B_3}, respectively. It is then found that

$$R_{T_1} = \frac{1}{1/30,000 + 1/15,000 + 1/1880} = 1590 \text{ ohms}$$
$$R_{i_1} = 1890 \text{ ohms} \qquad (76)$$
$$A_{p_1} = 1740 \text{ ohms}$$

The net gain, with the interstage loss subtracted is

$$Db_1 + db_2 = 32.4 \text{ db} - 0.73 \text{ db} = 31.67 \text{ db} \qquad (77)$$

The only remaining gain calculation is for the interstage network preceding the first stage. If R_{B_1} is made equal to 15,000 ohms, the loss is

$$\text{loss} = 10 \log_{10} \frac{R_T}{R_i} = 10 \log_{10} \frac{1590}{1890} = -0.75 \text{ db} \qquad (78)$$

The total gain is now found by adding all the decibel gains. The total is

$$\text{total gain} = 31.67 + 31.76 + 27.89 - 0.75 = 90.57 \text{ db} \quad (79)$$

Since the total gain is greater than required, a volume control may be placed in the circuit and will be shown in the final design.

The amplifier is now suitable for the a-c aspects. We have now to determine the proper d-c conditions. This is mainly a problem of setting the operating points of each stage so that the signal swing of each stage can be properly handled. Since from the above power calculations we know the maximum power out, we will begin with the last stage and work to the left.

The maximum power output will be 10 db above 1 mw. Let us assume that a volume control is inserted so that the maximum power of 1 mw occurs. To find a suitable operating point, then, we must find the peak-to-peak values of voltage and current.

Remembering that for a sine wave,

$$I_{\text{rms}} = 0.707 I_{\text{max}} \qquad (80)$$

the following peak-to-peak values can be found by

$$I_{pp} = \sqrt{\frac{8P}{R_L}} = \sqrt{\frac{(8)(1 \times 10^{-3})}{600}} = 3.6 \text{ ma}$$
$$E_{pp} = \sqrt{8PR_L} = \sqrt{(8)(1 \times 10^{-3})(600)} = 2.19 \text{ v} \qquad (81)$$

The minimum I_C, then, is given by

$$\min I_C = \frac{I_{pp}}{2} + I_{CEO} = \frac{3.6}{2} + 0.5 = 2.3 \text{ ma} \tag{82}$$

The minimum collector battery can now be determined by adding the minimum allowable voltage $(2.19/2 = 1.09)$ to the voltage drop across the load resistor. Note that it is R_{L_3}, 10,000 ohms, that controls the d-c load line. The voltage, with the minimum allowable I_C is

$$V_{R_{L_3}} = (I_C)(R_{L_3}) = (2.3)(1 \times 10^4) = 23 \text{ v}$$
$$\min E_{CC} = V_{CE} + I_C R_{L_3} = 1.09 + 23 = 24.09 \text{ v} \tag{83}$$

We will select a 27-volt battery. On the characteristics of the 2N43 in Figure 10-20 we can now draw the a-c and the d-c load lines. An

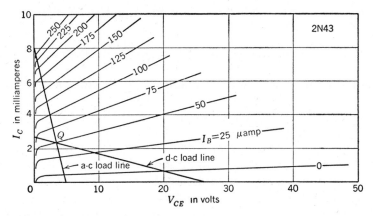

Fig. 10-20. A-c and d-c load lines for the third stage (2N43) transistor.

operating point at $I_C = 2.4$ ma is selected, and this requires an I_B of about 50 μa. Since the biasing resistor (R_{B_3}) is 15,000 ohms, a voltage of 0.75 v is required from the bleeder biasing circuit. This circuit will be determined after the bias voltages for all three stages are determined.

For the second stage the power output is about 28 db lower than 1 mw (about 2 μw). The I_{pp} and E_{pp} then are

$$I_{pp} = \sqrt{\frac{8P}{R_L}} = \sqrt{\frac{(8)(2 \times 10^{-6})}{1640}} = 0.0987 \text{ ma}$$
$$E_{pp} = \sqrt{8PR_L} = \sqrt{(8)(2 \times 10^{-6})(1640)} = 0 \tag{84}$$

Although an I_C of 0.5987 ma would be sufficient, the value of

0.7 ma will be selected. It is noted that due to the required swing, only a 0.08 value for V_C is required. Since this is down in the nonlinear region, we must make it greater than this. Since we wish to use a single battery, an E_{CC} equal to that of the third stage will be assumed (27 volts). The V_C will then be, for an I_C of 0.7 ma,

$$V_C = E_{CC} - I_C(R_L)_{\text{d-c}} = 27 - (0.7)(3.0 \times 10^4) = 6 \text{ v} \qquad (85)$$

This is satisfactory for V_C.

From the characteristics we see that an I_B of 10 μa is required. With the R_{B_2} of 15,000 ohms the required voltage from the bleeder circuit is 0.15 v. The a-c and d-c load lines for the second stage are shown in Figure 10-21.

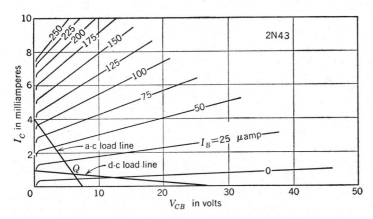

Fig. 10-21. A-c and d-c load lines for the second stage.

The operating point for the first stage is chosen identical to that of the second. Thus the load lines will be practically identical and the bias voltage for the R_{B_1} is 0.15 v.

The bleeder biasing circuit can now be determined. A total of 70 μa base biasing current is required for the three stages. If we make the total current of the bleeder circuit appreciably larger than this, we can calculate the resistance values separately—that is, we do not need to consider the simultaneous conditions of the three separate loops. A total bleeder current of 1 ma is chosen as being appropriate. For the voltage of 0.15 for the first two stages, then, a 1500 ohm resistance is required. For the 0.75 v of the third stage, a total of 7500 ohms is required. Hence an additional resistor of $7500 - 1500 = 6000$ ohms is used. In order to draw 1 ma from the 27 v battery, a total resistance

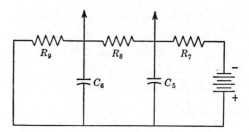

Fig. 10-22. Bleeder biasing network.

of 27,000 ohms is needed. Therefore, a 19,500 ohm resistor is finally required. The biasing circuit then appears as shown in Figure 10-22.

Since the coupling capacitors determine the low-frequency response, we must use Equations (39) and (31):

$$f_L = \frac{1}{2\pi(R_g + R_p)C} \tag{86}$$

where $R_g = \dfrac{R_o R_L}{R_o + R_L}$ and $R_p = \dfrac{R_B R_i}{R_B + R_i}$.

We will use this equation for each interstage. Since the values of R_o have not been previously calculated, we will first do this. By using the relations of Table 3,

$$(R_o)_{\text{1st stage}} = \frac{h_{ie} + R_g'}{\Delta^{h\bullet} + h_{oe}R_g'} = \frac{2000 + 148.5}{2.15 \times 10^{-2} + (5 \times 10^{-5})(148.5)}$$

$$= 74{,}400 \text{ ohms}$$

where $R_g' =$ total resistance preceding the stage

$$= R_{B_1} \parallel R_{\text{source}} = 15{,}000 \parallel 150 \text{ ohms.}$$

$$(R_o)_{\text{2nd stage}} = \frac{2000 + 8820}{2.15 \times 10^{-2} + (5 \times 10^{-5})(8820)}$$

$$= 23{,}100 \text{ ohms}$$

$$R_g' = R_{B_2} \parallel R_{L_1} \parallel R_{o_1}$$

$$= 15{,}000 \parallel 30{,}000 \parallel 74{,}400 \text{ ohms} \tag{87}$$

$$(R_o)_{\text{3rd stage}} = \frac{2000 + 7000}{(2.15 \times 10^{-2}) + (5 \times 10^{-5})(7000)}$$

$$= 24{,}200 \text{ ohms}$$

$$R_g' = R_{B_3} \parallel R_{L_2} \parallel R_{o_2}$$

$$= 15{,}000 \parallel 30{,}000 \parallel 23{,}400 \text{ ohms}$$

Using these values, in combination with the previously calculated values of R_i in Equation (86), we can find the value of C if we know the proper f_L for each interstage. Since we are allowed a 3 db drop-off at 100 c, and since there are four coupling capacitors, we can afford a 0.75 db loss in each interstage at 100 c. Referring to the low-frequency chart of Figure 10-13, we find the f_L of 40 c is proper. The values of the coupling capacitors may then be found to be

$$C_1 = \frac{1}{2\pi(R_{g_1} + R_{p_1})40} = \frac{1}{6.28(150 + 1680)40} = 2.17 \ \mu f$$

$$C_2 = \frac{1}{2\pi(R_{g_2} + R_{p_2})40} = \frac{1}{6.28(21,300 + 1670)40} = 0.173 \ \mu f$$

$$C_3 = \frac{1}{2\pi(R_{g_3} + R_{p_3})40} = \frac{1}{6.28(13,150 + 1735)40} = 0.268 \ \mu f$$
$$\hspace{11cm}(88)$$

$$C_4 = \frac{1}{2\pi(R_{g_4} + R_{p_4})40} = \frac{1}{6.28(7100 + 600)40} = 0.386 \ \mu f$$

The capacitors C_5 and C_6 used in the bleeder circuit to prevent a-c feedback from the bias network can be calculated from the criterion that the X_C presented at the lowest frequency used (100 c) must be at least 10 times less than the loop impedance in which it appears. Referring to Figure 10-19, the loop impedance for C_5 is $R_{o_2} \parallel R_{L_2} \parallel R_{B_3}$ in series with R_{i_3}:

$$R_{\text{loop}} = 7000 + 1960 = 8960 \text{ ohms}$$

Then
$$X_{C_5} = \frac{1}{10} \times 8960 \hspace{3cm} (89)$$

$$C_5 = \frac{10}{2\pi f_L 8960} = \frac{10}{(6.28)(100)(8960)} = 1.77 \ \mu f \approx 2.0 \ \mu f$$

For C_6, the series loop is

$$R_{\text{loop}} = 148.5 + 1890 = 2038.5 \text{ ohms}$$

Then
$$C_6 = \frac{10}{(6.28)(100)(2038.5)} = 7.81 \ \mu f \approx 8 \ \mu f \hspace{2cm} (90)$$

We can now exhibit the final design, and it is shown in Figure 10-23.

Although we estimated the high-frequency response in the beginning of this design, it was impossible to ascertain since the various components were not yet evaluated. It is useful, now, to check whether the high-frequency response is sufficient (3 db down at 5000 c). We will first note the loss due to the collector capacitance in the emitter connection C_{oe}. Using Equation (43) and (47) at each interstage, and then referring to the chart of Figure 10-16 to deter-

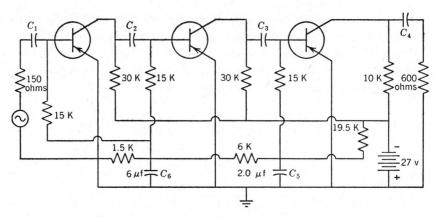

Fig. 10-23. Final design for *RC* coupled amplifier.

mine the loss at 5000 c, the calculations are

$$C_T = C_{oe} + C_W = \frac{C_{ob}}{1 + h_{21}} + C_W$$

$$= \frac{40}{1 - 0.98} + 100 \ \mu\mu f = 2.1 \times 10^{-9} f \qquad (91)$$

where a wiring capacity of 100 $\mu\mu f$ is assumed.

$$f_{H_3} = \frac{1}{2\pi R_T C_T} = \frac{1}{(6.28)(553)(2.1 \times 10^{-9})} = 128,000 \ c$$

db$_3$ (at 5000 c) $\cong 0$

$$f_{H_2} = \frac{1}{2\pi R_T C_T} = \frac{1}{(6.28)(1530)(2.1 \times 10^{-9})} = 49,500 \ c$$

db$_2$ (at 5000 c) $\cong 0$ $\qquad (92)$

$$f_{H_1} = \frac{1}{2\pi R_T C_T} = \frac{1}{(6.28)(1590)(2.1 \times 10^{-9})} = 48,500 \ c$$

db$_1$ (at 5000 c) $\cong 0$

These calculations agree with our former statement that the collector capacitance will not present a problem for the high-frequency drop-off. The calculations are shown here merely to illustrate the process.

For the drop-off due to h_{21}, we note that the $f_{\alpha 0}$ is given by the manufacturer as 1.0 megacycle. Then $f_{\beta 0}$ for the emitter connection is

$$f_{\beta 0} = f_{\alpha 0}(1 + h_{21}) = (1.0)(1 - 0.98) = 2 \times 10^4 = 20,000 \ c$$

From Figure 10-16 we see that the loss at 5000 c is then 0.27 db per transistor. The total loss due to h_{21} drop-off is then 0.81 db. Therefore at 5 kc, the high-frequency response exhibits only a 0.81 db drop-off and this is all due to the h_{21} effect.

Comparison of the Two Designs

As noted, the transformer design required only two transistors stages, whereas the RC case required three. The choice of coupling rests with the cost and space considerations. Usually the RC case is chosen because the additional transistors cost less and require less space than the combination of transformers.

The two designs, depicted above, were carried by using the design center values for the transistor quantities. In order to certify that the amplifier is suitable with any transistors of the same type, the gain and frequency response should be checked under the worst possible conditions. For frequency response this would mean recalculation, using the maximum value of C_{oe} and the minimum value for $f_{\alpha 0}$; for gain, the minimum value of h_{fe} would be used. The manufacturer usually specifies the maximum and minimum quantites along with the design center quantities. This recalculation is left as an exercise for the student.

The above two designs should not be construed as representing all aspects of transistor amplifier designing. In the next chapter we will consider the stabilizing of the d-c operating points, and following this the use of feedback will be considered. The frequency response of the above amplifier, for example, could be improved by the use of feedback.

Problems

1. Using the maximum value of collector capacity and minimum value of $f_{\alpha 0}$ stated by the manufacturer for the 2N43, determine whether the transformer coupled amplifier designed in the text would be satisfactory.
2. Using the minimum value of h_{21} given by the manufacturer for the 2N43, check the mid-frequency gain of the transformer coupled design. Will this amplifier still give the required gain?
3. Using the conditions set forth in Problem 1, determine whether the RC coupled amplifier design will give the required frequency response.

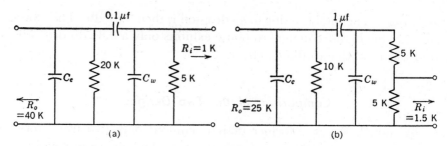

Fig. 10-24. Transistor interstages.

4. Using the conditions of Problem 2 check the mid-frequency gain of the *RC* coupled amplifier. Is there still sufficient gain?

5. What is the mid-frequency loss through the interstages shown in Figure 10-24?

6. What are the upper and lower half-power frequencies for the interstages of Figure 10-24? Use a collector capacitance C_c of 2500 $\mu\mu f$ and a wiring capacity C_w of 150 $\mu\mu f$.

7. If the upper cutoff frequency of the transistors used with the interstages of Figure 10-24 is 10 megacycles and the grounded-base short-circuit current gain h_{fb} is -0.96, what is the limiting factor in the high-frequency response?

8. What value of coupling capacitance would be required in the interstages of Figure 10-24 to improve the frequency response such that the low-frequency cutoff will be 20 c?

II

Bias Stability and Direct-Current Amplifiers

When considering bias conditions for power amplifiers and for cascaded amplifiers, the methods of obtaining a desired d-c operating point were studied. It is now necessary to consider the available measures for *retaining* the desired operating point under actual operating conditions.

There are two major reasons for the difficulty in sustaining a desired operating point. First, as was noted in the physics portion, the characteristics of the transistor are temperature dependent. Although this affects both the a-c parameters and the d-c conditions, the latter are most important. Second, the characteristics of different transistors of the same type will vary from unit to unit. Consequently, when various transistors are placed in the same circuit, the operation will vary somewhat unless stabilizing measures are taken.

It will be the purpose of this chapter, then, to study the various stabilizing measures and to evaluate the resulting stabilized circuit. All the stability considerations will concern the grounded-emitter connections, since this is the most frequent amplifier connection. The same procedures may, of course, be used for the other two connections.

We will first consider the manner in which temperature and unit-to-unit variation affect the transistor. For purposes of evaluating a given circuit, a stability factor S will be defined and explained. Following this, the various methods of stabilizing a circuit will be studied in terms of the resulting S. Since the question of stability is very critical for d-c amplifiers, some basic circuits and the resulting stability for such circuits will be considered.

Important Factors

We shall now consider the effect that temperature changes and unit-to-unit variation have on transistors. In addition, the effect of a relatively high cutoff component of collector current will be considered.

Temperature variation. The transistor characteristics specified by a manufacturer are actually valid only for a given junction temperature (usually 25°C). The actual junction temperature of a transistor in a circuit will depend upon both the power dissipated in the transistor and the means for removing heat from the transistor. In small-signal applications, where the dissipation power of the transistor is small, *we can regard the transistor junction temperature as being approximately equal to the temperature of the surrounding air*. As larger signals are encountered, however, the transistor power and its dissipating means must be considered in order to approximate the junction temperature. The method for doing this was described in the chapter on power amplifiers. For our purposes here we will assume that the junction temperature coincides with the ambient temperature.

The effect of the temperature variation can best be described by referring to the collector characteristics. When the temperature varies, the characteristics move from their original position. In general, the characteristics keep the same spacing with respect to each other, but the entire set of curves moves upward when temperature increases. This situation is caused by the fact that the I_{CO} for a transistor varies greatly with temperature. The dependence upon I_{CO} can be seen in Figure 11-1(a). Here it is noted that for any bias current I_C the current can be written as

$$I_C = I_{CO} + \alpha I_E = I_{CO} - h_{21}I_E \tag{1}$$

Note that this equation holds for *any* I_C so long as the proper values of I_{CO} and I_E are used. It is remembered that the I_{CO} is the bias current flowing through the reverse-biased collector junction (when the $I_E = 0$) and h_{21} is the short-circuit current amplification that is determined by the spacing between the curves. If the spacing between curves remains essentially constant with temperature, Equation (1) tells us that the set of curves will vary directly as I_{CO} varies.

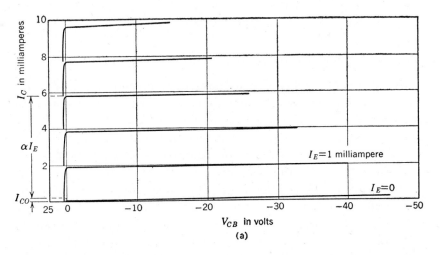

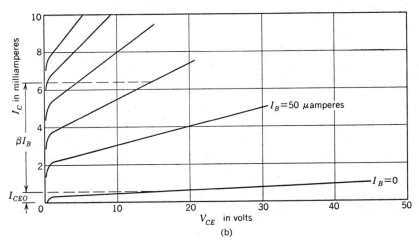

Fig. 11-1. Characteristics showing I_C, I_{CO} relationships: (a) grounded-base; (b) grounded-emitter.

Figure 11-1(b) shows the reverse-current dependence for the grounded-emitter connection. The equation here is

$$I_C = I_{CEO} + \beta I_B = I_{CEO} - h_{fe}I_B \qquad (2)$$

Again, since the h_{fe} does not vary appreciably, the set of curves will vary directly with I_{CEO}.

The relation between I_C and I_{CEO} is given by

$$I_{CEO} = \frac{I_{co}}{1 + h_{21}} \tag{3}$$

where h_{21} = grounded-base short-circuit current gain.[1]

When it is remembered that h_{21} is a negative number close to 1, it is seen that I_{CEO} is much greater than I_{co}. This means also that *any variation in I_{co} causes a much greater variation in I_{CEO}.* This is the reason, then, for the grounded-emitter connection being less stable than the grounded-base; hence we shall deal mostly with the stability of the emitter connection in this chapter.

Although the a-c parameters (such as h_{21}) remain essentially constant with temperature variation, which accounts for the curves remaining in the same relative position, there is some tendency for them to vary. The h_{11} and h_{21} will usually rise slightly with temperature increase, while the h_{12} and h_{22} would be expected to increase more substantially.

The important situation, then, when temperature increases are encountered is depicted in Figure 11-2(a). The solid lines show the characteristics of 30°C, and the dashed lines portray the change when temperature increases. The variation is exaggerated here to illustrate the action. If we now attach a circuit load line as shown in Figure 11-2(b), we may note the shift of operating point with temperature. Since the load line does not change with temperature, the operating point will shift along the stationary load line until the point where approximately the same I_B is encountered as before. It is seen that, with the new operating point, the permissible swing on the upper half of the load line is reduced. If a relatively large signal is being used under the conditions of (b) above, the shifting operating point will induce clipping if the signal now moves into the saturation region.

If the temperature were to continue increasing, the action shown in Figure 11-2 would continue until finally the operating point would lie on the I_C axis. It is easily seen now why it is necessary to stabilize the operating point for transistor amplifiers whenever a temperature variation is expected. The object of all stabilizing measures is to minimize the effect of the shift in characteristics shown above.

For any particular transistor, the amount of variation, such as in

[1] The reader will remember that we may use either h_{21} or h_{fb} for this quantity. Since practically all a-c parameters used in this chapter are grounded-base quantities, the authors have chosen the numerical subscript notation for the entire chapter.

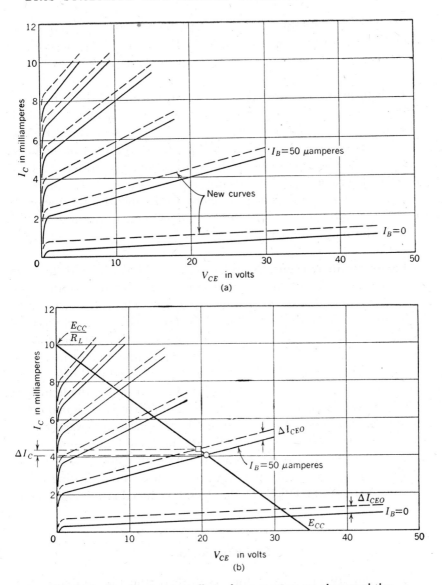

Fig. 11-2. Graphs showing effect of temperature on characteristics and operating point: (a) shift of characteristics with temperature; (b) shift of operating point with temperature.

Figure 11-2, can be found by using the temperature dependence of the I_{CO}, listed by the manufacturer, in Equation (3). If no data on the I_{CO} are given, it must be measured to find this dependence.

Unit-to-unit variation. When two transistors of the same type are manufactured, their characteristics are never identical. Again it is found that, although the a-c parameters vary somewhat, it is the I_{CO} that shows the chief deviation. This I_{CO} deviation will again be magnified, in the grounded-emitter connection, according to Equation (3). Therefore *unit-to-unit variation, in the same circuit, produces the same general effect as temperature variation.* Consequently, the measures suitable for stabilizing the temperature dependence will also serve to stabilize the unit-to-unit variation.

Large cutoff current. Another factor to be considered, in transistor amplifiers, is the large cutoff current I_{CEO} of the emitter connection, compared to the grounded-base I_{CO}. The relation between I_{CEO} and I_{CO} is given by Equation (3). The relatively high value of I_{CEO} is undesirable from the standpoint of efficiency. Although not a major factor, the efficiency of a large signal amplifier will be improved if the cutoff component of the collector current is reduced below I_{CEO}. The signal may then swing closer to the V_{CE} axis along the load line. This is especially true if the transistor amplifier is designed for a constant high-temperature operation. In this case the characteristic would be elevated according to Figure 11-2, and the signal swing would be limited, at the lower end, by the high value of I_{CEO}.

Those measures, then, that serve to stabilize the operating point, will also increase the efficiency due to the reduced cutoff component of current.

Stability Factor

The stability factor S is the measure of the bias stability of a transistor amplifier; S is defined as the change in collector current I_c per change in cutoff current I_{CO}.

$$S = \frac{\Delta I_C}{\Delta I_{CO}} \tag{4}$$

where I_{CO} = cutoff current in the grounded-base connection.

The Δ in Equation (4) stands for a small change in the quantity which it precedes. Equation (4) thus states that for a small change in $I_{co}(\Delta I_{co})$ a resulting change in $I_c(\Delta I_c)$ results and the ratio of these two changes is the stability factor S.

We can see why this method of measuring stability is useful by referring to Figure 11-2. There we note that the change in I_c is the measure of how much the operating point moves. Also, it is remembered that it is the I_{co} that varies with temperature and various transistors. By referring to Equation (3) we can quickly note the *stability factor of an unstabilized grounded-emitter circuit.* Since, for this condition, the ΔI_c equals ΔI_{CEO}, it is true that

$$S = \frac{\Delta I_c}{\Delta I_{co}} = \frac{\Delta I_{CEO}}{\Delta I_{co}} = \frac{1}{1 + h_{21}} \tag{5}$$

where h_{21} = grounded-base short-circuit current amplification.

Thus the stability factor of the unstabilized emitter circuit equals the circuit current gain. We will see below how this value is improved by the various stabilizing schemes.

The optimum value of S would be 1. If this were the case, the ΔI_c would always equal the ΔI_{co}. This is an idealized objective and is not realizable with ordinary measures; the value of S is always greater than 1 for the grounded-emitter configuration. However, it should be remembered that the closer the value of S is to 1, the better.

The stability factor then should be taken into consideration whenever a temperature variation is expected or when transistor replacement is necessary. If an a-c amplifier consists of cascaded stages, the S is considered separately for each stage. In the a-c amplifier, where coupling capacitors (or transformers) appear between the stages, the I_c change of any one stage does not affect the other stages. It is for this reason that the S is considered separately for each stage. For d-c amplifiers any change in I_c *will* affect all succeeding stages; therefore other considerations are involved and these will be considered later in this chapter.

In using the stability factor in a design situation one may begin by finding the allowable value of S and then, by the use of a number of d-c equations, adjust the various circuit values to obtain the desired S. Usually, however, the best procedure is to adjust the circuit components according to the a-c considerations, as was done in the previous design examples, and then check the S of the resulting circuit.

If the ensuing S is not low enough, the proper circuit values may be changed, always keeping in mind the a-c considerations, to obtain a suitable S.

In order to illustrate the use of the stability factor, let us consider the following example:

Assume that a temperature range of 50°C is encountered, and that the I_{co} varies by 20 μamp in this range. Assume also that the given circuit exhibits a stability of $S = 5$. The I_c will then vary by

$$\Delta I_c = S\Delta I_{co} = 100 \ \mu\text{amp} \tag{5a}$$

The next step would consist of estimating the total signal swing of the circuit. Using this swing in conjunction with the load line, it may be determined whether the ΔI_c is tolerable. If not, the circuit must be altered so as to provide a *lower* value of S.

Stabilized Circuits

There are, in general, four methods of stabilizing the operating point of transistor amplifiers: (1) direct current feedback; (2) direct voltage feedback; (3) use of temperature-sensitive circuit elements; and (4) particular tandem connections.

D-c current feedback. Feedback can be defined generally as the condition where part of the output is applied to the input circuit. For stabilizing purposes we are interested in inverse feedback; that is, if the output increases, the part fed back to the input serves to decrease the output. In current feedback the amount of signal fed back to the input depends upon a current flowing in the output circuit.

For the grounded-emitter connection, current feedback is achieved by simply placing a resistor R_3 in the emitter lead. We can examine how this serves to stabilize the operating point, intuitively, by noting Figure 11-3. The by-pass capacitor across R_3 is used to prevent the resistor from also providing a-c feedback; this capacitor will be used on all the current-feedback circuits. Let us assume that, due to an increase in temperature, the characteristics as shown in Figure 11-2 are moved upwards. Regarding the I_B as being constant, momentarily, this means that the I_c would increase. When the I_c increases, an additional voltage will appear across R_3 in the direction shown. It is seen that this voltage opposes the input bias voltage; hence the I_B will be reduced. Referring to Figure 11-2 again, it is seen that this

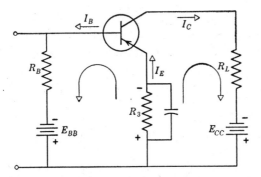

Fig. 11-3. Conventional grounded-emitter circuit using current feed-back.

tends to return the operating point to its original position. Thus, although the characteristics of the transistor itself have moved, the operating point tends to stay in the same position with respect to the axes. In addition, if R_3 is considered part of the transistor, the characteristics of the combination are stabilized so that their shift with temperature is not so great as the shift for the transistor alone. It is in this manner, then, that the current feedback resistor R_3 counteracts the effect of temperature and unit-to-unit variation. When the temperature acts to raise the set of transistor characteristics the voltage developed across R_3 acts to restrict the shift of the effective characteristics of the transistor-R_3 combination.

We can now calculate the stability factor of this stabilized circuit. Noting the definition of Equation (4), we wish to find how I_C varies with any change in I_{CO}. To find this relationship, for any circuit, we need to write the proper d-c equations, and solve them for I_C. Since a two-loop circuit is involved, we might begin by writing the usual two d-c mesh equations. They are, referring to Figure 11-2,

$$E_{BB} = I_B(R_3 + R_B) + I_C R_3 + V_{EB}$$

$$E_{CC} = I_B R_3 + I_C(R_3 + R_L) - V_{CE} \qquad (6)$$

These are the two d-c mesh equations of the basic grounded-emitter circuit. It is also evident, from the circuit, that

$$I_E = I_B + I_C \qquad (7)$$

Again it is necessary to emphasize that we are here writing the *d-c equations;* earlier in Chapter 8, we were mainly interested in the a-c conditions. It is remembered that, for electronic circuits in general, the a-c and the d-c conditions are treated separately.

We note that I_{CO} does not appear in any of the above equations. Since the relation between I_C and I_{CO} is desired, we need an equation that contains I_{CO}. The necessary d-c relation is given by Equation (1) and is

$$I_C = I_{CO} + \alpha I_E = I_{CO} - h_{21}I_E \qquad (8)$$

where I_{CO} = grounded-base cutoff current,
$\quad \alpha$ = grounded-base short-circuit current amplification
$\quad = \Delta I_C / \Delta I_E = -h_{21}$.

Since this equation is based upon the transistor itself, it must be valid for any connection.[2]

We may use, then, any of the above equations to find the stability factor S. We will need two equations, of course, since two loops are involved. Instead of the conventional output Equation (6), however, we will use (8) as the output equation. This is perfectly valid if we make the following two assumptions:

1. The collector I_C does not vary with collector voltage, V_{CB}.

2. The value of h_{21} (or α) is constant over the operating range. Both of these are reasonable assumptions for the transistor as can be seen by referring to any grounded-base characteristics. The output equation, then, is

$$I_{CO} = I_C + h_{21}I_E \qquad (9)$$

Note that I_C and I_E are the variables of this relation. For the input loop the conventional Equation (6) is used. In addition, the assumption is made that V_{EB} is negligible compared with the other quantities; the input equation then is

$$E_{BB} = I_B(R_3 + R_B) + I_C R_3 = (I_E - I_C)(R_3 + R_B) + I_C R_3 \quad (9a)$$

The two simultaneous equations suitable for finding the S are found to be

$$I_{CO} = I_C + h_{21}I_E, \qquad E_{BB} = -R_B I_C + (R_3 + R_B)I_E \qquad (10)$$

The variables are I_C and I_E. Solving for I_C by the use of determinants, we find

[2] The reader may be surprised to find a grounded-base, a-c parameter h_{21} appearing in this grounded-emitter circuit analysis. This is remedied if one remembers that Equation (8) states a relation that applies only to the transistor, regardless of attached circuitry. Therefore its use in this analysis is quite justified.

$$I_C = \frac{I_{CO}(R_3 + R_B) - E_{BB}h_{21}}{R_3 + R_B + h_{21}R_B} \tag{11}$$

$$I_C = \frac{R_3 + R_B}{R_3 + R_B + h_{21}R_B} I_{CO} - \frac{E_{BB}h_{21}}{R_3 + R_B + h_{21}R_B}$$

Since stability is defined as the *change* in I_C when I_{CO} varies, only the first term will affect the stability.

$$S = \frac{\Delta I_C}{\Delta I_{CO}} = \frac{R_3 + R_B}{R_3 + (1 + h_{21})R_B} \tag{12}$$

Equation (12) states how the I_C, and hence the operating point, will vary with a given change in I_{CO}. This stability, it is noted, is affected by R_3, R_B, and the h_{21} of the transistor. Note that the stability does not depend on the R_L: this is reasonable when it is remembered that the I_C is virtually independent of V_{CE}.

We can compare the result of Equation (12) with that of the un-stabilized circuit (where $S = 1/[1 + h_{21}]$) by changing the form of the equation. It can be written

$$S = \frac{\Delta I_C}{\Delta I_{CO}} = \frac{1}{1 + h_{21} - h_{21}R_3/(R_3 + R_B)} \tag{13}$$

It is seen that the stability is improved by the addition of a factor in the denominator. From either Equation (12) or (13) it can be found that the S is improved as R_3 is raised and R_B is decreased. One cannot make R_3 larger and R_B smaller indefinitely, however. Even though R_3 can be a-c by-passed by a capacitor, the input bias battery must be made larger as R_3 is increased. For R_B, a lower limit is set by the shunting effect on the a-c signal if the stage is capacitance coupled; if it is transformer coupled the lower limit on R_B is set only by the small size of the input battery. These considerations may be verified by referring to the bias circuits of the previous chapter.

As an example of the use of the stability factor let us assume the following component values:

$$R_3 = 1000, \quad R_B = 10,000, \quad h_{21} = -0.98 \tag{14}$$

The S is then

$$S = \frac{1}{1 + h_{21} - h_{21}R_3/(R_3 + R_B)} = 8.5 \tag{15}$$

Let us also assume that, either from manufacturer's data or from experimental tests, we will experience an I_{CO} variation of 5 μa to 25 μa due to temperature change or unit-to-unit variation. Equation (15) then tells us that when I_{CO} varies by 20 μa the I_C will vary by 170 μa instead of by 1000 μa for the unstabilized case.

Following this calculation we would estimate the maximum signal swing expected for the particular stage, and determine whether the I_C variation is permissible. If not, the R_3 must be raised or the R_B lowered until a suitable condition is found.

By referring to Equation (11) we may note the effect of reduced cutoff component of collector current. The first term of this equation represents the cutoff component and it does no useful work; i.e., it is the cutoff current for the transistor-R_3 combination. It is this component which should be kept low if greater efficiency is to be achieved. Note that this term is lower than the I_{CEO} (for the unstabilized case) due to the $h_{21}R_3/(R_3 + R_B)$ factor. Now it is seen why the stabilizing measures also serve to reduce the cutoff component of current. .

When finding the bias point for the stabilized circuits, it is again recommended that a load line be used for the output side, and a d-c equation for the input side. The I_B, for the circuit of Figure 11-3, can be found by writing the two ordinary d-c loop equations [Equation (6)]. Note that here the two loop equations are required, whereas in the circuits of the previous chapter only one was necessary. The difference lies in that here the R_3 *couples* the input loop to the output loop; hence two simultaneous equations are required. When the two equations are solved, the I_B is found to be

$$I_B \approx \frac{E_{BB}}{R_B + R_3/(1 + h_{21})} \qquad (16)$$

We will now apply the current feedback resistor to the three types of grounded-emitter bias circuits exhibited in the previous chapter. Since the S derivation was followed closely in the above case, we will show only the circuit and the resulting S and I_B here. They may be derived in the same manner as the previous one.

The circuit of Figure 11-4 is the same circuit of Figure 10-2(a) except that now a d-c feedback resistor R_3 is added. The two equations necessary for finding the stability are

$$I_{CO} = I_C + h_{21}I_E, \qquad E_{CC} = -R_B I_C + (R_3 + R_B)I_E \qquad (17)$$

Solving these for the variable I_C, the result is

$$I_C = \frac{R_3 + R_B}{R_3 + R_B(1 + h_{21})} I_{CO} - \frac{h_{21}E_{CC}}{R_3 + R_B(1 + h_{21})} \qquad (18)$$

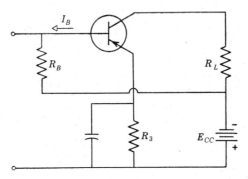

Fig. 11-4. Single battery grounded emitter circuit using current feedback.

The stability factor S is then

$$S = \frac{R_3 + R_B}{R_3 + R_B(1 + h_{21})} \tag{19}$$

To compare this with the unstabilized condition of Equation (5), we can change the form of Equation (19):

$$S = \frac{1}{1 + h_{21} - h_{21}R_3/(R_3 + R_B)} \tag{20}$$

It is seen that the stability is improved by the addition (h_{21} is negative) of the $h_{21}R_3/(R_3 + R_B)$ factor in the denominator.

By writing the ordinary d-c equation for this circuit, the I_B is found to be

$$I_B \approx \frac{E_{CC}}{R_B + R_3/(1 + h_{21})} \tag{20a}$$

Using this equation with the load line on the output characteristics, the operating point may be determined.[1]

In Figure 11-5 the same circuit as in Figure 10-3 is shown with

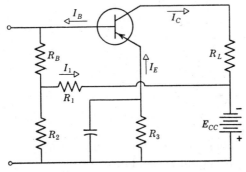

Fig. 11-5. Another stabilized single battery, grounded-emitter circuit.

[1] Since R_3 is in the collector circuit, the d-c load line must be drawn for $R_3 + R_L$ instead of R_L.

the feedback resistor added. It is evident, from the additional mesh, that three equations are required to find the S. They are

$$I_{CO} = I_C + h_{21}I_E + 0I_1$$
$$E_{CC} = R_2I_C - R_2I_E + (R_2 + R_1)I_1 \tag{21}$$
$$E_{CC} = -R_BI_C + (R_3 + R_B)I_E + R_1I_1$$

where I_1 = current flowing through R_1. Solving these for I_C and then finding the change with I_{CO}, the result is

$$S = \frac{K}{K + h_{21}(R_1R_B + R_2R_B + R_1R_2)} \tag{22}$$

where $K = R_1R_2 + (R_3 + R_B)(R_1 + R_2)$. This can be rearranged to compare with Equation (5):

$$S = \frac{1}{1 + h_{21} - h_{21}(R_3R_2 + R_1R_3)/K} \tag{23}$$

The I_B of this circuit can be found by using the three d-c mesh equations. The result is:

$$I_B \approx \frac{E_{CC}R_2 - I_{CO}R_3 \dfrac{R_2 + R_1}{1 + h_{21}}}{R_B[R_2 + R_1] + R_1R_2 + \dfrac{R_2R_3 + R_1R_3}{1 + h_{21}}} \tag{24}$$

Figure 11-6 shows a conventional single-battery grounded-emitter circuit. This circuit is identical with that of Figure 11-5, except that

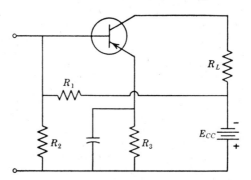

Fig. 11-6. A frequently used grounded-emitter circuit.

R_B equals zero. Therefore we can find the stability by using Equation (22) and letting R_B equal zero. Thus

$$S = \frac{K'}{K' + h_{21}R_1R_2} \tag{25}$$

where $K' = R_1R_2 + R_3(R_1 + R_2)$. Rearranging, it appears

$$S = \frac{1}{1 + h_{21} - h_{21}(R_3R_2 - R_1R_3)/K'} \tag{26}$$

The I_B for this circuit is found to be

$$I_B \approx \frac{E_{cc}R_2 - I_{co}R_3 \dfrac{R_2 + R_1}{1 + h_{21}}}{R_1R_2 + \dfrac{R_2R_3 + R_1R_3}{1 + h_{21}}} \tag{27}$$

The previous equations, then, are the appropriate ones for finding the stability of the grounded-emitter connection using direct-current feedback for the stabilizing means.

D-c voltage feedback. Another method for stabilizing the operating points of transistor amplifiers consists of using direct-voltage feedback. Voltage feedback is defined as that situation when the amount of signal fed back to the input (from the output) depends upon a voltage in the output circuit.

The simplest type of circuit using voltage feedback is shown in Figure 11-7. Whenever a voltage appears across the load resistor R_L, a part of this voltage is fed back to the input through R_F. Note that the R_F also applies the correct sign for bias voltage to the input side. In fact, bias-wise this circuit is similar to that of Figure 10-2; here the combination of R_L and R_F acts as the R_B of that circuit. It should also be noted that the circuit of Figure 11-7 will provide a-c feedback also (to be discussed in the next chapter) unless the R_F is broken up according to the manner of Figure 11-8.

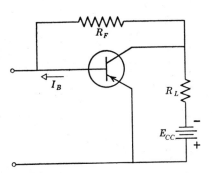

Fig. 11-7. The basic circuit using voltage feedback for stabilization.

The stability for this circuit is found by writing two d-c equations. Like the case of current feedback, the equation for the output side must involve I_{co} and hence the equation is again

$$I_{co} = I_c + h_{21}I_E \tag{28}$$

The other equation, corresponding to the input equation, is

$$E_{cc} = V_{EB} - R_F I_C + (R_F + R_L)I_E \tag{29}$$

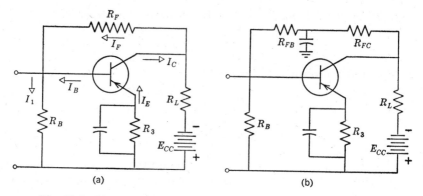

Fig. 11-8. Circuit using two stabilizing resistors and one bias resistor.

Neglecting V_{EB} as being small compared to the other quantities and solving for I_C, the result is

$$I_C = \frac{R_F + R_L}{R_L + R_F(1 + h_{21})} I_{co} - \frac{h_{21}E_{cc}}{R_L + R_F(1 + h_{21})} \tag{30}$$

For S we want the *change* of I_C with I_{co}; Equation (30) then says that

$$S = \frac{R_F + R_L}{R_L + R_F(1 + h_{21})} = \frac{1}{1 + h_{21} - h_{21}R_L/(R_F + R_L)} \tag{31}$$

Since we cannot use a load line on the output side because of the R_F connected to the collector, the operating point must be found by solving the equations for I_B and I_C. The I_B is found to be:

$$I_B \approx \frac{E_{cc}}{R_F + \dfrac{R_L}{1 + h_{21}}} \tag{32}$$

We will now move directly to the most general case for stabilization by voltage feedback. The circuit is shown in Figure 11-8(a), and it is seen that resistors R_3 and R_B are added to that of Figure 11-7. The resistor R_3 is an additional stabilizing resistor and the R_B enables the bias point to be controlled somewhat independently.

Part (b) of the figure shows a circuit identical to that of (a) except that the feedback resistor is broken up into two parts and alternating current is by-passed to ground. This arrangement serves to eliminate the a-c feedback due to resistor R_F. If the straight resistor is used, as in (a), the circuit will exhibit both a-c and d-c feedback. The d-c equations for both circuits are identical.

To find the S for these circuits, the following equations may be written:

$$I_{CO} = I_C + h_{21}I_E + 0I_1$$
$$0 = 0 + R_3I_E + R_BI_1 \tag{33}$$
$$E_{CC} = -R_FI_C + (R_F + R_L)I_E - (R_B + R_F + R_L)I_1$$

Using these equations, the S is found to be

$$S = \frac{1}{1 + h_{21} - h_{21}K''} \tag{34}$$

where $K'' = \dfrac{(R_B + R_F + R_L)R_3 + R_BR_L}{(R_B + R_F + R_L)R_3 + R_BR_L + R_FR_B}.$

The I_B for this circuit is

$$I_B \approx \frac{E_{CC}R_B[1 + h_{21}] - I_{CO}[R_3R_B + R_3R_F + R_3R_L + R_BR_L]}{R_BR_F(1 + h_{21}) + R_BR_L + R_3R_B + R_3R_F + R_3R_L} \tag{35}$$

Equation (34) is a general result since we have only to modify this equation for any cases where not all the resistors are used. Figure 11-9

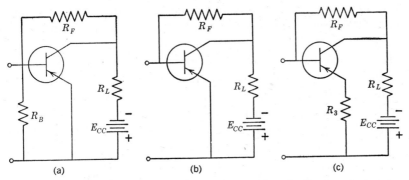

Fig. 11-9. Different combinations using voltage feedback and the corresponding K'' values.

$$K'' = \frac{R_BR_L}{R_FR_B + R_LR_B}, \quad K'' = \frac{R_L}{R_F + R_L}, \quad K'' = \frac{R_3 + R_L}{R_F + R_3 + R_L}$$
$$\text{(a)} \qquad\qquad\qquad \text{(b)} \qquad\qquad \text{(c)}$$

shows these modifications and the values of K'' that apply. The K'' values are obtained from Equation (34) by letting the proper resistance values go to zero or to infinity. Note that the circuit of (b) is identical with the first case treated. It is included to complete the use of the general Equation (34).

The circuit of (b) above is the simplest application of voltage feedback. The resistor R_F provides both stabilization and proper biasing conditions. If it is desired to separate the control of the bias and stabilization aspects, the resistor R_B may be added, as in (a). The circuit of (c) also allows separate control of bias and stabilization, and it usually provides the greatest stabilization (of the three circuits).

Each of the circuits of Figure 10-9 can make use of the no a-c feedback scheme shown in Figure 11-8(b). All the above equations apply directly but the R_F is always the sum of R_{FB} and R_{FC}.

These, then, are the stabilizing schemes and equations for the voltage feedback case. The choice between voltage and current feedback is largely determined by the size of the d-c load resistance. If the d-c R_L is large, as is usually the case for RC coupled cases, the voltage feedback is as effective as the current type. For transformer coupling, where the d-c R_L is low, current feedback is much more effective than the other.

Temperature-sensitive elements. In addition to the feedback stabilizing means just considered, another stabilizing method consists of the use of temperature-sensitive circuit elements. The idea here is to cause the circuit conditions to change with temperature so that the changes effected by the transistor are compensated.

It is remembered that the basic change in transistors, when temperature changes occur, consists of the entire set of characteristics moving with respect to the axis. This, in turn, is caused by the fact that the collector junction is biased in the reverse direction and the ensuing reverse current is a function of the existing temperature.

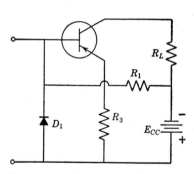

One temperature-sensitive element, then, would be a junction diode whose temperature properties are similar to that of the collector junction in the transistor. Thermistors, varistors, and special types of resistors may also be used as the temperature-sensitive elements.

Figure 11-10 shows a stabilized circuit in which a junction diode is used as the stabilizing means. The current flowing through the resistance R_1 and the diode D_1 furnishes the biasing voltage for the input of the transistor. We can describe the operation of this circuit generally by momentarily assuming that the diode is not temperature sensitive. When the temperature increa-

Fig. 11-10. Biasing network stabilized by a diode.

ses, the characteristics and the operating point will move upward according to the illustration of Figure 11-2. In order to return the operating point (and effectively the entire characteristics) to the original position it is necessary to reduce the I_B.

The presence of the temperature-sensitive diodes accomplishes this I_B reduction in two ways. First the decreased forward resistance of the diode (with temperature) makes the stabilizing resistor R_3 more effective, as will be remembered from the previous section on current feedback. Second, the reduced resistance of the diode means that a smaller bias voltage is supplied to the base by the voltage dividing network of $R_1 - D_1$. With the I_B properly reduced, the displaced characteristics of the transistor are effectively returned toward their original positions.

There are many special ways in which diodes and other temperature-sensitive elements can be used to stabilize a transistor circuit. We will not treat these special cases here, but refer the student to the literature for additional information.

Since the temperature dependence of diodes is a nonlinear phenomenon, it is not possible to calculate a stability factor for such circuits in any simple manner. Therefore the only method recommended for finding the S is by experiments with the circuit. The operation of the diode may be altered to suit the designer by adding ordinary series and shunt resistors. By a process of trial and error the circuit may be adjusted for a suitable stability factor.

Tandem operation. Another stabilizing method consists of appropriately connecting two or more transistors directly in cascade. By the use of special connections the circuit may be made stable with respect to temperature changes.

One such method consists of using two transistors of different types; i.e., an N-P-N followed by a P-N-P. This is done because the direction of collector current increase, when the temperature rises, is opposite for the two transistors. Thus the variation in one transistor tends to cancel that in the other. This is suitable only if the transistors are directly connected without a coupling capacitor or transformer. Assuming that the variation with temperature is approximately equal for both transistors, the first transistor would have to be stabilized by some other means, since the second transistor amplifies any temperature-induced variations. Since the alternative to this would be to stabilize each transistor by one of the methods discussed previously, it is worth while to consider using this method. A small saving in efficiency is achieved, since the second transistor would not require any explicit stabilizing.

Another way to utilize tandem operation in improving the stability is to use the first transistor as a constant-current source for the second transistor. The first transistor, of course, would still provide amplification. If the I_E of the second transistor, for example, is held relatively fixed, the sum of I_B and I_C will have to adjust so as to remain constant. In this way the I_B will be caused to decrease (the desired effect when the I_C increases due to temperature changes).

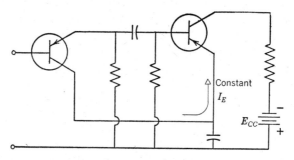

Fig. 11-11. An example of the use of tandem operation to obtain stabilization.

Figure 11-11 shows one application of this scheme. The fact that the I_E of the second transistor passes through the high-resistance collector junction of the first guarantees that it will be relatively constant if the first transistor is stabilized. Thus here again the net saving comes from the fact that only one of the two transistors must be stabilized to obtain a two-stage stabilized circuit.

Comment on grounded base stabilized circuits. All the previous stability considerations were devoted to the grounded-emitter connection because: (1) this is the most suitable connection for amplifiers; and (2) the stability problem is more critical for this connection. It is worth while, however, to make some comment about the grounded-base case.

The use of negative feedback for the grounded-base connection is not possible unless transformers (for phase shifting) are used and these will not work for d-c conditions. Therefore the simple method of shunt and series resistors, shown above for the emitter case, is not applicable here. For example, if a resistor is placed in the base lead of a grounded-base connection, the circuit has positive feedback and the stability is *reduced* (S increased). This is also true for a shunt resistor connected from collector to emitter.

One simple method of stabilizing the base connection is to insert a resistor in series with the emitter (input) lead, thus driving with a constant current source. This would be by-passed, of course, to avoid attenuating the a-c signal. This is still a relatively costly solution, however, since the large I_E (compared to I_B) causes an appreciable d-c power loss in the stabilizing resistor.

The use of temperature-sensitive elements and tandem operation are also applicable to the grounded-base case.

Design Considerations

As mentioned previously, the stability factor S should be considered whenever a temperature variation or a unit-to-unit variation is expected. Two general procedures are available for incorporating

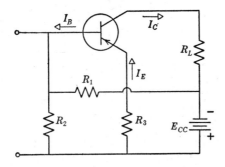

Fig. 11-11(a). Circuit of Fig. 11-6 shown repeated.

the S in any design situation: (1) determine the appropriate S value and then use the various d-c equations to fix the circuit component values which will give this S; or (2) decide upon the component values by the usual a-c considerations and then check the resulting S.

In order to illustrate the first method, we will find the appropriate equations for the circuit of Figure 11-6, shown repeated in Figure 11-11(a). Since the operating point and S factor will usually be fixed by a-c considerations, we will assume that we know the following values: I_C, V_C, h_{21}, I_{CO}, R_L, and S. Our object then is to find the values of R_1, R_2, R_3, and E_{CC} that will result primarily in the chosen S, and fulfill the other chosen quantities. This process requires manipulation of the d-c equations which are, as given before,

$$I_{CO} = I_C + h_{21}I_E + 0I_1$$
$$E_{CC} = R_2I_C - R_2I_E + (R_2 + R_1)I_1 \qquad (36)$$
$$E_{CC} = -R_BI_C + (R_3 + R_B)I_E + R_1I_1$$

From previous calculation we know the S is given by

$$S = \cfrac{1}{1 + h_{21} - h_{21}\cfrac{(R_3R_2 - R_1R_3)}{R_1R_2 + R_3(R_1 + R_2)}} \qquad (37)$$

Since none of the above equations contains V_C, we need the additional relation

$$E_{CC} = I_ER_1 + I_CR_L + V_C \qquad (38)$$

Putting each of the quantities in terms of the known values, we have

$$R_3 = \frac{-h_{21}(E_{CC} - I_CR_L - V_C)}{I_C - I_{CO}}$$

$$R_1 = \frac{E_{CC}(S - 1)}{I_C - SI_{CO}} \qquad (39)$$

$$R_2 = \frac{R_1R_3(S - 1)}{-R_3Sh_{21} - (S - 1)(R_1 + R_3)}$$

We would begin by selecting an E_{CC} and then finding R_3 and R_1. Using these values, we are able to find R_2. This is the method, then, by which it is possible to select the circuit components so as to provide a specified S. The principles shown in this derivation may be applied to any transistor circuit.

Many times the designer will prefer to avoid the lengthy calculations of the above method and use the system whereby all circuit components are selected on the basis of the a-c considerations. After this is done, the stability may be checked and suitable alterations made to improve the stability if necessary. It is recommended that, after some experience is achieved, this latter method be employed.

d-c Amplifier

Although it is generally the case that electronic amplifiers are designed to amplify alternating voltage or power it is sometimes necessary to construct amplifiers that will amplify a change in a direct potential or power. The essential difference between a d-c and an a-c amplifier is that, in the d-c case, a capacitor (or transformer) cannot be used as a coupling element between the stages. This, of course, changes the biasing conditions for the d-c amplifier. We shall find, that, as in the case of vacuum tubes, it is very difficult to construct a stable d-c amplifier. Since this is the case it is often desirable, when amplification of a d-c signal is required, to avoid the d-c amplifier and rather to use a chopping method; in this method an a-c signal is formed whose magnitude is proportional to the d-c signal being amplified, and the resulting a-c signal is then amplified by the conventional method. After sufficient amplification is acquired, the signal is then converted to direct current by a filtering process.

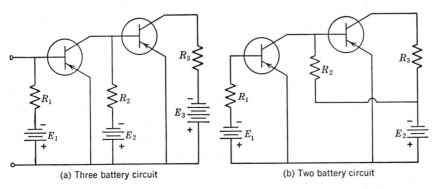

(a) Three battery circuit   (b) Two battery circuit

Fig. 11-12. Two basic d-c amplifier circuits using grounded-emitter: (a) three battery circuit; (b) two battery circuit.

In order to illustrate the stability problems of the d-c amplifier we shall show some basic d-c amplifier circuits. Figure 11-12(a) shows the simplest type of grounded-emitter d-c amplifier. Here it is seen how the absence of any coupling element alters the biasing situation. The battery E_2 provides both the collector bias for the first transistor and the base bias for the second transistor. The scheme of Figure 11-12(a) cannot be carried out to many stages since each succeeding battery must be larger than the previous in order to provide a negative collector-to-base voltage for each transistor. Part (b) of this figure shows a slight alteration of the same basic scheme, in which only two batteries are used. In this circuit care must be taken that the base of the second transistor remains negative with respect to the emitter for all values of signal on the first transistor.

Still another basic circuit utilizing a grounded-base and a grounded-emitter connection is shown in Figure 11-13. Here the in-

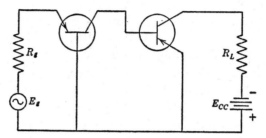

Fig. 11-13. D-c amplifier using grounded-base to grounded-emitter.

put of the second transistor acts as the only load on the first stage. Note that the collector bias for the first transistor is obtained *through* the collector-to-base junction of the second transistor. This biasing through another transistor, not possible with vacuum tubes, should always be kept in mind as a possibility when devising transistor circuits.

Although each of the above amplifiers provides the desired d-c amplification, it is very difficult to maintain a stable operation with them. We can readily see the reason for this. If the I_C of the first transistor, in either of the cases, changes because of temperature variation, the second transistor will *amplify* this change and will also add its own temperature variation. Thus due to the amplification of any changes in the previous stages, the operating point stability is very low for d-c amplifiers (S high). Note that, for a-c amplifiers, the d-c conditions of each stage are separated by the coupling element and hence the cumulative condition is not encountered.

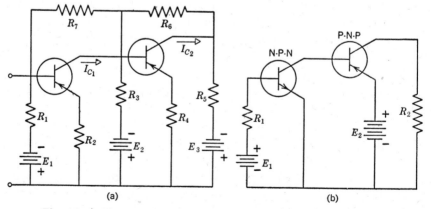

Fig. 11-14. D-c amplifiers with stabilizing measures: (a) stabilizing by current and voltage feedback; (b) stabilization by tandem operation.

The stability situation can be improved, somewhat, by applying the stabilizing measures discussed in the previous section. The basic circuit of Figure 11-12, with both series and shunt resistors added for stabilization, is shown in Figure 11-14. The gain of this circuit will, of course, be less than that for the unstabilized circuit; for here it is undesirable to by-pass the d-c feedback resistors. Therefore the stabilizing resistors will provide d-c as well as a-c feedback.

Figure 11-14(b) shows another application of a stabilizing method to d-c amplifiers. Here use is made of tandem operation, where one transistor is of the N-P-N type and the other is of the P-N-P type. As noted in the previous section, the stabilizing action stems from the fact that the direction of I_C change with temperature is opposing for the two transistors. Note that here again, in the biasing circuit, the collector bias for the first transistor is obtained *through* the second transistor.

In order to illustrate the stability calculation for d-c amplifiers, and compare it to the a-c case, we will calculate the stability of the circuit in Figure 11-12(b). If the temperature changes so as to vary the I_{CO}, the variation in I_{C_2} will be

$$\Delta I_{C_2T} = A_{i2}\Delta I_{C_1} + \Delta I_{C_2} = A_{i2}S_1\Delta I_{CO_1} + S_2\Delta I_{CO_2} \qquad (40)$$

where A_{i2} = current gain of the second stage,
$\quad S_1 = \Delta I_{C_1}/\Delta I_{CO_1}$,
$\quad S_2 = \Delta I_{C_2}/\Delta I_{CO_2}$.

If the I_{CO} change with temperature is approximately the same for both transistors, then

$$\Delta I_{CO_1} \cong \Delta I_{CO_2} \qquad (41)$$

and Equation (40) may be written

$$S_{\text{total}} = \frac{\Delta I_{C_2T}}{\Delta I_{CO}} = A_{i2}S_1 + S_2 \qquad (42)$$

We can now see why the stabilizing problem is more difficult for d-c than for a-c amplifiers. In a-c amplifiers, when each stage is isolated d-c-wise from the others, a stability factor applies to only one stage and affects only the operation of that one stage. In Equation (42), however, we note that the current gain multiplies the first stage stability. This exhibits, mathematically, the statement that the I_C variation is cumulative in d-c amplifiers.

Using Equation (42) we can now find the stability of Figure

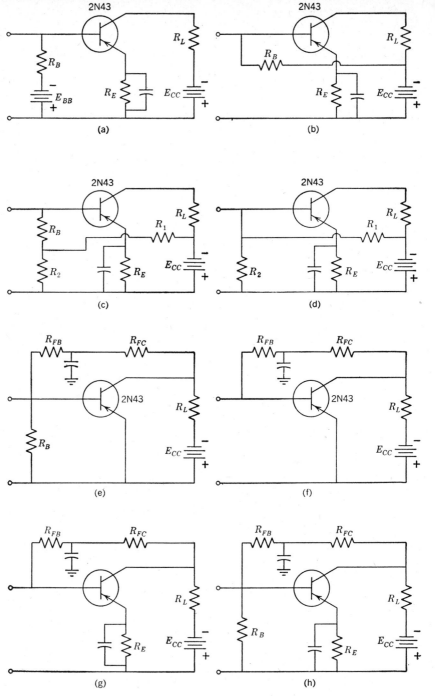

Fig. 11-15. Typical bias stability circuits. (a) $R_B = 10$ K, $R_E = 500$ ohms, $R_L = 20$ K; (b) $R_B = 30$ K, $R_E = 1$ K, $R_L = 40$ K; (c) $R_B = 20$ K, $R_E = 1$ K, $R_L = 20$ K, $R_1 = 5$ K, $R_2 = 1$ K; (d) $R_L = 10$ K, $R_E = 100$ ohms, $R_1 = 50$ K, $R_2 = 5$ K; (e) $R_{FB} = 5$ K, $R_{FC} = 25$ K, $R_B = 20$ K, $R_L = 20$ K; (f) $R_L = 30$ K, $R_{FB} = 10$ K, $R_{FC} = 50$ K; (g) $R_{FB} = 20$ K, $R_{FC} = 80$ K, $R_E = 1$ K, $R_L = 20$ K; (h) $R_B = 5$ K, $R_E = 1$ K, $R_L = 20$ K, $R_{FB} = 10$ K, $R_{FC} = 50$ K

11-12(b). It has been shown previously that

$$S_1 = \frac{1}{1 + h_{21_1}}, \qquad S_2 = \frac{1}{1 + h_{21_2}}$$

For finding the A_{i2} we can use the a-c relation for current gain as given by Table 3 of Chapter 8.

$$S_{\text{total}} = \left(\frac{h_{fe}}{R_{L2}h_{oe} + 1}\right)\left(\frac{1}{1 + h_{21_1}}\right) + \frac{1}{1 + h_{21_2}}$$

Although the stability calculation for d-c amplifiers is distinctly different from that of the a-c case, the other performance quantities are calculated in an identical manner. Therefore *the equations of Table 3 in Chapter 8 are used to calculate the performance quantities of d-c amplifiers.*

As stated previously, it is generally best to avoid the use of d-c amplifiers if possible. If they are required, the above methods may be used to stabilize them as much as possible.

Problems

1. What are the stability factors of the circuits shown in Figure 11-15?
2. What should the values of R_E be in Figure 11-15(a,b) for a stability factor S of 10, leaving the other components the same?
3. If R_1 is increased in Figure 11-15(c), what happens to the stability factor S?
4. Does the presence of R_B in Figure 11-15(c) improve the stability factor S over that of Figure 11-15(f) if R_{FB}, R_{FC}, and R_L remain constant in both cases?
5. What effect does an increase in R_L have upon the stability factor S of Figure 11-15(g,h)?
6. What would be the stability factor S of the circuits in Figure 11-15(a,f,h) if the 2N243 silicon transistor were used instead of the 2N43?

12

Feedback

The application of feedback to an electronic circuit consists essentially of adding additional elements (usually passive) to the basic circuit in order to favorably change the performance quantities. Feedback, then, represents a general method by which we may alter the a-c performance quantities of the transistor. In the previous chapter, d-c feedback was considered as a means of stabilizing the operating point. In this chapter we are interested in a-c feedback, where the a-c performance quantities are influenced.

If we are dealing with a circuit in which an input and an output can be identified, as is true for all active circuits, then any element that couples the output to the input is a feedback element. For a passive circuit this means that the element appears in both the output and the input portions; for an active circuit it means that either a voltage source in the input depends upon a current or voltage in the output, or a passive element may directly couple the input to the output. It is interesting to note that the transistor itself contains a feedback element; the h_{12} term of the equivalent circuit (Chapter 8) couples the output circuit to the input circuit. This is distinctly different from the vacuum tube where the output is normally isolated from the input circuit.

In this chapter our purpose will be to consider the effects and methods of treating externally added feedback elements in transistor amplifiers. We will begin by noting the qualitative effect of feedback upon each of the a-c performance quantities. A simplified feedback theory, not generally applicable to transistors, will be used to illustrate these effects. Following this, a method of treatment applicable to transistors will be described. The common transistor feedback circuits will be portrayed, and design curves presented to facilitate the quick determination of a given feedback upon the amplifier performance.

It is the object here to present the fundamentals concerning feedback. For this reason only single-stage feedback circuits will be considered. In addition, it will be assumed that the transistor is operating in the mid-frequency range, i.e., the transistor parameters will all be assumed resistive and the h_{21} is regarded as constant. Finally, the feedback theory described here is limited to small-signal analysis where the equivalent circuit representation is valid.

Effects of Using Feedback

In order to show the effect of feedback on the gain and the other performance quantities, it is useful to consider a simplified and elementary treatment of feedback. The assumptions made in this treat-

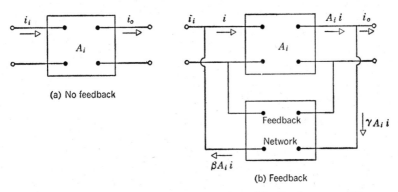

Fig. 12-1. Block diagram illustrating effect of feedback on amplifier gain.

ment are not, in general, applicable to transistors so it will not give us much aid in analyzing transistor circuits. It does, however, serve to clearly show the effect of feedback upon the various quantities.

To illustrate this simplified theory, consider a general current amplifier as depicted in Figure 12-1(a). We will label the current amplification A_i. This value would be determined, for any particular amplifier, by the amplifier parameters and the load conditions as described in Chapter 8. For any value of input current i_i, then, the output current will appear as

$$i_o = A_i i_i \qquad (1)$$

If feedback is applied to this general amplifier, the resulting circuit can be represented as in Figure 12-1(b). The input and output currents are still i_i and i_o, respectively; however, the currents associated with the active amplifier are now i and $A_i i$. The symbol γ is used *to represent the fraction of $A_i i$ that flows to the feedback network* (it may be only a single element). Hence the current flowing to the network is $\gamma A_i i$. That portion of $A_i i$ that flows out of the feedback network to the amplifier input is labeled $\beta A_i i$. Thus β *is the fraction of $A_i i$ that is sent back to the input.* The relation between β and γ is determined by the feedback network in conjunction with the input to the amplifier. With these defining quantities, then, the various currents appear as shown in the block diagram of Figure 12-1(b).

We now wish to find the current gain for the feedback case. Referring to the figure, the following equations may be intuitively verified:

$$i_o = A_i i - \gamma A_i i = i A_i (1 - \gamma)$$
$$i_i = i - \beta A_i i = i(1 - \beta A_i) \qquad (2)$$

The ratio of i_o to i_i then is

$$A_{if} = \frac{i_o}{i_i} = \frac{A_i(1 - \gamma)}{1 - \beta A_i} \qquad (3)$$

where A_{if} = current gain with feedback applied.

For many cases the feedback network consists of a single series element, usually a resistor. For these cases the γ equals β, and Equation (3) appears

$$A_{if} = \frac{i_o}{i_i} = \frac{A_i(1 - \beta)}{1 - \beta A_i} \qquad (4)$$

Comparing this with Equation (1), it is noted that the current gain has been changed by a factor of $(1 - \beta)/(1 - \beta A_i)$. The feedback gain can be written as the product of the nonfeedback gain and the above factor:

$$A_{if} = A_i \frac{1 - \beta}{1 - \beta A_i} \approx A_i \frac{1}{1 - \beta A_i} \qquad (5)$$

For most feedback circuits the β is small compared with unity, so that a further simplification may be made by neglecting the β term in the numerator. The expression we are interested in, then, is given by the right side of Equation (5).

Under the conditions assumed in this development, Equation (5) states that when feedback is added to a single-stage amplifier, the current gain is altered by the factor of $1/(1 - \beta A_i)$. If the quantity βA_i is negative, the gain will be reduced and this is called *negative* or *inverse* feedback. If the sign of βA_i is positive, the situation is termed *positive* feedback. The sign of this quantity, of course, depends upon the sign of both β and A_i. Actually βA_i is a phasor and can take on any angle from 0 to 360°. For simplicity we have referred to two possibilities only.

The sign of A_i in turn depends upon the basic amplifier circuit; we noted in Chapter 8 that A_i is positive for grounded-base and grounded-collector connections, and negative for grounded-emitter connections. The feedback network is often made up of only resistors; then its sign will be positive since this means that the current flows through the feedback network without changing its direction. With a resistive feedback, then, the $A_i\beta$ term will be negative for grounded-emitter connections and positive for both grounded-collector and grounded-base connections. This in turn *means that the grounded emitter will have negative feedback and the other two connections will experience positive feedback.* A simple method of reversing the feedback sign consists of using a transformer. This is usually undesirable, however, in terms of cost and space consumption.

For most purposes negative feedback is desired. We shall see below that, although the gain is reduced with negative feedback, the circuit stability, frequency response, and distortion are all improved. Positive feedback, where the gain is increased, is used where the absolute maximum gain is required at the sacrifice of the other quantities—regenerative radio receivers, where a sufficient sensitivity is achieved with only a minimum of circuitry, is an example of positive feedback.

It is interesting to note here that if the sign of $A_i\beta$ is positive and exactly equal to 1, the denominator of Equation (5) goes to zero. This would imply that the current gain is now infinite. The circuit under these conditions will not operate as an amplifier because $A_i\beta$ equal to 1 defines one of the conditions necessary for an oscillator. *Thus any oscillator can be regarded as a feedback amplifier whose value of $A_i\beta$ equals 1.*

Since negative feedback is the one usually utilized, we shall consider this type in the present chapter. We wish to see, then, how negative feedback affects the gain, the frequency response, the distortion, and the input and output impedances of a single-stage amplifier. It must be remembered that the analysis method utilizing Equation (5) is chosen primarily for its clarity in showing the effects of the feedback; this method is not generally applicable to the analysis of transistor amplifiers for reasons we shall describe later.

Gain. It has been seen above that the current gain of the amplifier is reduced by the factor $1/(1 - A_i\beta)$ when negative feedback is applied. It can be shown that the voltage gain is reduced by approximately the same factor. Since the power gain is proportional to the square of the current gain, this quantity will be reduced by the square of the $1/(1 - A_i\beta)$ term.

Gain stability. The stability of the d-c operating point was considered in the previous chapter. It was mentioned there that although of less consequence than the operating-point change, the a-c parameters do tend to change with temperature. In addition, these a-c parameters vary from transistor to transistor and with aging. Therefore if an amplifier is to be completely stable it may be necessary to consider stabilizing the effect of the a-c parameter variation. We will see here that negative feedback acts to stabilize the effect of variations in the a-c performance quantities.

Referring to Equation (5), it is easily seen that if the quantity $A_i\beta$ is large with respect to 1, then the equation will reduce to

$$A_i \approx \frac{A_i}{\beta A_i} = \frac{1}{\beta} \qquad (6)$$

It is noted that the gain now depends only upon the β feedback term. If sufficient gain remains, this is a very desirable condition for electronic amplifiers since the β is determined almost entirely by the feedback network. It, in turn, is usually very stable with temperature and aging changes since it is usually composed of resistors, capacitors, and inductors.

Although it may not always be desirable to apply feedback to the extent depicted in Equation (6), any negative feedback has the general effect of tending to stabilize variations in the active amplifier circuit. Positive feedback, on the other hand, tends to accentuate any circuit changes.

Frequency response. It is remembered that the frequency band-pass of an amplifier is defined by the two points where the response is down 3 db from its mid-band value. In the usual notation used, f_L is the low-frequency and f_H is the high-frequency 3 db down point.

If Equation (5) is taken to be the relation between the feedback and no-feedback current gain, and if in addition the β network has no frequency-dependent quantities (capacitors or inductors), then the 3 db points of the amplifier will be changed to

$$f_{Hf} = (1 - A_i\beta)f_H; \qquad f_{Lf} = \frac{f_L}{(1 - A_i\beta)} \qquad (7)$$

where f_{Hf} = upper 3 db down point with feedback,

f_{Lf} = lower 3 db down point with feedback.

It is seen that the upper limit is increased by the factor $(1 - A_i\beta)$ and the lower limit is decreased by the same factor. The negative

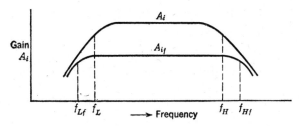

Fig. 12-2. Sketch illustrating the effect of negative feedback on gain versus frequency characteristic.

feedback therefore improves the frequency response of the basic amplifier by affecting both 3 db down points. The combination of decreased gain and increased frequency response is illustrated by the gain versus frequency curves in Figure 12-2. One curve applies to the basic amplifier and the other depicts the use of the negative feedback.

Input and output impedances. The application of feedback affects both the input and the output impedances of the resulting amplifier. Whether the impedances are increased or decreased depends upon the manner in which the negative feedback is achieved. We will show how the impedances are affected when considering the analysis of transistor feedback circuits later in this chapter.

Non-linear distortion. Feedback improves an amplifier from the standpoint of distortion. Distortion can be considered a change in the signal produced by the amplifier. The change in the signal is applied back at the input of the amplifier by the feedback network and if the feedback is negative, at the opposite sign. Thus the distortion is effectively reduced. If the distortion is equivalent to an input current of i_d before feedback is used, the distortion output is

$$i_{od} = \text{distortion output current} = i_d A \qquad (8)$$

After feedback is applied the output from Equation (5) is

$$i_{odf} = \text{distortion output current with feedback}$$

$$= \frac{A_i i_d}{1 - A_i \beta} \qquad (9)$$

The ratio of i_{odf} to i_{od} is

$$\frac{i_{odf}}{i_{od}} = \frac{A_i i_d / (1 - A\beta)}{A_i i_d} = \frac{1}{1 - A_i \beta} \qquad (10)$$

From Equation (10) it is seen that the distortion may be reduced considerably with negative feedback.

Methods of Treating Feedback in Transistors

In the foregoing section the effects of feedback were illustrated by using an approach which resulted in

$$A_{if} = A_i \frac{1}{1 - \beta A_i} \qquad (11)$$

where A_{if} = current gain with feedback,
A_i = current gain without feedback,
β = fraction of current sent back to input.

For those schooled in vacuum tubes the above will be a familiar representation of the feedback case; there, however, the voltage gain is used instead of the current gain of Equation (11). For transistors we shall see that Equation (11) is usually not a suitable tool for designing or analyzing feedback circuits. The reasons for this are the following:

1. Since the input side of a transistor is affected by the loading conditions on the output, it is usually true that the A_i varies with changes in β. Therefore the A_i would have to be recalculated if β is varied. The result is that the β method loses its utility of being a useful circuit tool.

2. The values of A_i and β are usually difficult to calculate since all parts of the circuit are interrelated. Thus again the method fails to fulfill its objective as being a short cut.

3. Any signal passing from the input through the passive feedback network is neglected in the above analysis.

For these reasons we will not use the method of Equation (11) when calculating the effect of feedback. As stated, its previous presentation was for the purpose of clearly showing the *effects* of feedback. It is fairly difficult to thus exhibit the properties of feedback when delving into the calculations.

Before leaving the approach of Equation (11) it is interesting to note that this procedure is usually quite valid for vacuum tubes. In vacuum tubes it is true that the output is isolated from the input (except at such frequencies where the electrode capacitances become important). Also, the other two objections listed above are usually not present for the vacuum tube case.

For transistors, then, we will handle the feedback properties by returning to the equivalent circuit and adding the feedback element (or elements) to this circuit. The resulting modified network may now be handled in a manner identical to that used in Chapter 8. That is, a new set of h parameters can be found by writing the necessary equations. These h parameters are then used to calculate the a-c performance quantities by the use of the equations in Table 3 of Chapter 8. In the next sections we will show the resulting h parameters for two common types of transistor feedback.

For relatively simple feedback networks, where the network equations are still solved without undue difficulty, the above procedure is recommended. If the feedback network becomes complex, or if the feedback extends over more than one stage, it is virtually necessary to move to a matrix method of analysis. Since a discussion of matrix algebra is not within the goals of this book, the reader is referred to the many sources available for information about this matrix method.

A Transistor Connection Using Current Feedback

In this section we will apply the principle discussed in the foregoing section to a common feedback connection. Figure 12-3 shows a grounded-emitter connection to which a resistor R_{se} has been added. It can easily be shown that this resistor affords *current feedback;* that is, the signal fed back to the input is proportional to the *current* flowing in the output side. This type of feedback is often termed *series* feedback.

It is remembered from the previous chapter that this circuit was used to stabilize the d-c operating point; there, however, a by-pass capacitor was used to produce only a d-c feedback. The only change, then, is that the by-pass capacitor is removed so that a-c feedback is now achieved.

From the material in the beginning of this chapter it can be seen that the current feedback of this circuit is of the negative type. When a positive signal is applied, for example, the amplified current appears in the output side in the direction shown. This current causes a positive voltage to appear across the R_{se}, which is in a direction to

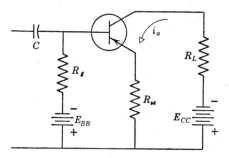

Fig. 12-3. Transistor circuit using "current" or "series" feedback.

oppose the input signal. The greater the input signal, the greater the feedback voltage, etc. In this manner, then, the circuit provides negative current feedback.

It may be noted here that if such a "series" resistor were used in the grounded-base or the grounded-collector connection, the resulting feedback would be positive. This is because these connections do not exhibit a 180° phase shift as does the grounded-emitter connection.

To analyze the circuit of Figure 12-3 we will return to the concept of using the equivalent circuit of the transistor, as in Chapter 8, and add the feedback element to this circuit. Then, proceeding as before, we can write the mesh equations to find the new h^{e*} parameters in terms of the transistor h^e parameters and the feedback element. Since the principle of finding the proper equations was fully covered in Chapter 8, it will not be repeated here.

The results can be shown to be

$$h_{ie}^{*} = \frac{h_{ie} + R_{se}(1 + h_{fe} + \Delta^{h\prime} - h_{re})}{1 + R_{se}h_{oe}}$$

$$h_{re}^{*} = \frac{h_{re} + R_{se}h_{oe}}{1 + R_{se}h_{oe}}$$

$$h_{fe}^{*} = \frac{h_{fe} - R_{se}h_{oe}}{1 + R_{se}h_{oe}}$$ \hfill (12)

$$h_{oe}^{*} = \frac{h_{oe}}{1 + R_{se}h_{oe}}$$

Note that the feedback parameters are expressed in terms of the transistor grounded-emitter parameters. Thus the analysis steps can be summarized:

1. Find the transistor grounded-emitter parameters by use of the manufacturer's data and Table 1 of Chapter 8.

2. Use the above equations to determine the feedback parameters for the R_{se} used.

3. Use these resultant parameters, then, in the same manner as described in Chapter 8. In other words, any cascaded circuit can be analyzed on a stage-by-stage basis using the feedback parameters for each stage that incorporates a feedback element. If any stage has no feedback, of course, the proper h parameters are used directly.

The above procedure, then, represents a simple way of taking account of the current feedback situation. In a following section, design curves adapted to Equations (12) will be given to facilitate a quick determination of the effects of a given feedback resistance.

A Transistor Connection Using Voltage Feedback

Another grounded emitter feedback circuit that is frequently used is shown in Figure 12-4. Here a resistor R_{sh} is connected from the collector to the base input. In this way, by feeding part of the output signal back through the resistor to the input, a *voltage* feedback is achieved. Voltage feedback occurs when the signal fed back to the input is proportional to a voltage on the output side. This type of feedback is also termed shunt feedback.

Assume for a moment that positive input signal is applied; due to the current amplification an amplified current appears in the output. This increase in output current causes a greater voltage drop across the load resistor and hence the collector voltage *decreases*. Thus the voltage fed back to the input opposes the positive input signal and consequently negative feedback is provided.

The $h^{e'}$ parameters of this transistor circuit-plus-feedback can be found by adding the feedback resistor to the equivalent circuit of the transistor and then writing the mesh (or nodal) equations to determine the parameters. It is convenient to express these resultant $h^{e'}$ parameters in terms of the usual h^e parameters for the transistor part

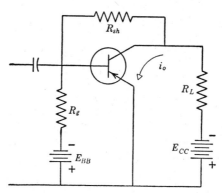

Fig. 12-4. Transistor circuit using "voltage" or "shunt" feedback.

of the circuit and the resistor R_{sh}. The parameters can be shown to be

$$h'_{ie} = \frac{h_{ie}R_{sh}}{R_{sh} + h_{ie}}$$

$$h'_{re} = \frac{R_{sh}h_{re} + h_{ie}}{R_{sh} + h_{ie}}$$

$$h'_{fe} = \frac{R_{sh}h_{fe} - h_{ie}}{R_{sh} + h_{ie}}$$

$$h'_{oe} = \frac{R_{sh}h_{oe} + (1 + h_{fe} + \Delta^{h^e} - h_{re})}{R_{sh} + h_{ie}}$$

(13)

The procedure then is identical to that enumerated in the previous section. In the next section, design curves are given to facilitate the selection of the feedback quantity to achieve a desired change in circuit performance. It should be noted that both Equations (12) and (13) can be used for the grounded-base or grounded-collector connections. However, in these cases the resulting feedback is positive unless some **means** is taken to shift the phase of the feedback signal.

Design Curves for Series and Shunt Feedback

Although Equations (12) and (13) can be used to find the effect of feedback on the circuit performance, it is useful, from the design point of view, to have curves which quickly show the effect of the feedback.

In the curves which follow, both shunt and series feedback will be considered. Since these curves (and the preceding equations for that matter) can be applied to any transistor connection, we shall change the symbols to those of the *general h* parameters; i.e., h_{11} may be h_{ie}, h_{ic}, or h_{ib}. It is remembered, however, that positive feedback results in the grounded-base and grounded-collector connection. From Equations (12) and (13) the following relations can easily be verified, where the h' quantities refer to shunt feedback and the h^* quantities refer to series feedback.

$$\frac{h'_{11}}{h_{11}} = \frac{1}{1 + \dfrac{h_{11}}{R_{sh}}}$$

$$\frac{h'_{21}}{h_{21}} = \frac{1 - \dfrac{h_{11}}{R_{sh}h_{21}}}{1 + \dfrac{h_{11}}{R_{sh}}} \simeq \frac{1}{1 + \dfrac{h_{11}}{R_{sh}}} \qquad \left(\frac{h_{11}}{R_{sh}h_{21}} \text{ usually} \ll 1\right)$$

$$(14)$$

$$\frac{h^*_{22}}{h_{22}} = \frac{1}{1 + R_{se}h_{22}}$$

$$\frac{h^*_{21}}{h_{21}} = \frac{1 - \dfrac{R_{se}h_{22}}{h_{21}}}{1 + R_{se}h_{22}} \simeq \frac{1}{1 + R_{se}h_{22}} \qquad \left(\frac{R_{se}h_{22}}{h_{21}} \text{ usually} \ll 1\right)$$

where h = parameters of any one of the three transistor connections,
  h^* = parameters when series feedback is applied,
  h' = parameters when shunt feedback is applied.

It is noted that each of the above relations between a feedback parameter and a nonfeedback parameter has the same form. Hence it is convenient to plot all these relations on the same graph. The resulting curve is shown in Figure 12-5 and shows the variation of the feedback parameters versus the feedback terms. The feedback term for the series connection is $R_{se}h_{22}$ and h_{11}/R_{sh} for the shunt connection.

The remaining relations are somewhat more complex. The equa-

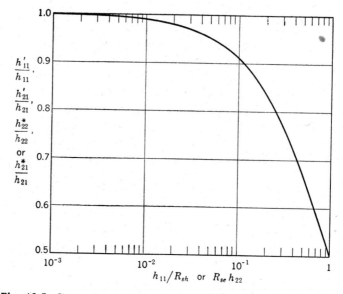

Fig. 12-5. Curve showing the relations of Equations (12) and (13).

tions, with the proper approximations, are

$$\frac{h'_{12}}{h_{12}} = \frac{1 + h_{11}/R_{sh}h_{12}}{1 + h_{11}/R_{sh}} = \frac{1 + (h_{11}/R_{sh})(1/h_{12})}{1 + h_{11}/R_{sh}}$$

$$\frac{h'_{22}}{h_{22}} = \frac{R_{sh}h_{22} + (1 + h_{21} - h_{12} + \Delta^h)}{h_{22}(R_{sh} + h_{11})} \simeq \frac{1 + (1 + h_{21})/R_{sh}h_{22}}{1 + h_{11}/R_{sh}}$$

$$\simeq \frac{1 + [(1 + h_{21})/h_{11}h_{22}](h_{11}/R_{sh})}{1 + h_{11}/R_{sh}} \tag{15}$$

In a similar manner it can be shown:

$$\frac{h^*_{12}}{h_{12}} = \frac{h_{12} + R_{se}h_{22}}{h_{12}(1 + R_{se}h_{22})} = \frac{1 + (1/h_{12})R_{se}h_{22}}{1 + R_{se}h_{22}}$$

$$\frac{h^*_{11}}{h_{11}} = \frac{h_{11} + R_{se}(1 + h_{21} - h_{12} + \Delta^h}{h_{11}(1 + R_{se}h_{22})}$$

$$\simeq \frac{1 + [(1 + h_{21})/h_{11}h_{22}]R_{se}h_{22}}{1 + R_{se}h_{22}}$$

It is seen that the equations above are similar, and that the feedback resistor occurs in both numerator and denominator. For this reason, it is necessary to have a set of curves as shown in Figure 12-6. The quantity that is held constant on each of the curves is as follows:

$$\frac{1 + h_{21}}{h_{11}h_{22}} \quad \text{for} \quad \frac{h_{22}'}{h_{22}} \quad \text{and} \quad \frac{h_{11}^*}{h_{11}}$$

$$\frac{1}{h_{12}} \quad \text{for} \quad \frac{h_{12}'}{h_{12}} \quad \text{and} \quad \frac{h_{12}^*}{h_{12}} \tag{16}$$

The procedure for using these curves, then, is as follows:

1. Calculate the h parameters for the particular transistor and connection being used.

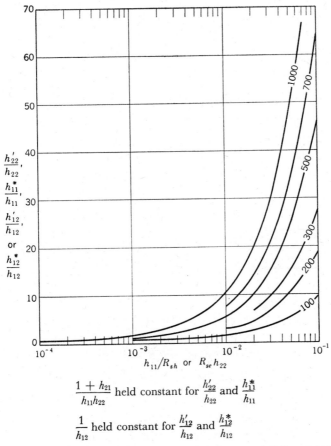

$\dfrac{h_{22}'}{h_{22}}$, $\dfrac{h_{11}^*}{h_{11}}$, $\dfrac{h_{12}'}{h_{12}}$ or $\dfrac{h_{12}^*}{h_{12}}$

h_{11}/R_{sh} or $R_{se}h_{22}$

$\dfrac{1 + h_{21}}{h_{11}h_{22}}$ held constant for $\dfrac{h_{22}'}{h_{22}}$ and $\dfrac{h_{11}^*}{h_{11}}$

$\dfrac{1}{h_{12}}$ held constant for $\dfrac{h_{12}'}{h_{12}}$ and $\dfrac{h_{12}^*}{h_{12}}$

Fig. 12-6. Curves expressing the relations of Equations (12) and (13).

2. Calculate $(1 + h_{21})/h_{11}h_{22}$ and $1/h_{12}$ from these values.

3. Find the ratio of the desired feedback parameter to nonfeedback parameter for any value of R_{se} or R_{sh} by moving to the proper

value on the horizontal axis and reading the vertical value on the curve of $(1 + h_{21})/h_{11}h_{22}$ or $1/h_{12}$.

The curves shown in Figure 12-7 are the same as those of Figure 12-6 except that the vertical scale has been expanded to give more accuracy in the low region.

Note that the curves of Figure 12-5 and 12-6 can be used for shunt and series feedback of any transistor connection. However,

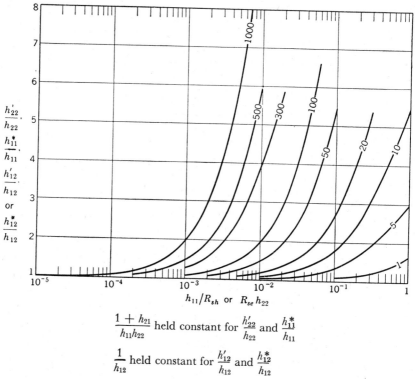

$$\frac{1 + h_{21}}{h_{11}h_{22}} \text{ held constant for } \frac{h'_{22}}{h_{22}} \text{ and } \frac{h^*_{11}}{h_{11}}$$

$$\frac{1}{h_{12}} \text{ held constant for } \frac{h'_{12}}{h_{12}} \text{ and } \frac{h^*_{12}}{h_{12}}$$

Fig. 12-7. An expansion of the lower region of Fig. 12-6.

attention must be paid to the sign of the h parameters. Shunt and series feedback in both the grounded-base and the grounded-collector connections result in positive feedback.

Example 1. The input impedance of the grounded-emitter amplifier of Figure 12-8 is approximately 1500 ohms. It is desired to double this value in order to match the impedance of the generator with the aid of an unby-passed emitter resistor. What value should this resistor be?

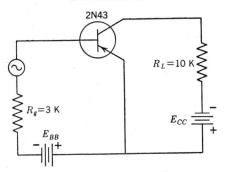

Fig. 12-8. Grounded-emitter amplifier.

$$h_{ie} = 2000, \quad h_{re} = 16 \times 10^{-4}, \quad h_{fe} = 49, \quad h_{oe} = 5 \times 10^{-5}$$

Referring to the equation for R_i, which is

$$R_i = \frac{\Delta^{h\cdot}R_L + h_{ie}}{h_{oe}R_L + 1}$$

it is noticed that h_{ie} is the predominant term. Thus if we choose an unby-passed emitter resistor that will double h_{ie} we should be close to the desired value.

Referring to Figure 12-7 it can be determined that h^*_{21}/h_{11} equals 2 occurs when a series resistance of 40 ohms is used. This is obtained by noting that $(1 + h_{21})/h_{11}h_{22}$ for this transistor is 500. The intersection of the line representing this parameter and the line representing the 2 multiplier for h^*_{11}/h_{11} occurs at a value of $R_{se}h_{22} = 2 \times 10^{-3}$. Thus

$$R_{se} = \frac{2 \times 10^{-3}}{5 \times 10^{-5}} = 40 \text{ ohms}$$

The parameters for the circuit with feedback obtained in a similar manner from Figures 12-5, 12-6, and 12-7 are

$$h^*_{ie} = 4000$$
$$h^*_{re} = 33.6 \times 10^{-4}$$
$$h^*_{oe} = 5 \times 10^{-5}$$
$$h^*_{fe} = 49$$
$$\Delta^{h\cdot*} = 0.036$$

Using these parameters, the value of the input resistance is

$$R_i = 2906 \text{ ohms}$$

This is accurate enough for most practical purposes.

Example 2. The output impedance of the circuit in Figure 12-8 is approximately 30,000 ohms. It is desired to reduce it to match the 10,000 ohm load resistor by use of shunt feedback. What value of R_{sh} will be necessary?

Upon inspection of the equation for R_o, which is

$$R_o = \frac{h_{ie} + R_g}{\Delta^{h^e} + h_{oe}R_g}$$

it is noticed that h_{oe} will be the determining parameter for the value of R_o. Thus if we increase h_{oe} by a value of 3, R_o should decrease by approximately the same factor.

The parameter $(1 + h_{21})/h_{11}h_{22}$ for this transistor, as found in the last example, is 500. With reference to Figure 12-7 the intersection of the line representing this value and h'_{22}/h_{22} equals 3 gives h_{11}/R_{sh} a value of 4×10^{-3}.

The value of R_{sh} is thus

$$R_{sh} = \frac{2000}{4 \times 10^{-3}} = 500,000 \text{ ohms}$$

The other parameter values from the curves are

$$h'_{ie} = 2000$$
$$h'_{re} = 49.6 \times 10^{-4}$$
$$h'_{fe} = 49$$
$$h'_{oe} = 15 \times 10^{-5}$$
$$\Delta^{h^{e'}} = 0.05$$

Calculating R_o, we obtain

$$R_o = \frac{2000 + 3000}{0.05 + 0.45} = 10,000 \text{ ohms}$$

The above examples give some idea of the use of the curves in determining the new h parameters when feedback is used.

Problems

1. Calculate the remaining performance quantities of the circuit of Figure 12-8 with the unby-passed emitter resistor.

Much of the material in this chapter has been taken from an unpublished doctorate thesis by R. L. Riddle, Dept. of Electrical Engineering, State University of Iowa, Iowa City.

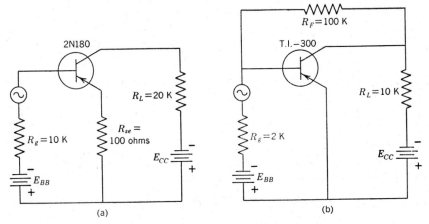

Fig. 12-9. Transistor circuits with feedback.

2. Calculate the remaining performance quantities of the circuit of Figure 12-8 with the shunt feedback.

3. What are the parameters of the transistor with feedback of the two examples in the text if both forms of feedback are used at the same time? Also calculate the performance quantities of this circuit using generator and load resistances shown in Figure 12-8.

4. In Figure 12-9 are shown two transistor circuits with feedback. What are the current and voltage gain and input and output resistances with the feedback shown? See Appendix III for transistor parameters.

13

Noise

Whenever an amplifying device is dealing with extremely small signals it is necessary to consider the *noise* aspects of the devices. The noise of the amplifying device, in conjunction with the inherent noisiness of the signal source, determines the smallest signal that can usefully be handled by the device.

We are all familiar with the situation where a distant radio or television station provides such a small signal that the sound or picture is buried in noise. In the case of radio, the noise comes almost wholly from the source; in the television picture, the "snow" present with a weak signal is caused mostly by the set and partially by the noise within the source (the electromagnetic wave). Many times the signal versus noise problem becomes very critical in radar sets; here an operator must determine the presence or absence of a target among the various noises, and this often is a delicate choice. Much research has been devoted to improving this situation in the radar area. Since the topic of noise is a rather profound subject, we can do little more than present the fundamental ideas and apply them to transistors in this chapter.

One of the items of data supplied by the manufacturer of a transistor is a *noise figure*. Hence, it may be considered that the foremost object of this chapter is to note how this noise figure can be used to evaluate the noisiness of any amplifier we build with a transistor. Before dealing with this directly, however, it is necessary to consider the basic concepts of noise and noise figure.

We will begin by describing noise in very general terms in order to note the fundamental aspects. *Thermal noise* will be introduced as the basic noise phenomenon, and the equivalent circuit of a noise source will be treated. Following this, the sources of noise in a transistor are described and their effects are noted by placing fictitious noise sources in the transistor equivalent circuit.

The concept of noise figure is then introduced and its significance is noted. The chapter is concluded with consideration of the consequence of a given amplifier noise figure.

General Noise Considerations

In the broadest possible definition, noise can be defined as *any undesired signal*, and can be divided into two categories: externally induced noise, and internally generated noise. *External noise*, as the name implies, includes those disturbances that appear in the system as a result of an action outside the system. Two examples of external noise are hum pick-up from the 60-cycle power lines, and radio static caused by electric storms. *Internal noise*, on the other hand, includes all those noises that are generated within the system itself. It is now well known that every resistor produces a discernible noise voltage and also every electronic device (the vacuum tube and the transistor) has internal sources of noise. This internal noise can be thought of as an ever-present limit to the smallest signal that can be handled by the system.

In this chapter we will consider only the effect and sources of *internal* noise. The external noise considerations are well established and many references to this can be found. Usually these external noises can be eliminated by proper shielding of the equipment.

As mentioned in the introduction, internal noise needs be considered only when the signals are very small. Although the noise is still present with large signals, the noise is masked by the signal in this case, and need not be considered. Because of this we would expect that noise is important only in the initial stages of a cascaded set of amplifiers. Since the signal is amplified with each succeeding stage, the noise of all except the first few stages will be completely masked. Usually, then, the first stage, and at the most the first and second stages, determine the noise properties of an entire set of amplifiers.

Description of noise. The first thing to note about noise is that it cannot be described in the same manner as the usual electric voltages and currents. It is common for us to think of a current or voltage in terms of its behavior with time. For example, we think of a sine wave as periodically varying with time, a direct current as being constant with time, etc. Now, if we look at the *noise* output of any electric circuit as a function of time it will be found that the result is completely erratic; that is, we cannot predict what the amplitude of the output will be at any specific instant. Also, there would be no indication of regularity in the wave. When completely unpredictable conditions such as this exist, the situation is described as *random*.

The internal noise being considered here is characterized, then, as *random noise*. If we were to look at an oscilloscopic trace of random noise, it would appear as shown in Figure 13-1.

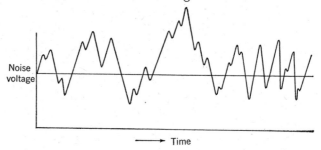

Fig. 13-1. General appearance of a random noise voltage.

Because the noise is random, it is impossible to specify the noise voltage (or current) as a function of time, as we do for the sine wave, for example. In order to gain useful knowledge about the action of a random noise one has to utilize the concepts of probability. We shall not, of course, discuss probability theory here but will consider the important results of such an analysis.

By using highly specialized probability theory it can be shown that there are two things which can be determined about random noise: (1) the *average energy* (or power) produced by the noise; and (2) the average frequency distribution of this energy—commonly called *power spectrum*. The average power can be thought of as the net effect of the many actions in the random phenomenon. In a sense, this average power is analogous to the square of the root-mean-square (rms) value of any a-c wave. When one speaks about the rms value of a sine wave, for example, one refers to the *average* effect without considering the time behavior. Therefore this average effect should not be entirely unfamiliar.

The concept of power spectrum, although strange on first encounter, is very important and very basic to noise considerations. The power spectrum refers to the amount of power in a small band of frequencies, and to the variation in this power density as the small band varies over a whole range of frequencies. A pure sine wave, for example, has a power spectrum that has a value for one frequency (the frequency of the sine wave) and is zero everywhere else. If we have a complex wave that is periodic we can regard it as the sum of a number of sine waves of different frequencies; the power spectrum then would consist of finite values at each of the frequencies of the component waves and would be zero at all other frequencies. The power spectrum of a random noise is an extension of this idea to the case where the wave is purely random. When specifying the power spectrum of a random wave we are doing the equivalent of specifying the *frequency* of a sine wave or of a group of sine waves.

Of the many possible power spectrums of random waves there are two types that will be of interest to us: a power spectrum that is "flat"—that is, the power density at all frequencies is equal; and a power spectrum that varies (with frequency) as the inverse of the frequency $(1/f)$. We shall find in the next section that the most basic type of noise, thermal noise, has a flat frequency spectrum and this type is called *white noise*. Later we shall see that the most important noise within the transistor has a $1/f$ spectrum.

In conclusion, then, we cannot speak about random quantities in terms of their behavior as a function of time, as we would for a sine wave, but must describe them in terms of the average effect they produce and how this average effect varies over the frequency spectrum.

Thermal noise. The most basic type of noise, and one that can never be evaded, is thermal noise. Thermal noise is present in every electric conductor (whether or not it is connected) and hence is present in every electric circuit. This noise is pictured as being due to the random motion of free electrons (the current carriers) from thermal energy. Because of this thermal agitation the electrons fly about in a random fashion and the resulting current due to these moving charges produces a voltage across the ends of the conductor.

Thus, even when no current flows, this thermal noise may be observed. When current does flow, the random motion is still present, but now the noise phenomenon is superimposed on the flowing current.

In 1928 H. Nyquist showed that the average noise power *available* from any conductor is

$$\text{available noise power} = kTB \tag{1}$$

where T = temperature of conductor in degrees Kelvin (273.1 + centigrade),

k = Boltzmann's constant = 1.38×10^{-23} watt-sec/deg,

B = bandwidth of measuring system in cycles per second = $f_H - f_L$.

Note first that this is *available power*. From Chapter 8, Equation (59), it is remembered that available power is obtained if the load is matched to the source. Suppose then that a given conductor has a resistance R; Equation (1) says that, if a noiseless resistance of R were connected to the noise resistance, the load R would absorb kTB watts of power. This example is only illustrative since it is impossible to produce a noiseless resistance; we noted above that every conductor has thermal noise.

We can now find what noise voltage appears across the conductor of resistance R. Since available power can always be expressed as $E^2/4R$, we can write

$$\frac{\overline{E_n^2}}{4R} = kTB \quad \therefore \quad \boxed{\overline{E_n^2} = 4RkTB} \tag{2}$$

where $\overline{E_n^2}$ = rms value of noise voltage squared,

R = resistance (or the real part of a complex impedance).

Equation (2) specifies the value of rms noise voltage that appears across any resistor R. This voltage could be read on a high-impedance voltmeter if precaution is taken to find the rms value of the random wave. Note that expressing the rms voltage in terms of its square corresponds to expressing the average power, as discussed in the preceding section. We can always find the square root of Equation (2) and thus have the rms voltage. However, for random waves, it is usually left in the squared form.

There are two important things to observe from Equation (2). First, the noise voltage-squared is proportional to the value of resistance. Secondly, the noise voltage-squared is proportional to bandwidth, *no matter where the $f_H - f_L$ occurs. This means that the power spectrum of thermal noise is flat.* For example, the noise power between 0 and 1000 cycles is the same as the power between 1,000,000 and 1,001,000 cycles. Whenever noise has a flat power spectrum it can be regarded as containing components of all frequencies and is usually called *white noise.*

Although thermal noise theoretically possesses power at all frequencies, as seen above, any electric system that we connect to a resistor has a finite bandwidth. If our object is to measure the noise, the measuring instrument itself would have a finite bandwidth and this bandwidth would determine the amount of noise power that the instrument would accept. If we have an amplifying system connected to a resistor, the bandwidth[1] of the system will determine the amount of thermal noise that is accepted. Thus we can think of the thermal noise source (the resistor) as supplying power at all frequencies possible, but when we use the resistor in any electric circuit the bandwidth of the circuit selects only a part of the total possible power—that part that corresponds to the bandwidth of the circuit.

Other thermal-type noises. It was stated in the previous section that thermal noise is the most basic type of noise encountered in electric circuits. It is also true that, in electronic devices, there are a number of noises present that, although not strictly thermal in nature, behave much like a thermal noise. Examples of this type of noise are the shot effect and the induced grid noise of vacuum tubes. Although both of these noises arise from physical sources within the tube that are not strictly thermal in nature, we can treat the noise *as though they were due to a fictitious resistor.* This is the basis for using an equivalent resistance in the grid circuit of a vacuum tube to account for the shot and the induced grid noise. Although we are not interested in vacuum tube noises here, the above was included as an example since the concept of using the noise equivalent resistance of a vacuum tube is familiar to most electronics designers.

We shall find that an analogous situation holds for one type of transistor noise. The shot noise or *diffusion recombination* noise of a

---

[1] For noise considerations the bandwidth refers to an ideal, straight-sided bandpass characteristic. For any system having a reasonably flat characteristic between half-power points, however, the half-power points may be taken to define the bandwidth. [Chapter 6, Equation (83).]

transistor is a noise that acts essentially like a thermal noise. Its power spectrum is flat and hence it can be called white noise.

Equivalent circuit of a noise source. When we wish to take account of the various noise sources in a given circuit, it is useful to have an equivalent circuit of the source itself so that we may treat the noise in a manner similar to the usual voltage source.

In the case of thermal noise it is noted that the noise voltage appearing across a resistor is always given by Equation (2). We may say, then, that the equivalent circuit of any resistor (noisewise) is given by a fictitious noise generator in series with the given resistance.[2] This is depicted in Figure 13-2. To account for all thermal noise sources,

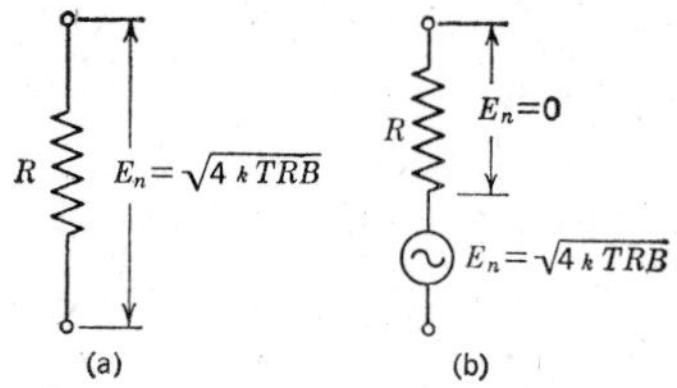

Fig. 13-2. The noise voltage of a resistor and its equivalent circuit: (a) thermal noise across resistor; (b) equivalent circuit of the resistor.

then, we would replace every resistor by its equivalent circuit; as noted earlier, however, only those thermal sources in the *first stages* of an electronic amplifying circuit need be considered.

If we have noise sources within the transistor that are not strictly thermal in physical nature, but act as though they were thermal noises, we can again use a fictitious generator to represent this source of noise. To do this, we need to know the value of the fictitious resistance in order to assign the proper voltage to the source, as given by Equation (2). Note that in this case *the equivalent noise source does not contain a series resistor;* the value of the noise voltage is determined by the value of a fictitious resistance, but this resistance does not appear in series with the voltage source.

If we encounter a noise source that is not like a thermal source (it does not have a flat power spectrum) we may still represent it by an

---

[2] Note that Norton's equivalent circuit is also acceptable and is found in the usual way. The result is a current generator $I^2 = \dfrac{4KTB}{R}$ in parallel with a resistance R.

equivalent voltage source. It must always be kept in mind, however, that the power spectrum is not flat. Again, no equivalent resistance will appear in series with the fictitious source.

Transistor Noise Sources

The important noise sources of a semiconductor device, such as the transistor, fall into two categories: the *shot noise* or *diffusion recombination noise* makes up one type, and the *surface noise* and *leakage noise* make up the other. The physical phenomenon that acts to create these noises is not well understood and we shall not attempt to describe the phenomenon here. The important properties of the noises, however, have been measured and it is these that interest us.

The *diffusion recombination noise* (shot noise) is similar to thermal noise in its action. Its power spectrum is flat with frequency and its voltage-square value is given by Equation (2). This means that we can assign a fictitious resistance to this noise, for any particular transistor, and use a voltage source to account for the noise. Again, it must be remembered that the fictitious resistor will not appear in series with the noise source.

The other types of transistor noise, surface noise and leakage noise, both exhibit a phenomenon that is common to all semiconductors. This noise is distinguished by the fact that it exhibits a $1/f$ power spectrum. This means that if the frequency is increased the noise decreases for a given bandwidth. These two noises are commonly grouped together and called *semiconductor or $1/f$ noise*.

The two types of noises encountered in transistors then are *white noise* and *semiconductor noise*. Since the semiconductor noise decreases as the frequency goes up, we may expect that at some frequency this noise will become less than the white noise. The noise power versus frequency will then appear, for a transistor, as shown in Figure 13-3. As shown, the frequency range can be considered in terms of two regions: the region where the semiconductor noise is predominant, and the region where the white noise is important. For a typical transistor the frequency where the $1/f$ noise is equal to the white noise (shown as f_b on the figure) is in the range of 1 kc to 10 kc.

We have just seen above that the noises generated within a transistor can be considered as belonging to two types, based on the power spectrum of the noise. It may be concluded, then, that the noise of a transistor can be analyzed, circuitwise, by using two fictitious noise sources: one to represent the $1/f$ noise, and the other to depict the white noise. This is the procedure we shall adopt in describing the transistor noise.

The two questions that remain are: (1) What values shall be assigned to the fictitious noise sources? and (2) Where shall the noise sources be placed in the transistor equivalent circuit?

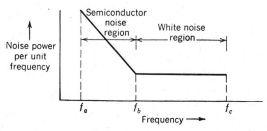

Fig. 13-3. Sketch showing transistor noise power versus frequency.

Dealing with the first question we note that the shot noise is a thermal-type noise and hence we can use the Nyquist equation:

$$\overline{E_s^2} = 4kTR_{eq}B \qquad (3)$$

where $\overline{E_s^2}$ = rms-voltage squared of transistor white noise,

R_{eq} = the equivalent resistance that would produce $\overline{E_s^2}$.

In order to evaluate this quantity we would need to know R_{eq}. Since, in many transistor applications the bandwidth is entirely in the $1/f$ region, the manufacturer gives no information about the white noise (R_{eq}). Hence if it is necessary to evaluate it, the noise must be measured.

For the $1/f$ noise we know that the power per unit frequency can be written

$$\text{power density} = C\frac{1}{f} \qquad (4)$$

where C is a constant.

If we wish to find the power available in a given bandwidth between f_H and f_L it is necessary to sum up the noise power contained between f_L and f_H expressed by the above equation. This is the mathematical process of integration. The result is

$$1/f \text{ noise power} = C \ln\frac{f_H}{f_L} \qquad (5)$$

where f_H = upper frequency limit of bandwidth,

f_L = lower frequency limit of bandwidth.

Since power is proportional to E^2 we may write

$$\overline{E_n^2} = K \ln\frac{f_H}{f_L} \qquad (6)$$

where K = constant differing from C,

$\overline{E_n^2}$ = squared rms value of $1/f$ noise voltage.

We shall find, when discussing *noise figure*, that the transistor manufacturer does specify information that amounts to assigning a proper value to K under certain specified conditions.

Although Equations (3) and (6) provide expressions for the two types of transistor noise, it is necessary to point out that the constants in these relations vary from unit to unit and, more important, these

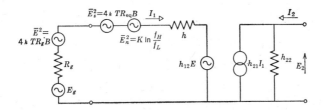

Fig. 13-4. Equivalent circuit of a transistor showing the fictitious noise generators.

constants vary with operating point and temperature. It is known that the constant K, for example, varies rather widely with collector voltage. Since these variations do occur, the manufacturer, when giving noise data, specifies the operating point and the temperature used for his measurements.

Given that we can now add the two noise sources to the transistor equivalent circuit; we must decide where to place them. The noises are generated internally in the transistor and, of course, make their appearance, along with any signal, at the output. One might surmise, then, that the proper place for the fictitious noise generators is at the output of the transistor. It turns out, however, that for purposes of calculating the noise figure it is more convenient to have the fictitious noise sources appear in the *input* side of the transistor equivalent circuit. It is clearly allowable to place the noise sources at the input if these sources, multiplied by the gain of the transistor, cause a noise in the output equal to the actual noise observed there.

We can now draw a proper representation of the transistor with its internal noise sources. The result is shown in Figure 13-4. Note that here the noise voltage of the source resistance (thermal noise) is also included.

Having dealt with the question of the sources of transistor noise, we are now ready to consider the practical effect of this noise in a given circuit. It is the noise figure that is universally used to evaluate the effect of noise in electronic circuits.

Noise Figure

It is clearly evident that whenever extremely small signals are encountered in any amplifying circuit, the noise quality of the circuit must be considered. In the past, various measures of this noise quality have been used. The most important is that of noise figure.

The aim of defining a quantity such as the noise figure is to provide a basis of comparison between similar electronic circuits (or devices) and also to provide a method whereby the noisiness of the component parts of a circuit may be related to the noisiness of the complete circuit. In transistors, for example, the manufacturer always specifies a noise figure for the transistor; using this value the noise figure of an amplifier in which that transistor is used may be found. From such a resultant noise figure the smallest signal that can be accepted for specified conditions can be calculated.

The noise figure for our purposes is defined as "the ratio of the total noise power appearing in the load to the noise power in the load due to amplified thermal noise from the source resistance R_g." The source resistance may be an antenna resistance, an actual voltage source resistance, or the output impedance of a previous stage.

$$\text{noise figure} = F = \frac{\text{total noise power in load}}{\text{load noise from source resistance}} \qquad (7)$$

It is of great importance to note that the noise figure is independent of the load resistance. In the definition above this comes about because, when taking the ratio of the two noise powers, the R_L cancels out. It is equally important to observe that the noise figure does depend upon the source resistance R_g.

It is useful to discuss the concept of noise figure before proceeding with the calculations. Although we refer to the transistor here, the noise figure concept can be applied to any two-terminal network. First, it is noted that the noise figure gives the measure of *how much noise is added by the transistor.* If the transistor were completely noiseless the numerator of (7) would equal the denominator, i.e., the total noise power appearing in the load would consist of only the amplified source resistance noise power. Thus it is seen that the most desirable value of F is 1. For any noise contributed by the transistor the F will increase correspondingly from 1. In general, then, the closer F is to 1, the better.

This can be looked at in still another way. We know that the *least* amount of noise that can be achieved in a circuit is the thermal noise of the resistances. Therefore if we connect any electronic amplifying device to a source, the ideal minimum amount of noise in the output will be the amplified thermal noise of the source resistance. Achieving only this amount of noise in the output can be regarded as being the *ideal* condition. The noise figure as defined above, then, gives us a measure of how far from the ideal we are. If we have a noise figure of 2.0, for example, this means that the transistor is providing a noise power (in the output) equal to the thermal source resistance noise power. The output noise power is twice the *ideal* value. It is useful, then, to rewrite the F in the following manner:

$$F = \frac{\text{thermal noise power} + \text{transistor noise power}}{\text{thermal noise power}}$$

$$= \frac{P'_{RN} + P'_{TN}}{P'_{RN}} = 1 + \frac{P'_{TN}}{P'_{RN}} \tag{8}$$

where P'_{RN} = thermal noise power in load,
P'_{TN} = transistor noise power in load.

As a final thought, it should be emphasized that the noise figure is a function of the source resistance. Hence the F may be regarded, basically, as a means of comparing the noise properties of different amplifying devices (or circuits) *used with a given source.*

We can now illustrate the noise figure for the general transistor amplifier in terms of the noise sources described earlier. Although the result of this will not be very useful for practical calculations, it does show how the transistor noise sources affect the noise figure. After having done this, we will see how to use the manufacturer's data and certain noise measurements.

As a first step we may note that, if we think of moving the transistor noise sources *outside* the transistor (to the left of the input) the transistor itself can be thought of as being noiseless. The advantage of this is that now we can calculate the *output* noise conditions at the *input*, i.e., now the transistor adds no noise, since we have theoretically moved its sources outside the unit, and hence the noise figure at the input is the same as at the output. Using this simple principle, the equivalent circuit of Figure 13-4 is redrawn in Figure 13-5 below.

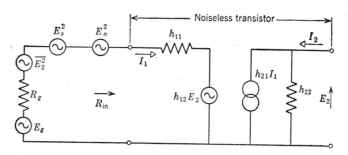

Fig. 13-5. Circuit of Fig. 13-4 redrawn to move the noise generators outside the transistor unit.

We can now consider the quantities of Equation (8) as being the *input* power from the thermal source and the transistor sources, respectively. Since the input powers in numerator and denominator of Equation (8) will be amplified by the same amount, the gain will cancel out; hence the noise figure at the input will equal the noise figure at the output.

We then proceed to calculate the noise figure at the input side. The thermal noise power supplied to the transistor by the source resistance is

$$P_{RN} = I^2 R_{in} = \frac{\overline{E^2}}{(R_g + R_{in})^2} R_{in} = \frac{4kTR_g B}{(R_g + R_{in})^2} R_{in} \qquad (9)$$

where P_{RN} = thermal noise power from R_g absorbed by transistor,
R_{in} = input resistance of transistor with any particular load.

The noise power supplied by the two transistor noise sources is

$$P_{TN} = \frac{\overline{E_s^2} + \overline{E_n^2}}{(R_g + R_{in})^2} R_{in} = \frac{K \ln (f_H/f_L) + 4R_{eq}kTB}{(R_g + R_{in})^2} R_{in} \qquad (10)$$

where P_{TN} = transistor noise power at the input.

Equations (3) and (6) were used to obtain the right side of (10).

The F of a transistor, with a given R_g, is then found by using Equation (8):

$$F = 1 + \frac{P_{TN}}{P_{RN}} = 1 + \frac{K \ln (f_H/f_L) + 4R_{eq}kTB}{4R_g kTB} \tag{11}$$

The above equation, then, shows how the transistor noises which were described in the previous section combine to form the noise figure of a given transistor and a given source resistance. One possible procedure now consists of taking a transistor and measuring the noises in a manner to determine the values of K and R_{eq} in the above equation. The manufacturer, however, always states some information about the noise properties of the given transistor. This information, however, is not in the form where one can evaluate the two constants directly. Nevertheless, as shall be seen in the next section, many times we will not have to make additional measurements to predict the noise figure of the transistor in our application; sometimes, however, it will be necessary.

Before proceeding with the topic of using the manufacturer's data it is useful to make some concluding remarks about noise figure in general. If the student pursues the topic of noise figure more thoroughly, he will find that the general definition differs somewhat from the one stated in Equation (7). The most basic definition is "the ratio of the ideal signal-to-noise ratio to the actual signal-to-noise ratio," and here the signal and noise are expressed in terms of *available* power. For the case of transistors the available signal power is the same in both the noiseless and the actual cases. Taking this into consideration, it can easily be shown that the definition of Equation (7) is the same as the basic definition—and somewhat easier to visualize.

Also, further investigation of noise figure will uncover the concept of *spot noise figure* versus *integrated noise figure*. If the frequency spectrum of the noise sources were somewhat erratic with frequency, and if our electronic device were fairly broadband, then the total effective noise figure would have to be calculated by considering the F at a series of frequencies within the pass band (spot noise figures) and then sum the resulting F variation over the pass band to obtain the total effective F (integrated noise figure). Since, as seen in the preceding section, the transistor noise sources are either a simple $1/f$ relation or constant with frequency, we could present the total effective F as in Equation (7) without introducing the spot noise concept.

Finally, it must be remembered that the noise figure is independent of the load resistance, but is dependent upon the source resistance.

Use of Manufacturer's Stated Noise Figure

One of the items of data supplied by the manufacturer of transistors is a noise figure F_o, stated under specified conditions. It is our object, in this section, to determine how to use this data to evaluate the noise figure of a given transistor application.

At present, the noise figure F_o stated by the manufacturer usually applies to a noise measurement at a frequency of 1000 c and for a bandwidth of 1 c. The value of source resistance (R_g) used in the measurement is usually given since the noise figure depends upon its value.

Although the noise characteristics of transistors are constantly being improved, it is still true that the frequency of 1000 c is well within the $1/f$ noise region for most transistors. Consequently we can regard the manufacturer's data as supplying information about the transistor noise in the $1/f$ region; if our application demands evaluating the noise in the higher-frequency regions, where the white noise is predominant, we will have to measure it. (The methods of noise measurement for transistor circuits are identical to those for vacuum tube circuits.)

The question we then deal with is "How is the F_o, measured for a 1-c bandwidth, related to a given bandwidth we may encounter?"

First, we consider the case where our bandwidth lies wholly in the $1/f$ region (between f_a and f_b of Figure 13-3). In addition, for this first case we will consider the bandwidth as being small.

In this region the $1/f$ noise is much larger than the white noise. Consequently, in Equation (11), we may neglect the "$4R_{eq}kTB$" term and write the noise figure as

$$F = 1 + \frac{K \ln (f_H/f_L)}{4kTR_g B} \tag{12}$$

Now, if the bandwidth is small $[(f_H - f_L) \ll f_L]$, we can make the following approximation:

$$\ln \frac{f_H}{f_L} \simeq \frac{f_H - f_L}{f_L} \tag{13}$$

The F may then be written

$$F = 1 + \frac{K'}{f_L} \qquad (14)$$

where $K' = \dfrac{K}{4kTR_g}$.

If, at a frequency of 1 c, a value of F_o is measured, it must be true that

$$F_o = 1 + \frac{K'}{1000}; \qquad K' = 1000(F_o - 1) \qquad (15)$$

Substituting this K' into Equation (14), we have the important result:

$$F = 1 + \frac{1000(F_o - 1)}{f_L} \quad \text{if} \quad \left\{ \begin{matrix} (f_H - f_L) \ll f_L \\ f_a < f_L < f_b \end{matrix} \right\} \qquad (16)$$

where F_o = noise figure measured at 1000 c.

Equation (16) enables us to calculate the noise figure for an amplifier with any center frequency in terms of the noise figure at 1000 c (F_o). The restrictions on Equation (16) are that the f_L lie in the $1/f$ region and the bandwidth be small. *Also, the F given by this equation will result only if we are using an R_g close to the value used to measure F_o.* This is usually the case since we generally operate the transistor with circuit values close to the recommended ones. However, if this R_g criterion is not filled, it simply means that the F_o data do not apply. We would then have to measure the noise figure to obtain any accuracy.

Next, we consider the case where the $f_H - f_L$ occurs wholly within the $1/f$ region, but the bandwidth (of our amplifier) is not small. This means that we cannot use the approximation given in Equation (13). However, the approximation does still apply to the F_o measurement (supplied by the manufacturer) so that Equation (15) holds. Substituting this value of K' in Equation (12) we find

$$F = 1 + \frac{(F_o - 1)1000 \ln (f_H/f_L)}{f_H - f_L} \quad \text{for} \quad f_a < f_H, f_L < f_b \qquad (17)$$

Equation (17) then is the more general equation that applies when the pass band is within the $1/f$ region, but the bandwidth is not small. At first thought it may appear that the noise figure of the circuit with the greater bandwidth will be the higher since the greater bandwidth allows more $1/f$ noise. However, the larger bandwidth also allows more source resistance thermal noise to be present, so that the F in the application of Equation (17) may well be less than for the case where Equation (16) applies.

Now suppose that we have an amplifier whose bandwidth lies above the $1/f$ region; i.e., in the white noise region of Figure 13-3. In this case the $1/f$ noise is negligible and Equation (11) may be written

$$F = 1 + \frac{R_{eq}}{R_g} \quad \text{if} \quad f_b < f_H, f_L \tag{18}$$

Since the transistor data give no information about the noise in this region, a measurement is required to find the noise figure. In this case, any bandwidth that is above the $1/f$ region may be used for the measurement. The F measured in any bandwidth in the white noise region is identical to that in any other bandwidth as long as it also is in the white noise region.

The last case to be considered is where the amplifier bandwidth lies in *both* the $1/f$ and the white noise region. For this case we need merely *add* the noise powers obtained by calculating the $1/f$ portion and the addition supplied by the white noise portion. The result is

$$F = 1 + \frac{(F_o - 1)1000 \ln (f_b/f_L) + (R_{eq}/R_g)(f_H - f_b)}{f_H - f_L} \tag{19}$$

The above relation, then, provides the means for calculating the noise figure of a transistor amplifier with any given bandwidth. It is seen that if the amplifier bandpass lies completely in the $1/f$ region, the transistor data can be used to find the noise figure. If this is not true, a measurement must be taken to find F.

One important restriction must be repeated: in order to use the manufacturer's value of F_o with reasonable accuracy, it is necessary that the given amplifier have a source resistance close to the R_g used in evaluating F_o.

The noise figure supplied by most manufacturers is given in decibels; the noise figure we have used here is in terms of a power ratio. The relation between these two different forms is as follows:

$$F_{db} = 10 \log_{10} F_o \tag{20}$$

where F_{db} = manufacturer's noise figure in decibels,

F_o = manufacturer's noise figure as used in this text.

Use of the Noise Figure

Having now explored the meaning and the method of calculating the noise figure of transistor amplifiers, it follows to see what information this gives us.

In the first place the F_o data of a transistor allow us to compare the noisiness of one transistor versus another. The transistor with the lowest noise figure, of course, is the most desirable from the noise standpoint. Remember that comparing F_o's is only valid if the same source resistances are involved.

This means, then, that if we are comparing different transistors for use in a given amplifier (given R_g and bandwidth) that transistor with the lowest F_o will provide the lowest F for the amplifier.

As indicated in the introduction, we need only consider the noise figure of the first stage—or at most the first and the second stage of a string of cascaded amplifiers. After the first few stages the signal has been amplified to the extent that the noise in the following stages is completely negligible. Therefore the noise figure of the first few stages may be regarded as being the noise figure of the entire set of cascaded circuits.

Many times it is necessary to know the smallest signal that can be handled by an amplifier or a set of amplifiers. We can use the noise figure to calculate this. Suppose that it is agreed that the signal is recognizable if the signal-to-noise ratio at the output is equal to 1.0. Given that our circuit has a noise figure F and a source resistance R_g, and remembering that the noise figure gives the ratio of total output noise to thermal noise in output, we can write

$$\frac{P_{\text{noise}}}{P_{\text{signal}}} = 1$$

$$P_{\text{noise}} = P_{\text{signal}} = F \times P_{\text{thermal}} = F \times 4kTR_g B \qquad (21)$$

We may regard the signal power of Equation (21) as a *minimum detectable signal* for a signal-to-noise ratio of 1. In this way we can determine the smallest signal that can be handled by the given amplifier.

References

1. H. T. Friis, "Noise Figures of Radio Receivers," *Proc. Inst. Radio Engrs*, **32**, 419, 1944.

2. H. Goldberg, "Some Notes on Noise Figures," *Proc. Inst. Radio Engrs.*, **36,** 1205, Oct. 1948.

3. A. van der Ziel, *Noise.* New York: Prentice-Hall, Inc., 1954.

Problems

1. What would be the noise figure of an amplifier employing a 2N130 transistor if the band pass of the amplifier were 100 to 10 kc? See characteristics of the transistor in Appendix III. Assume that the band pass lies wholly within the $1/f$ noise region.

2. If the noise figure of a transistor in the white region is 10 and the noise figure measured at 1 kc is 100, at what frequency (f_b) will the noise due to the $1/f$ contribution be equal to that of the white noise?

3. What would be the over-all noise figure of the transistor of Problem 2 over a frequency band pass of 100 c to 100 kc?

4. If the CK790 is used in place of the 2N130 of Problem 1, what would the noise figure be?

5. What would be the minimum detectable signal for the amplifiers in Problems 1, 3, and 4 if the generator resistance in all cases were 1000 ohms?

14

Transistor Oscillators and Multivibrators

In addition to amplifiers, oscillators are electronic circuits common to most communications equipment. Their basic function is to generate the sine wave currents and voltages utilized in these equipments. It is usually true that the oscillator is used to furnish sine wave power, although sometimes only a voltage is used. Consequently, we can regard the oscillator as the electronic equivalent of a power generator that supplies the low-frequency sine wave power to our homes. As an example of an oscillator we may note that every modern radio has a local oscillator and it is the frequency of this oscillator that is adjusted when we turn the dial. The power output of this oscillator is combined with the incoming signal to form a *beat frequency* signal and this is then further amplified.

In performing the function of sine wave generator, the oscillator circuit acts essentially as a *converter*. It converts power from the d-c plate supply to a-c power whose wave shape is a sine wave, and whose frequency is determined by the reactive components of the circuit.

Since the *multivibrator*[1] performs a function similar to that of the oscillator, it is convenient to discuss it briefly in this chapter.

The multivibrator is also a generator of power for electronic circuits. In multivibrators, however, the waveform of the generated wave is always nonsinusoidal. In fact, this difference may be regarded as the definition: a multivibrator performs the same functions as an oscillator, but the generated wave is always nonsinusoidal. For ex-

---

[1] Often the term "multivibrator" is taken to include monostable, bistable, and astable trigger circuits. We here refer only to the astable or free-running type.

ample, multivibrators are used to produce the *sweep* voltages necessary in oscilloscopes and television sets.

At the outset it is important to stress a basic difference between the considerations of this chapter and of the entire preceding material. Thus far in this book we have concentrated upon the operation of the transistor in its active region, i.e., the region wherein it serves as an amplifier. Although this active region is still of prime importance in oscillators and multivibrators, both the saturation and the cutoff regions are also involved. Hence we shall have to take account of the transistor in all three regions when dealing with oscillators and multivibrators.

In this chapter we will deal mainly with oscillators. The circuit descriptions and analyses developed will be general enough so that the multivibrator can be treated briefly in terms of the oscillator considerations.

General Description of Oscillators

We may observe first that the process of amplification is very basic to an oscillator. Certainly, most oscillators involve an amplifying element such as a transistor or a vacuum tube. We may regard the oscillations as representing an unstable amplifying condition; it is also implied that the instability is regulated so that a constant amplitude sine wave results.

We remember from Chapter 11 that if positive feedback is applied to an amplifier circuit, the circuit may become unstable. This, then, represents *one* fundamental way to achieve an oscillator: apply sufficient positive feedback to an amplifier circuit.

In any unstable circuit we will need a *frequency-determining* circuit if we wish to control the frequency of oscillation. This, of course, means the use of either a series or a parallel resonant circuit. An oscillator, then, is the combination of an unstable amplifying circuit and a frequency-determining circuit.

Although we could approach the oscillator from the viewpoint of feedback, it is more basic to consider it in terms of a *negative resistance*. It can be shown that in *any* oscillating circuit, the amplifying part of the circuit serves to supply an a-c negative resistance. This negative resistance in combination with the resonant circuit makes up the oscillator. Since this concept is sufficiently basic to require emphasis, we can regard the circuits of Figure 14-1 as being the equivalent

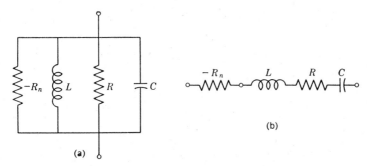

Fig. 14-1. Basic equivalent circuits of an oscillator: (a) parallel resonant circuit oscillator; (b) series resonant circuit oscillator.

circuit of any oscillator. The R in these circuits accounts for the resistance present in every coil and the negative resistance shown is supplied, in an oscillator circuit, by the transistor or vacuum tube. A few comments on this very simple representation are pertinent. As is immediately suspected, the negative resistance is necessary to balance out the positive resistance encountered in every resonant circuit. This amounts to the same thing as saying the losses in the resonant part are compensated for by the negative resistance portion.

If the R_n equals R in Figure 14-1, we are left with a lossless resonant circuit. If an oscillation is once started in such a circuit, it is evident that it will continue without decreasing. In actuality, the electric energy is oscillating between the coil and the capacitor. The energy first appears in the coil, then in the capacitor, then in the coil, etc. Although this is a frequent occurrence in all transients of electric circuits, the unique situation here is that the oscillations remain constant without decreasing. Note that this is true only so long as the negative resistance balances the inevitable losses in the resonant circuit. For any oscillator, then, we can think of the circuit as consisting essentially of a frequency-determining part and a negative-resistance part, as shown in Figure 14-2.

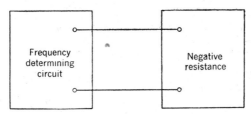

Fig. 14-2. General equivalent circuit for an oscillator.

With this simple picture, then, the remaining consideration is to determine how the negative resistance is affected by the transistor (or vacuum tube). We are aware of the fact that the concept of negative resistance is often a strange one. It is such a useful tool, however, that it is worth while to treat it in some detail.

Oscillators are separated into two basic types, based on the manner in which the negative resistance appears in the circuit. The two types are the *two-terminal oscillator* and the *feedback oscillator*. The chief distinguishing feature between the two types is that in the two-terminal type the negative resistance portion can be separated from the frequency-determining part. This means that the negative resistance can be obtained without connecting the resonant circuit. In the feedback type, on the other hand, the resonant circuit is necessary to produce the negative resistance. Thus the two portions cannot be physically separated, although it is still useful to think of the two functions separately.

We proceed to consider the negative resistance obtained in the two-terminal type; we can then show how the same effect is achieved in the feedback type.

Negative Resistance Characteristic

When considering the transistor as an active circuit element in the previous chapters, we considered the two major methods of treating the circuit as (1) the equivalent circuit method, and (2) the graphical analysis method. Now, when considering the total three regions of operation of the transistor, we shall introduce another method: this method consists essentially of obtaining the input characteristic of the transistor connection. The input may be at either the emitter, the collector, or the base terminals. After obtaining the input characteristic, the d-c circuitry attached to the input terminals forms a load line to the input.

The usefulness of this method, for oscillators and multivibrators, lies not in its ability to permit quantitative analysis, but rather in its ability to provide a picture of the operation of these devices. The mathematical analysis itself is a rather simple technique that gives us no insight into the physical operation.

Although we are interested in those input characteristics that give us a negative resistance in some region, we will begin by considering the input characteristic generally.

Use of the input characteristic. The basic idea of the input characteristic consists essentially of selecting two terminals of the transistor as the input, and then plotting the voltage versus current for this input. Note that it is assumed that some circuitry is attached to the other set of terminals.

For example, let us consider that we have a junction transistor connected in the grounded-base connection, and the input terminals we choose are those of the emitter to base. If now we vary the input current (d-c wise) and note the resulting voltage at each point, the curve will appear as shown in Figure 14-3. We note that three differ-

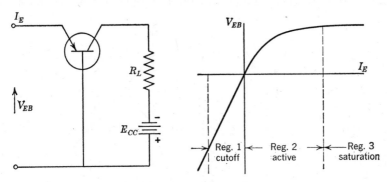

Fig. 14-3. Input characteristic of emitter terminals for the three different regions.

ent regions are apparent: the cutoff region, the active region, and the saturation region. Since the input resistance *for a-c varying signals* is given by the slope of the curve, we can justify the general shape of this curve for the three regions.

In region I, the cutoff region, a negative voltage must be applied to the emitter junction, as shown on the curve. This means that the emitter junction is reverse-biased. Hence in the cutoff region both the emitter and the collector junction are back-biased. With this back bias of the emitter junction we would expect the input resistance to be very high, and hence the steep slope of the curve in this region.

In the active region the transistor is biased as described earlier in this book. The emitter junction is forward-biased and the collector junction is reverse-biased—this is the region of normal amplification treated thus far in the book. As we remember, the input resistance in this region varies with the input current; as shown in the curve, the input resistance decreases as the current increases. It is this varying resistance, in the active region, that accounts for the nonlinear input resistance as discussed in Chapter 9.

In the saturation region the input voltage is high enough to cause the collector junction to become forward-biased; hence in this region both the emitter and the collector junction are *forward-biased*. As would be expected for this condition, the curve shows that the input resistance is very low for this region.

The important consequence of this characteristic is that now we can consider any d-c circuitry attached to the input terminals *in terms of a load line on the input graph*. This concept is perfectly analogous to the concept of drawing a load line on a set of collector characteristics,

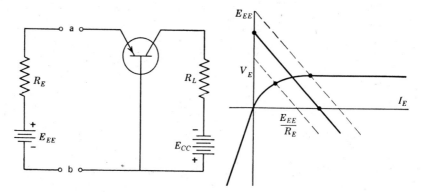

Fig. 14-4. Illustrating use of d-c load line on input characteristic.

as is done for the usual graphical analysis. The graphical analysis was treated in Chapter 7, Figure 7-4. It will be remembered that the idea presented there was that the load line portrays a graphical simultaneous solution of the circuit to the left and to the right of the breaking point. In Figure 14-4 we consider that the circuit is broken at *a-b*; consequently, the input characteristic portrays the circuit to the right of these points and the load line portrays the circuit to the left. As previously, the voltage intercept of the load line equals the open-circuit voltage of the circuitry, and the current intercept is the short-circuit current. This is illustrated in Figure 14-4. If we had a signal alternating voltage placed in the load circuit, we could envisage the operation on Figure 14-4 in terms of moving the load line up and down. Remember that we can draw a simple load line only for resistive loads; if reactance forms part of the load, the load line concept **is** not nearly so useful.

Having noted the load line concept, we can now see how the input characteristic is obtained experimentally. One merely attaches a proper load resistance (R_E) with a variable direct voltage. Then as the voltage is varied, the respective currents and voltages will be given by the intersection, as shown by the dashed lines on Figure 14-4. By using a large enough voltage swing, including negative emitter voltages (for P-N-P), the entire characteristic in the three regions can be scanned.

Before leaving this topic of general input characteristic, it is worth while emphasizing the difference from the input characteristics as depicted by Figure 7-2. There the characteristics, and there are a number of them, give the transistor V_E versus I_E with various constant collector currents, i.e., this is information about the transistor alone. If we attach an emitter load line to these characteristics we have to know, in addition, the swing of the collector current if we are to depict the operation. The input characteristic, on the other hand, is a single curve that specifies information about the transistor *and the associated circuitry.* Here the collector current is not constant, but varies according to the collector circuitry (battery and resistor) and the input current. A different input characteristic will result if either the transistor, the collector battery, or the resistor is changed.

Although we have here regarded the emitter-to-base terminals as the input, it is clear that we can obtain an input characteristic for any two terminals, with the other pair attached to a given circuitry.

Negative resistance input characteristics. As mentioned previously, any oscillator can be considered in terms of a resonant circuit and a negative resistance. Using the above concepts, we can now show how a negative resistance is obtained at the input of certain transistor connections.

Let us consider the input characteristic of a point contact transistor to which an R_B has been added in series with the base. Remembering that the grounded-base connection has no phase shift, it can quickly be shown that the presence of R_B represents a *positive feedback* element. Hence this tends to make the circuit unstable, which is exactly what we wish for an oscillator. Also, we remember that the magnitude of h_{21} (or α) of the point contact type is always greater than 1.

If we now find the input characteristics, by the method of the previous section, we will find the characteristic as shown in Figure 14-5. Here we see that in region II, or the active region, *the slope of the curve is negative.* This means that a-c wise a negative resistance is exhibited. The d-c resistance, for any value of voltage and current, is given by the slope of the line through the origin to that point. The a-c resistance, on the other hand, is given by the slope of a line tangent to the characteristic.

It is useful to explain why the particular characteristic of Figure 14-5 results with the connection shown. First of all, in region I the emitter (and collector) junction is reversed-biased, and hence the high positive resistance occurs. In region II, where the transistor is in the amplifying region, the resistance R_B acts as an element that produces positive feedback. Thus when an increment of emitter current is applied, the resulting increment of collector current causes a

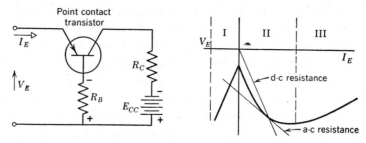

Fig. 14-5. Input characteristic showing negative resistance region for a point contact transistor.

voltage to appear across R_B in the direction shown in Figure 14-5. However, this voltage is in the direction to cause still a further increase in the emitter current, etc.; hence the positive feedback. Although many circuits utilize positive feedback, they are not necessarily unstable (exhibiting a negative resistance) as is the case here. The important factor that causes the negative resistance is that *the increment in collector current is greater than the original increment in applied emitter current*—since the h_{21} is greater than 1 for the point contact transistor. It is this situation, then, that makes the point contact transistor a unique item for any circuits that require a negative resistance characteristic. A single unit junction transistor, for instance, will not exhibit such a negative resistance property since its h_{21} is always slightly less than 1. We can, however, obtain an effective negative resistance characteristic with a single unit junction transistor by using external positive feedback, as shall be seen later. If we sought to have a negative resistance looking in at two terminals, as in Figure 14-5, with a

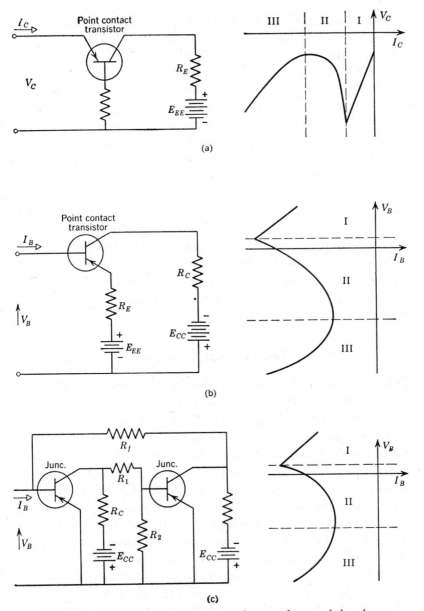

Fig. 14-6. Circuits and the negative resistance characteristics given at the input terminals: (a) input characteristic at the collector terminals of a point contact transistor; (b) input characteristic at the base terminals of a point contact transistor; (c) input characteristic of two junction transistors, d-c coupled and with positive feedback.

junction transistor, we would need two junction transistors that were d-c coupled in a manner to provide positive feedback.

It was mentioned previously that a negative resistance can be acquired looking into the various terminals of the point contact transistor. These additional characteristics and the one using two junction transistors are shown in Figure 14-6. Note that the characteristic for the collector input case is similar to that for the emitter case treated previously, except that the regions have been transposed— region III now appears on the left and region I on the right.

For the base input characteristics, however, we note that the curve appears to be rotated 90° from the two previous cases. This is an important difference from the emitter and the collector input cases. We shall see the meaning of this in the next section. Part (c) of Figure 14-6 shows the negative input characteristic obtained when two junction transistors are d-c coupled and positive feedback (R_1) is applied. It is remembered that since the junction transistor has an h_{21} slightly less than 1, two units are required to obtain an isolated negative characteristic.

Two-Terminal Oscillators

We now proceed to consider the simplest type of oscillator, the two-terminal type. This is effected simply by joining a resonant circuit (frequency-determining circuit) to the negative resistance characteristics, obtained in the previous section. We are calling this type the two-terminal negative resistance oscillators since the negative resistance part of the circuit can be separated from the frequency-determining circuit. This is not true for the feedback type of oscillator.

To make an oscillator, then, we need to connect either a series or a parallel resonant circuit to the input terminals of any of the circuits of Figure 14-5 or 14-6. Also, we must connect a battery and a load line to these input terminals in order to establish the d-c operating point. (This can be done by other means, but we shall consider the basic case here.) In fact, just as for the case of the amplifier, it is profitable to separate the d-c and the a-c problems. We will consider the d-c problem first.

To form an oscillator we want the d-c operating point to *appear in the negative resistance region of the input characteristic*. In addition, this d-c operating point must be *stable*. In other words, although the entire circuit represents an unstable condition, the point about which the operation oscillates must itself be stable or the output will indeed be very erratic. The d-c load line, then, must be such as to obtain operation in the negative resistance region and must provide a stable operating point in this region.

The condition on the a-c load, the frequency-determining network, is that the resonance shall appear at the desired frequency, and also that the impedance of the resonant circuit shall not load the d-c condition so as to move the operating point out of the negative resistance region.

We can now apply these considerations to the negative resistance characteristics of the previous section. For the emitter-input point contact case we need a d-c load line as shown in Figure 14-7. To be

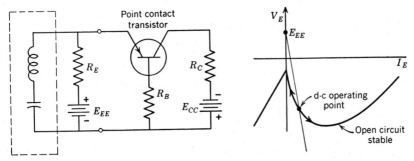

Fig. 14-7. Circuit and graphical picture of an oscillator utilizing the emitter-input of a point contact transistor.

d-c stable, the load line must be more vertical than the negative resistance characteristic. This means that the d-c load resistance is *greater* than the magnitude of the negative resistance.

Since this is the requirement for this circuit, any circuit exhibiting a characteristic similar to that in Figure 14-7 is termed *open-circuit stable*. This means that a d-c load impedance that is high (in the limit, an open circuit) results in a stable operating point.

In Figure 14-7, a series resonant circuit is used as the a-c load, or the frequency-determining circuit. A series rather than a parallel tank is chosen because the impedance of this is very low at resonance. If a parallel tank were used the impedance at resonance would be extremely high and this would mean that the R_E would load down the a-c load, and hence absorb much of the a-c power.

We can now gain some insight into how an oscillator operates. Assume first that the oscillations have begun. Then the current (I_E)

is periodically varying as a sine wave. This would normally damp out due to the inevitable resistance of the coil. However, the transistor input terminals exhibit an a-c negative resistance; this means that if the current increases slightly, the transistor makes it increase still more. Thus pictorially we can consider the transistor operation as proceeding back and forth along the input characteristic, about the d-c operating point. Although the d-c conditions are stable, the a-c conditions are definitely unstable and represent oscillations.

We can see how the *amplitude* of the oscillations is governed in this type of oscillator. As the amplitude of swing increases, the positive resistance region will eventually be reached. When the operation swings into the region where the negative resistance no longer balances out the coil resistance the amplitude rise will be stopped. This is the reason for labeling the oscillator a nonlinear circuit. It is the non-linearities that limit the amplitude of oscillation.

In a sense we can regard this type of oscillator as a circuit that has a stable operating point but which is never allowed to stay at this operating point because of the unstable a-c conditions effective in this region. It is in this way that the very simple representation of Figure 14-1 is achieved.

The frequency of oscillation of this type of circuit will be given approximately by the resonant frequency of the coil and capacitor combination.

We can now summarize the oscillators that can be built from the other input characteristics of Figure 14-5. They are shown in Figure 14-8. For the collector input case the characteristic is again open-circuit stable; hence again the R_C must be greater than the magnitude of the negative resistance and hence more vertical to obtain a stable d-c operating point. For the base-input case we have a different situation. The characteristic here represents a *short-circuit stable* circuit. This means that the d-c load line must be very low (in the limit a short circuit) to provide a stable d-c operating point.

Since both the open-circuit stable and the short-circuit stable characteristics look similar in the negative resistance region, it is useful to notice how we can distinguish them in any situation. The clue is to notice what resistance occurs in the transition between the positive and the negative resistance regions:

1. In the open-circuit stable case the resistance goes through zero; this can be seen by drawing a tangent line to the characteristic at the transition region.

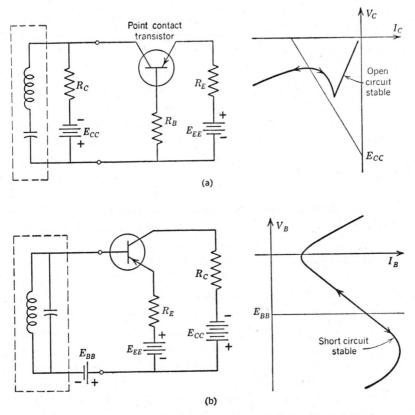

Fig. 14-8. Oscillators that can be formed with point contact transistors: (a) oscillator utilizing collector-input characteristic; (b) oscillator utilizing base-input characteristic.

2. In the short-circuit stable case the resistance goes through infinity. Using this criterion, then, we can always specify which characteristic we have.

To return to the base-input case of Figure 14-8, then, we note that we need a very low d-c load resistance in order to obtain a stable operating point. As seen in the figure, the load resistance used is practically zero since only the d-c resistance of the coil is used for the load. This then specifies that a parallel resonant circuit must be used as the frequency-determining element. Consider the alternatives a minute: if a battery and low resistance were placed in parallel with a series resonant circuit, the low resistance of the battery circuit would absorb much of the a-c power during oscillation; and if a parallel circuit were placed in parallel with the battery, the coil would be practically a direct short circuit on the battery. With these two considerations it can be seen that the arrangement shown in Figure 14-8 is the necessary one.

It will be noted that we have not shown an oscillator that utilizes the characteristic of Figure 14-6(c). This is because it is not profitable to construct the two-terminal type of oscillator with junction transistors since two units are required. If junction transistors are used, the feedback oscillator, to be discussed in the next section, is more practicable. The junction characteristic was presented formerly to indicate that a negative resistance can be achieved in this way.

Mathematical analysis of isolated oscillator. Having gained some insight into how an oscillator works in general, we proceed to considering the appropriate mathematical analysis.

The mathematical analysis implied here refers only to the *linear* considerations of the circuits. Any nonlinear calculations are quite involved, and we shall certainly not consider this here. Nevertheless, we remember that the amplitude of oscillations depends upon the fact that the input characteristic is nonlinear. It is so nonlinear, in fact, that it changes from a region of positive to a region of negative resistance. In spite of the limitation of not being able to predict the amplitude of oscillation from a linear analysis, we can predict the frequency and the circuit conditions necessary for oscillation. We proceed then to the analysis that involves only the linear considerations.

The general analysis of oscillators is based upon the ordinary mesh (or nodal) equation used throughout this book. For a circuit to be in a state of stable oscillation, it is required, mathematically, that the solutions to the mesh equations be *indeterminate*. This means that if the solution involves both a numerator and a denominator, they both equal zero (zero over zero is an indeterminate solution). Now, consider the case when we write a set of mesh equations. To solve them for any of the currents we obtain essentially one determinant as the numerator and one determinant as the denominator. Now the numerator of the determinant will automatically be zero since the oscillator is a completely closed loop situation; all the mesh voltages will total to zero.

The criterion remaining then is that the denominator determinant be zero. However, the denominator consists of the determinant of the circuit impedances; hence the linear criterion for any oscillator is that *the determinant of the mesh equations be equal to zero.*

This determinant, if expanded, will contain both a resistive and a reactive part, since every oscillator contains reactive elements. To extract the necessary information we separate the resistive and the reactive part. Then by setting the resistive part of the determinant equal to zero we find the necessary condition for oscillation, i.e., the necessary conditions to obtain a negative resistance region. Further,

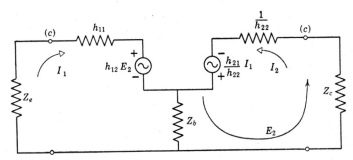

Fig. 14-9. General linear equivalent circuit of a two-terminal oscillator.

by setting the reactive part equal to zero, we can find the frequency at which the circuit will oscillate.

For the circuits treated thus far, this last part is trivial since we already know the approximate oscillation frequency from the resonant circuit. However, this maneuver is perfectly general and we shall find in the next section that this procedure may be necessary to find the frequency.

The circuit determinant for all three of the isolated oscillators can be written generally. We first write the general mesh equations based upon the equivalent circuit in Figure 14-9. Note that in the equivalent circuit of the transistor we have used Thevenin's theorem on the output side to obtain a voltage generator. The Z_e, Z_b, and Z_c represent the entire external impedances that appear at the respective terminals. The two mesh equations are

$$I_1(Z_e + Z_b + h_{11}) + I_2(Z_b) = -h_{12}E_2$$

$$I_1(Z_b) + I_2\left(Z_b + \frac{1}{h_{22}} + Z_c\right) = +\frac{h_{21}}{h_{22}}I_1 \tag{1}$$

where E_2 = voltage across output of transistor (shown in the diagram).

Using the fact that E_2 is found to be

$$E_2 = -I_2 Z_c - (I_1 + I_2) Z_b \tag{2}$$

the equations can be written

$$I_1(Z_e + Z_b + h_{11} - h_{12}Z_b) + I_2(Z_b - h_{12}Z_c - h_{12}Z_b) = 0$$

$$I_1\left(Z_b - \frac{h_{21}}{h_{22}}\right) + I_2\left(Z_b + \frac{1}{h_{22}} + Z_c\right) = 0 \tag{3}$$

The determinant for these two equations, after expansion, is

$$\Delta \equiv M\, Z_e Z_b + Z_e \frac{1}{h_{22}} + Z_e Z_c + \frac{Z_b(1 - h_{12})}{h_{22}} + Z_c Z_b + h_{11}Z_b$$

$$+ \frac{h_{11}}{h_{22}} + h_{11}Z_c + Z_b(1 - h_{12})\frac{h_{21}}{h_{22}} - \frac{h_{12}h_{21}}{h_{22}} Z_c = 0 \tag{4}$$

Using the fact that

$$h_{22} \ll 1, \qquad h_{11} \ll \frac{1}{h_{22}} \tag{5}$$

the determinant simplifies to

$$\Delta \approx Z_e Z_b + Z_e \frac{1}{h_{22}} + Z_e Z_c + Z_b\left(\frac{1 + h_{21}}{h_{22}}\right) + Z_c Z_b + \frac{h_{11}}{h_{22}}$$

$$+ h_{11}Z_c - \frac{h_{12}h_{21}}{h_{22}} Z_c \lessgtr 0 \tag{6}$$

We can use this equation, then, to find the conditions for oscillation and the frequency for any of the oscillators treated in this section.[2] As an example, let us evaluate the conditions for the emitter-input case, shown in Figure 14-7. Since we want to separate the resistive and reactive parts of Equation (6), we note that only Z_e contains a reactive part for the emitter-input case. Although Z_e consists of R_e in parallel with the series resonant circuit, the R_e is so much larger than the other that we can neglect it; hence the Z_e term will be purely imaginary. Using this fact, we can immediately write the resistive part of Equation (6) by simply deleting all terms containing Z_e. The resistive part is

$$Z_b\left(\frac{1 + h_{21}}{h_{22}}\right) + Z_c Z_b + \frac{h_{11}}{h_{22}} + h_{11}Z_c - \frac{h_{12}h_{21}}{h_{22}} Z_c \lessgtr 0 \tag{7}$$

Equation (7) specifies the relation between the transistor parameters and the other circuit quantities that will permit a negative

---

[2] The h parameters here refer specifically to the grounded-base parameters and not to the h parameters in general.

resistance to be realized. When it is remembered that h_{21} is a negative number, it is seen that the term $h_{21}Z_b/h_{22}$ is the only negative term in this equation. Remember also that for the point contact transistor the h_{21} is greater than 1. Thus it is seen how important the presence of R_B is to make oscillations possible.

To find the frequency, we set the reactive part of Equation (6) to zero. Since Z_e is purely imaginary, the equation is

$$Z_e \left(Z_b + \frac{1}{h_{22}} + Z_c \right) = 0 \tag{8}$$

To fulfill this equation, either of the terms may be set to zero. Since the term in parentheses cannot possibly be zero, we must set $Z_e = 0$. But Z_e is given by

$$Z_e = j\omega L + \frac{1}{j\omega c} = 0$$

$$\omega = \frac{1}{\sqrt{LC}}, \qquad f = \frac{1}{2\pi\sqrt{LC}} \tag{9}$$

Hence we have shown that the frequency is given by the resonant frequency of the tuned circuit, which we knew beforehand, of course.

This, then, is the manner in which the linear considerations of an oscillator are handled. For any oscillator of the type considered in this section, that is, where the negative resistance and the frequency-determining portion of the circuit can be separated, Equation (6) may be used.

It should also be noted that the h-parameters, used for all cases, are the *grounded-base parameters*. Since the general equation was derived by using these parameters, they must always be used if Equation (6) is to apply.

In general, we see from Equation (7) that a high R_B and a low R_C are the conditions conducive to oscillation.

Feedback Oscillators

As mentioned in the beginning sections, oscillators can be considered both as negative resistance circuits and as positive feedback circuits. It is felt by the authors that the negative resistance viewpoint is the more general and the more profitable intuitively, and hence the oscillator in general was presented in this light.

Nevertheless, there are two basic types of oscillators: (1) those in which the negative resistance portion can be considered separately from the frequency-determining portion, and (2) those in which the negative resistance is formed partly by the frequency network, and hence the two cannot be separated for analysis. Whereas we consider the first type in the preceding section, we now turn to the second type.

Even though both types involve feedback, it has been the practice in the past to label this inseparable type the *feedback oscillator.*

The feedback oscillator differs from the two-terminal type in that *any amplifying device can be made into an oscillator.* By this it is meant that the criterion of $h_{21} > 1$ is no longer necessary. Hence a single

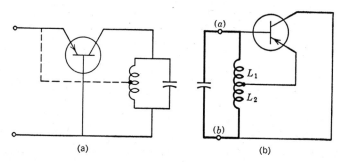

(a)   (b)

Fig. 14-10. The a-c equivalent of a Hartley oscillator: (a) an amplifier with feedback; (b) the Hartley circuit.

unit junction transistor can be used in a feedback oscillator (and usually is). The fact that single-unit junction transistors can be used for this type of oscillator means that transistor feedback oscillators are very similar to vacuum tube oscillators.

An additional fact concerning the feedback oscillators is that they usually follow one of two basic patterns, the Hartley and the Colpitts circuits, which are familiar to the vacuum tube field. We will treat only these two basic circuits, since other feedback oscillators are more or less variations on the same theme.

The basic Hartley circuit, without the biasing network, is shown in Figure 14-10(b). We have left the bias circuitry out at first to emphasize the a-c oscillating action; the entire circuit will be pictured later. In order to gain some concept of how the feedback oscillators perform, consider for a minute the circuit of Figure 14-10(a). As seen, the circuit consists essentially of a grounded-base amplifier having a tuned collector load. If we now consider driving this circuit with a source at a varying frequency, it is clear that we will obtain a maximum amplification only at the resonant frequency of the tuned circuit. As a matter of fact, the amplification on either side of this frequency will drop off sharply if the circuit has a high Q; this is simply because the effective load impedance drops to a low value at frequencies different from resonance. It should be noted that we are considering a junction transistor here; although the current gain is less than 1, there is a substantial voltage and power gain (Chapter 8).

Consider now that we connect a lead as shown by the dashed line in (a). We first note that the current fed back to the input is in *phase* with the input driving current. Since the phase is proper, it can be seen that if the amplification is sufficient, the power fed back to the input may be *equal* to the power being supplied by the external source. If this is the case, we can consider the circuit to be *supplying itself*, and of course this represents an oscillator. The basic idea here is that we have essentially an amplifier that is providing its own input. The actual source of power then comes from the bias battery; the circuit acts as a converter in that it converts d-c power from the bias battery into a-c power of a sine wave shape.

The two conditions to be fulfilled for an amplifier of this type are: (1) that the *amplitude* of current fed back to the input be the correct value to obtain the corresponding output, and (2) the *phase* of the fed-back current be in phase with the output, hence giving positive feedback.

The Hartley oscillator of Figure 14-10(b) is exactly the type of circuit we have described. Part (b) of the figure is obtained by merely rearranging the diagram. For feedback oscillators in general, it is profitable always to emphasize the tank circuit; for this reason the heavy lines are used in part (b) to emphasize this part of the circuit.

It should be noted that, although we have used a feedback description here, any feedback oscillator can be described in terms of a negative resistance property, as was used for the two-terminal devices previously. The essential difference here is that the circuit *cannot be separated into its negative resistance portion and its tank circuit*. The reason for this is that the tank circuit is required to form the negative resistance condition. This can be stated by saying that the negative resistance occurs in the *dynamic* characteristic of the circuit, rather than in the static characteristic as before.

Nevertheless, it is still useful to note that an effective negative resistance occurs across the tank circuit when the circuit is oscillating.

Hence in Figure 14-10(b) a negative resistance occurs across the points a-b.

The mathematical analysis of the feedback oscillators is identical in principle to that of the two-terminal type discussed previously. Again, a linear analysis specifies the frequency and the circuit conditions necessary for oscillation, but gives no information about the amplitude.

The linear analysis, then, consists of setting the resistive part of the circuit determinant to zero to find the circuit requirements, and setting the reactive part to zero to find the frequency. The determinant will be somewhat more complicated than for the previous case

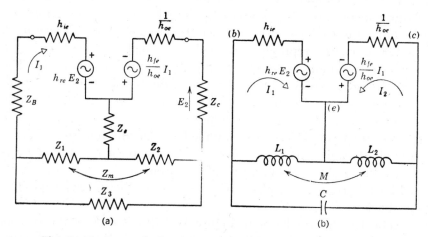

Fig. 14-11. A-c equivalent circuits of feedback oscillators: (a) the general equivalent circuit; (b) the Hartley circuit.

because we now have three mesh equations instead of two, and because we may have to deal with mutual impedances between inductors (as in the Hartley case). Because of this we will not solve for a general result, as previously, but will treat each case separately. Although we treat only the Hartley and the Colpitts oscillators here, the student may readily adapt the procedure to any feedback oscillator.

In order to achieve some uniformity in writing the mesh equations (to find the determinant) it is profitable to always consider the feedback oscillator in terms of the general circuit of Figure 14-11(a). Note that here the *grounded-emitter parameters* are used since the transistor is connected in the grounded-emitter manner. The terms Z_1, Z_2, and

Z_3 are the components of the resonant circuit, and the Z_m represents the mutual impedance between Z_1 and Z_2 (if any). In the case of the Hartley oscillator this Z_m is the mutual impedance between L_1 and L_2. Also, this general circuit contains the terms Z_b, Z_e, and Z_c. In many oscillators these impedances are frequency-stabilizing elements, but they shall be considered zero for our cases. Figure 14-11(b) shows the linear equivalent circuit of the Hartley oscillator.

To find the determinant for this Hartley oscillator, we first write the three mesh equations. They are

$$I_1(h_{ie} + jX_{L_1}) + I_2(-jX_M) + I_3(-jX_{L_1} - jX_M) = -h_{re}E_2$$

$$I_1(-jX_M) + I_2\left(\frac{1}{h_{oe}} + jX_{L_2}\right) + I_3(jX_{L_2} + jX_M) = +\frac{h_{fe}}{h_{oe}}I_1 \quad (10)$$

$$I_1(-jX_{L_1} - jX_M) + I_2(jX_{L_2} + jX_M)$$
$$+ I_3(jX_{L_1} + jX_{L_2} - jX_C + 2jX_M) = 0$$

Using the fact that E_2 is equal to $I_2/h_{oe} - h_{fe}I_1/h_{oe}$, the equations can be written

$$I_1\left(h_{ie} + jX_{L_1} - \frac{h_{re}h_{fe}}{h_{oe}}\right) + I_2\left(\frac{h_{re}}{h_{oe}} - jX_M\right) + I_3(-jX_{L_1} - jX_M) = 0$$

$$I_1\left(-jX_M - \frac{h_{fe}}{h_{oe}}\right) + I_2\left(\frac{1}{h_{oe}} + jX_{L_2}\right) + I_3(jX_{L_2} + jX_M) = 0 \quad (11)$$

$$I_1(-jX_{L_1} - iX_M) + I_2(jX_{L_2} + jX_M)$$
$$+ I_3(jX_{L_1} + jX_{L_2} - jX_C + 2jX_M) = 0$$

Since the determinant of these equations is extremely complex, we look for any simplifications. It may be noted that, at the resonant frequency, the series reactance of the tank circuit is practically zero (this assumes that the frequency of oscillations is close to the resonant frequency). With this approximation, the coefficient of I_3 in the third equation is zero. The resulting determinant then is

$$\Delta = \left(\frac{h_{re}}{h_{oe}} - jX_M\right)(jX_{L_2} + jX_M)(-jX_{L_1} - jX_M)$$
$$+ (-jX_{L_1} - jX_M)\left(-jX_M - \frac{h_{fe}}{h_{oe}}\right)(jX_{L_2} + jX_M)$$
$$- (-jX_{L_1} - jX_M)\left(\frac{1}{h_{oe}} + jX_{L_2}\right)(-jX_{L_1} - jX_M) \quad (12)$$
$$- (jX_{L_2} + jX_M)(jX_{L_2} + jX_M)\left(h_{ie} + jX_{L_1} - \frac{h_{re}h_{fe}}{h_{oe}}\right)$$

Solving for the real part of this equation, the result is

$$0 = \left(\frac{h_{re}}{h_{oe}} - \frac{h_{fe}}{h_{oe}}\right)(X_{L_1} + X_M)(X_{L_2} + X_M) + \frac{1}{h_{oe}}(X_{L_1} + X_M)^2$$
$$+ \left(h_{ie} - \frac{h_{re}h_{fe}}{h_{oe}}\right)(X_{L_2} + X_M)^2 \tag{13}$$

In this equation we solve for h_{fe}, using the fact that h_{re} is very much less than h_{fe}; the final result is

$$h_{fe} \gtreqless \left(\frac{X_{L_1} + X_M}{X_{L_2} + X_M}\right) + \Delta^{h\bullet}\left(\frac{X_{L_2} + X_M}{X_{L_1} + X_M}\right) \quad \text{or}$$
$$h_{fe} \gtreqless \left(\frac{L_1 + M}{L_2 + M}\right) + \Delta^{h\bullet}\left(\frac{L_2 + M}{L_1 + M}\right) \tag{14}$$

Equation (14) then gives the relation between the circuit components and the transistor parameters that are required if the circuit is to function as an oscillator. This equation can be reduced by regarding either ratio on the right side as a variable and solving the resulting quadratic equation. Using the fact that $h_{fe}^2 \ll 4\Delta^{h\bullet}$, the result is:

$$\frac{L_2 + M}{L_1 + M} < \frac{h_{fe}}{\Delta^{h\bullet}} \tag{15}$$

This is the result then of equating the resistive part of the determinant to zero; it states the circuit conditions necessary to cause oscillation for the Hartley circuit.

To find the frequency of oscillation we need to set the reactive part of the determinant to zero. Using Equation (12) the reactive part is found to be:

$$(X_C X_{L_2} X_{L_1} - X_C X_M^2) + \frac{h_{oe}}{h_{ie}}(X_{L_1} + X_{L_2} - X_C + 2X_M) = 0 \tag{16}$$

Solving this relation for frequency, the result is:

$$f = \frac{1}{2\pi\sqrt{C(L_1 + L_2 + 2M) + \frac{h_{oe}}{h_{ie}}(L_1 L_2 - M^2)}} \tag{17}$$

Figure 14-12 shows the complete Hartley oscillator with its bias circuitry. The resistor R_B is connected from collector to base in order to achieve a proper d-c bias on the base (the emitter is grounded). A proper bias point may be considered as being the center of the active region (on the collector characteristics) when the d-c load line corre-

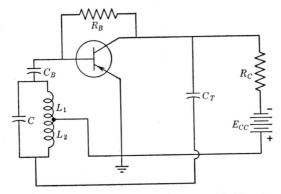

Fig. 14-12. The Hartley oscillator complete with bias circuitry.

sponding to V_{CC} and R_C is constructed. It is evident that the capacitor C_B is necessary to block the direct current from base to emitter, since otherwise they would be d-c short-circuited through the inductor winding. Likewise C_T prevents the collector from being d-c short-circuited to ground through the L_2 winding.

The addition of these components, if properly designed, will not influence the a-c analysis shown previously. The components simply provide the proper d-c operating point to the circuit.

The other basic type of feedback oscillator is the Colpitts, and its a-c circuitry is shown in Figure 14-13. As seen, the operation is very similar to the previous case except that now the capacitance is split to provide the necessary feedback, rather than the inductance. Its physical operation can

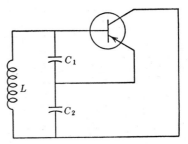

Fig. 14-13. A-c circuit for the Colpitts oscillator.

be described in a completely analogous way to that of the Hartley. If the three mesh equations are written for this circuit, and the resistive part of the determinant set equal to zero, it is found that the necessary condition for oscillation is

$$\frac{C_1}{C_2} \gtreqless \frac{h_{fe}}{\Delta^{h_\bullet}} \qquad (15)$$

It is left as an exercise for the student to show this in a manner identical to that used to find Equation (14).

General Considerations

We have found that every oscillator can be pictured in terms of a frequency-determining circuit in conjunction with a negative resistance. The unique function of the negative resistance is to compensate for the inevitable losses in the resonant circuit. In the two-terminal type of oscillator the negative resistance is available at two terminals, and the characteristic can be found with the resonant circuit disconnected. In the feedback type of oscillator the negative resistance is an integral part of the entire circuit, and hence this negative characteristic cannot be obtained separately. The resonant circuit itself is necessary to provide the negative resistance.

The linear analysis of both types of oscillators is identical. It consists of setting the resistive and the reactive parts of the circuit determinant to zero, as exhibited previously. From this linear analysis the relationship between the pertinent circuit components and the transistor parameters can be determined. If these conditions are not fulfilled, the circuit will not oscillate.

To predict the amplitude of oscillation would require a complicated nonlinear analysis. In many applications specific additional circuitry is incorporated to limit the amplitude to a known value. Usually this circuitry is an application of diodes, and the reader is referred to any standard handbook for specific circuits.

Another topic very pertinent to oscillators is the matter of frequency stability. The linear analysis illustrated previously assumed (1) the parameters of the transistor are resistive, and (2) the effective negative resistance characteristic is linear. The first is always a good approximation at low frequencies, but the second is never really true. For this reason the frequency of an oscillator may change with age, bias variations, etc., unless special circuitry is used. As mentioned earlier, inserting reactances in series with the transistor leads is a common way of stabilizing feedback oscillators.

Multivibrators

As mentioned in the introduction, we can regard the multivibrator as the nonsinusoidal equivalent of the oscillator. It is appropriately included with the topic of oscillators since an oscillator can often be made into a multivibrator by replacing the resonant circuit with a single energy-storage element (L or C).

As in the case of the oscillator, a negative-resistance characteristic is essential to the operation of a multivibrator. Hence we can make a multivibrator from any of the negative resistance circuits shown in Figures 14-5 and 14-6.

As an example, let us consider a multivibrator formed from the negative resistance characteristic of Figure 14-5. We will replace the resonant circuit by a single capacitor and note the action. The resulting circuit is shown in Figure 14-14.

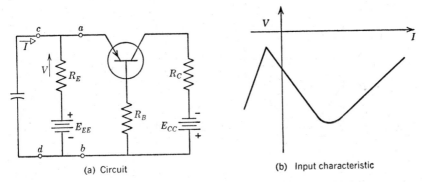

(a) Circuit   (b) Input characteristic

Fig. 14-14. A basic negative-resistance multivibrator: (a) circuit; (b) input characteristic.

In order to depict the operation of such a circuit, we first note that we cannot expect the action to shift smoothly about a d-c operating point, as in the oscillator. We are not interested, then, in constructing a d-c load on the $V_E - I_E$ input characteristic. Rather we are interested in noting the total characteristic that the capacitor faces. Because of this, we view the circuit in Figure 14-14 at points c-d, rather than that at a-b as before. In other words, we investigate the input characteristic, not at V_E versus I_E, but at V_E versus I_E plus the battery-resistor current. It is easy to verify that the input characteristic of Figure 14-5 will be shifted to the left as shown above. Also, no d-c load line can appear on this graph since we have already included the bias current.

The essential action now is that the operation moves about the characteristic in such a fashion that the capacitor alternately charges and discharges. Assume first that the operation is at point B in Figure

14-15. This point corresponds to a positive initial voltage on the capacitor. At point B the transistor is in saturation (region III) and hence the capacitor faces R_E in parallel with the saturation input resistance (relatively low) of the transistor. The capacitor then discharges through these two resistances and follows the characteristic as shown by the arrows. At point C the operation jumps from the saturation region to the cutoff region at D. The reason for this jump is that the voltage across a capacitor cannot change instantaneously, whereas the current changes abruptly. At D, since the current is negative, the capacitor begins to charge again and its voltage increases along the characteristic. Note that the charging is slower than the discharge

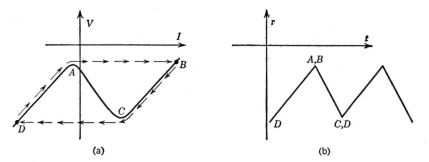

Fig. 14-15. Graphical description of multivibration action: (a) path of operation on input characteristic; (b) resulting waveform at input.

because the charging is via the high-resistance input of the transistor in the cutoff region. When A is reached the operation again experiences a jump to B.

In this manner, then, the multivibrating action is effected. The resulting capacitor voltage versus time is shown in Figure 14-15(b).

Note that now we cannot analyze the circuit by writing a circuit determinant, since we are not dealing with sine waves. An analysis of a nonsinusoidal operation, such as that of the multivibrator, requires finding the transient solution in each of the two regions of operation. With such a transient analysis the time spent in each portion of the waveform and the amplitude of the waveform can be calculated.

We have just seen that a multivibrator and a two-terminal oscillator are very similar in requirements and in physical operation, but differ greatly in mathematical analysis. We may note that there is no multivibrator equivalent to a feedback oscillator. In other words, a separable negative resistance characteristic is required. This means that either a point contact transistor, where the h_{21} is greater than 1, or two junction transistors are required. The process of using a reactive element to form a dynamic negative resistance, as in the feedback oscillator, is not possible for the multivibrator.

Analytical Expressions for the Transistor

We have seen in the previous sections how the cutoff and the saturation regions are important to the operation of many transistor circuits. Although we have performed no quantitative calculations in these regions, it is interesting to note how such calculations would be done.

Since the transistor graphical characteristics depict the operation of the transistor in all three regions of operation (see Chapter 7) we might expect that any calculations in either the saturation or the cutoff regions would have to be done with the use of these characteristics. The difficulty, however, is that the characteristics are usually not accurate in the saturation and the cutoff regions. For example, if we wish to read a V_{CE} from a set of collector curves for an I_B in the saturation region, the reader will quickly agree (see Figure 7-7) that it is practically impossible to achieve an accurate result. To remedy this situation one could always provide a number of detailed sets of characteristics.

A more reasonable solution, however, is to find a set of mathematical expressions which give the operation in any of the three regions. Such a set of equations was published by Ebers and Moll in December, 1954 (*Proc. I.R.E.*, page 1761). In essence these equations enable us to find the expressions for the entire set of characteristics; hence they describe the action of the transistor in all three regions.

As already mentioned, these equations have great practical value, among other uses, in finding the operating conditions in the saturation and the cutoff regions. Although the topics covered in this book do not require accurate calculations in these regions, such calculations are required in dealing with pulse circuits. In fact, two major items in pulse circuit analysis and design are the transient response of the circuit and the fixing of the stable states; many times the stable states occur in either the saturation or the cutoff region.

For the reasons given we are not interested here in a detailed study of the Ebers-Moll equations. Rather, we are interested only in mentioning their existence and referring the reader to the original source (or text on transistor pulse circuits) for a complete treatment. We are, however, interested in specifying what these equations say, and how this relates to the material that we have covered.

In Chapter 7 it was stressed that the graphical characteristics depict the operation in its entirety whereas the equivalent circuit is accurate only for a small region about a given bias point. When we have the equivalent circuit, of course, we also have mathematical expressions for the given region. It is also true that the a-c equivalent circuit always lies in the *active* region; i.e., the region where the transistor acts as an amplifier. It will be remembered that the a-c equivalent circuit (with h parameters) was used for the small signal amplifiers, feedback, noise, and for the linear analysis of oscillators and multivibrators.

The Ebers-Moll equations represent an alternative, in a sense, to the use of the characteristics. They, too, deal with the operation of the transistor in all three regions. In fact, the transistor characteristics can be derived from the use of the Ebers-Moll equations. Also, since the mathematical expressions do exist, we have available, in effect, an equivalent circuit of the transistor which is valid in all regions. Since such an equivalent circuit is nonlinear it is of little practical value except in some special cases, and it certainly does not supplant the a-c linear equivalent circuit that we have dealt with.

Although the Ebers-Moll equations give the same sort of information as the characteristics, it should not be construed that they replace these characteristics; it would be very tedious and impractical to use these equations for every purpose to which the characteristics have been put. In the saturation and the cutoff regions, however, these equations do have significant practical value as noted before.

In using the Ebers-Moll equations the essential idea is to measure certain quantities of the transistor and then insert these measured values into the given expressions. If any two of the four variables (2 currents and 2 voltages) are given, the remaining two may then be found by the use of the expressions.

Without any derivation, the Ebers-Moll equations are shown in equation (19). In this form the unknown currents are written in terms of the unknown voltages. All quantities in these two equations should be regarded as measured constants except V_E, V_C, I_C and I_E.

$$I_E = \frac{I_{E0}}{1 - \alpha_N \alpha_I}(e^{\,qV_E/kT} - 1) - \frac{\alpha_N I_{E0}}{1 - \alpha_N \alpha_I}(e^{\,qV_C/kT} - 1)$$

$$I_C = \frac{\alpha_I I_{C0}}{1 - \alpha_N \alpha_I}(e^{\,qV_E/kT} - 1) + \frac{I_{C0}}{1 - \alpha_N \alpha_I}(e^{\,qV_C/kT} - 1)$$

(19)

where V_E = voltage across emitter-base junction,

V_C = voltage across collector-base junction,

I_{E0} = emitter current when collector current is zero and with emitter junction reverse-biased,

I_{C0} = collector current when emitter current is zero and with collector junction reverse-biased,

α_N = normal transistor current gain, corresponding to $-h_{21}$,

α_I = inverse transistor current gain; the equivalent of $-h_{21}$ if the emitter is made to serve as a collector and vice versa.

The reader is warned that the voltages appearing in Equation (19) refer only to the junction itself, and not to terminal-to-terminal. This means that the bulk resistance of the three regions must be taken into account; usually only the base resistance need be considered.

Given all the measured quantities and two of the unknown variables, then, these equations can be used to find the remaining two variables. Note that this can be done for all three regions of transistor operation.

These are the equations, then, that enable us to accurately find the d-c conditions in the saturation and the cutoff region. As noted, this is especially important when dealing with pulse circuits. Since the objective here was only to call attention to their existence, the reader is referred to the sources mentioned earlier for complete information.

Problems

1. In the circuit of Figure 14-16 the capacitor C is large enough to short-circuit the resistor R_E effectively at the oscillating frequency. Determine the frequency of oscillation and the minimum value of R_B to produce oscillations.

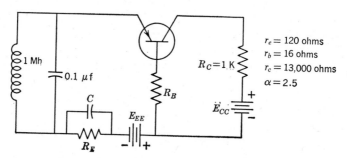

$r_e = 120$ ohms
$r_b = 16$ ohms
$r_c = 13,000$ ohms
$\alpha = 2.5$

Fig. 14-16. Point contact negative resistance oscillator.

2. What value of R_B would be required in Problem 1 if (1) $R_C = 10,000$ ohms; (2) $R_C = 100,000$ ohms; (3) $h_{12} = 10^{-2}$, and the other values remained as in Problem 1?

3. Using the T.I.-300 characteristics given in Appendix III determine whether the circuit shown in Figure 14-17 will oscillate.

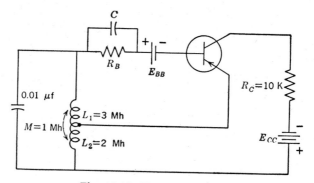

Fig. 14-17. Hartley oscillator.

4. Would this oscillator operate if $L_1 = 100$ mh, $L_2 = 1$ mh, and $M = 4$ mh?

5. In Problem 4 what value of M will cause the oscillator to operate correctly if it does not with the value of M given?

15

Transistor Experiments

The serious student of transistor circuits will want to check the results of his efforts of design in the laboratory. This chapter is included to guide the student toward this goal.

The experiments presented here cover the range from basic static characteristics through simple applied circuits. Where practicable, the design of the circuit to be tested is left up to the student and only the measuring techniques are outlined.

The list of necessary equipment to perform these experiments is as follows:

Resistors:
Assorted, should include the following:

100 ohm $\frac{1}{2}$ watt	1
1000 ohm $\frac{1}{2}$ watt	1
1000 ohm 1 watt	1
5000 ohm 3 watt	1
10,000 ohm $\frac{1}{2}$ watt	2
22,000 ohm $\frac{1}{2}$ watt	1
100,000 ohm $\frac{1}{2}$ watt	1
330,000 ohm $\frac{1}{2}$ watt	1

Capacitors:
Assorted, should include the following:

25 μf 25 v	1
0.05 μf	1
0.02 μf	1
0.01 μf	1
1000 $\mu\mu$f	1

350 $\mu\mu f$	1
45–380 $\mu\mu f$	1
Potentiometers:	
15,000 ohm 2 watt	1
25,000 ohm 2 watt	1
1 megohm 2 watt	1
Transformers:	
1:1 isolation or filament	
transformer	1
Diodes:	
1N64 or equivalent	1
1N34 or equivalent	1
Batteries:	
3 volt	1
15 volt	2
27 volt	1
Transistor sockets, minimum of	3
Inductors:	
Ferri-loop stick	1
1 henry choke	1
1 henry choke, center-tapped	1
radio frequency choke	1
Set of earphones	
2500 ohm 20 volt relay	1
Single-pole single-throw switch	1
Transistors:	
Assorted, should include both N-P-N and P-N-P, with a minimum	
of three of at least one type.	
Thermometer, glass, $\frac{1}{4}$-inch diameter	1
Cork, 1-inch diameter	1
Electric hot plate	1
Supply of crushed ice	
d-c Voltmeter, 20,000 ohms/volt	1
a-c Vacuum tube voltmeter	1
Signal generator	1
Graph paper:	
Cartesian	
Semilog	

The following equipment would be helpful but is not entirely necessary:

oscilloscope	galvanometer for thermocouple
115-volt Variac	supply of dry ice
thermocouple	

Experiment 1. Static Collector Characteristics of a Junction Transistor. The static collector characteristics of a transistor are probably the most important single design tool that an engineer can obtain on transistors. This experiment will describe a method of obtaining these characteristics.

The static characteristics are discussed in Chapter 7. With reference to this material it is seen that the collector family of curves describes the relationship between collector current and voltage for various values of emitter (grounded-base circuit) current, or base (grounded-emitter circuit) current.

The curves can thus be obtained by varying the collector voltage and noting the collector current for various values of emitter or base

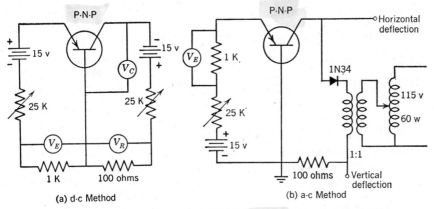

Fig. 15-1. Circuits for obtaining grounded-base static characteristics.

current depending upon whether the grounded-base or grounded-emitter curves are desired.

These curves may be obtained statically or dynamically. In the static method d-c sources are used. In the dynamic method a-c sources are used. Figure 15-1 shows the circuit diagrams for measuring the grounded-base characteristics. The circuits presented in Figure 15-2 show the methods used for the grounded-emitter circuit.

Equipment. The equipment required for this experiment is as follows:
1 transistor, N-P-N or P-N-P
2 25,000 ohm potentiometers
1 1-megohm potentiometer
1 100 ohm resistor, $\frac{1}{2}$ watt
1 1000 ohm resistor, $\frac{1}{2}$ watt
1 1:1 isolation transformer or filament transformer
1 115-volt Variac desirable but not necessary

1 1N34 or other suitable diode
1 5000 ohm resistor, 3 watt
1 1000 ohm resistor, 1 watt
1 50,000 ohm resistor, $\frac{1}{2}$ watt
2 15 volt batteries
1 d-c voltmeter
1 10,000 ohm resistor, $\frac{1}{2}$ watt
1 oscilloscope
1 transistor socket

Procedure. Let us first look at the d-c method of obtaining the static characteristics. The circuit of Figure 15-1(a) or 15-2(a) is connected

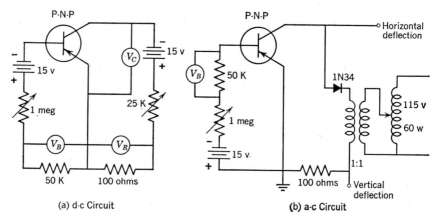

(a) d-c Circuit   (b) a-c Circuit

Fig. 15-2. Circuits for obtaining grounded-emitter static characteristics.

depending upon whether the grounded-base or grounded-emitter characteristics are desired. The collector voltage is read on voltmeter V_C, while the collector current is read by obtaining the voltage across the 100-ohm resistor and then dividing this reading by the resistance value. The emitter current is obtained in a similar manner by reading the voltage across the 1000 ohm resistor in the emitter circuit in the case of Figure 15-1(a), or the 50,000 ohm resistor in the base circuit of Figure 15-2(a).

The voltage across the collector is varied throughout its range for each setting of emitter and base current desired. These values of emitter and base current depend upon the transistor used, but for a 150 mw transistor, typical values are from 0 to 10 ma in 1 ma steps for the grounded-base circuit and from 0 to 200 μa in 20 μa steps in the case of the grounded-emitter circuit.

The circuits of Figures 15-1 and 15-2 are shown for P-N-P transistors.

It is necessary only to reverse the direct voltages and diode polarities if N-P-N transistors are used.

A word of caution here is that the product of collector current and voltage never be allowed to exceed the rating of the transistor being tested.

The circuits of Figures 15-1(b) and 15-2(b) allow the display of the characteristics directly on an oscilloscope.

The emitter or base currents are obtained in the same manner as in the d-c method. The collector voltage varies as a half sine wave, and as a result the collector current varies in a similar manner. These varying voltages are placed upon the horizontal and vertical deflection plates of an oscilloscope, the collector voltage being placed on the horizontal axis and the collector current on the vertical axis. The collector current is actually converted to a voltage via the 100 ohm resistor in the collector circuit. If the scope is calibrated in both horizontal and vertical deflection, the values for the static characteristics may be obtained by readings from the scope or by photographing the display. If a Variac is not available the circuit of Figure 15-3 may be used. The 1000 ohm

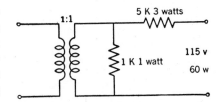

Fig. 15-3. Voltage dividing network for reducing as voltage to collector circuit.

resistor may be varied in value if larger or smaller voltages are desired. A 6.3 volt filament transformer may be used for low voltage devices.

The I_{COB} may be rather small (of the order of microamperes) for low-power units. In order to obtain the I_{COB} curve it might therefore be necessary to replace the 100 ohm resistor in the collector circuit with a 5000–10,000 ohm resistor. It depends upon the transistor whether this will be necessary in obtaining I_{COE}.

Problem. Obtain the static characteristics for an N-P-N or P-N-P transistor. Draw these static curves on Cartesian coordinate paper. Compare your results with those published by the manufacturer, if they are available.

Experiment 2. Bias and Bias Stability. The bias or operating point and the stability of this operating point are very important, especially for devices that must operate over a wide range of temperature. These subjects are covered in Chapters 10 and 11.

In grounded-base circuits the operating point is determined by the values of collector voltage and current along with the emitter current. The best way of stabilizing this type of a circuit is by using a constant-current emitter source. This is usually obtained by placing a large ·value of series resistance in the emitter circuit.

In the grounded-emitter circuit the operating point is determined by the values of the collector voltage and current along with base current. The same method of stabilizing is still used, but more caution must be used in applying it. This is discussed in Chapter 11.

Equipment. The following is the equipment necessary to perform this experiment.

    assorted $\frac{1}{2}$ watt resistors
    1 d-c voltmeter
    3 transistor sockets
    2 15-volt batteries
    1 temperature oven
    1 thermometer or thermocouple
    1 1-inch cork
    1 hot plate
    Source of crushed ice or dry ice
    1 transistor, N-P-N or P-N-P

Procedure. Set up grounded-base and grounded-emitter transistor circuits for any operating point you desire, using the material from Chapters 10 and 11. Check the operating points at room temperature and check the results against your desired operating points.

Design another grounded-emitter circuit with a stability factor of 5 according to the method outlined in Chapter 11. Using the temperature oven described at the end of this experiment, vary the temperature of the transistor connected in the three circuits designed above over a wide range. Do not exceed the maximum dissipation permissible at any given temperature. Record the three currents and voltages that determine your operating point at various temperatures.

Problems. Plot the collector current versus temperature for the three circuits investigated. The collector current for the unstabilized grounded-emitter circuit should vary to a greater extent than that for the grounded-base circuit. In fact, the following relationship should hold:

$$(I_{CB} - I'_{CB}) \frac{1}{1 + h_{fb}} = I_{CE} - I'_{CE} \qquad (1)$$

where I_{CB} = collector current of grounded-base circuit at room temperature,

    I'_{CB} = collector current of grounded-base circuit at elevated temperatures,

    h_{fb} = forward short-circuit current gain of the grounded-base circuit,

I_{CE} = collector current of grounded-emitter circuit at room temperature,

I'_{CE} = collector current of grounded-emitter circuit at elevated temperatures.

The relationship that should hold between the grounded-base circuit and the stabilized grounded-emitter circuit is

$$(I_{CB} - I'_{CB})S = I_{CE} - I'_{CE} \qquad (2)$$

where S = stability factor

The stability factor in the case under investigation is 5.

Temperature Oven. In Figure 15-4 is shown a simple temperature oven which is made from any easily worked material such as aluminum.

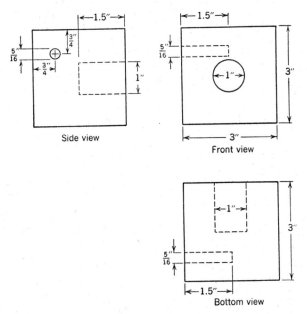

Fig. 15-4. Simple temperature oven.

The dimensions are not critical except that the $\frac{5}{16}$-inch hole should be large enough to accept a thermometer easily. If a thermocouple is used to obtain the temperature, this hole is not necessary.

The transistor socket is placed on the small end of a 1-inch cork with leads pushed through the cork to come out the large end.

The cork with the transistor mounted in the socket is placed in the 1-inch hole and the oven is placed on a hot plate to obtain temperatures above room temperature or placed in dry ice or crushed ice to obtain temperatures below room temperature.

A thermocouple placed directly on the case of the transistor will give the best temperature reading; however, the block assumes a rather uniform temperature due to its large size and a thermometer placed in the $\frac{5}{16}$-inch hole will give very good temperature measurements.

Experiment 3. Single-Stage Transistor Amplifiers. One of the first steps in building a multistage circuit is the design and construction of the individual stages. This experiment is intended to give the reader experience in designing these single-stage amplifiers.

The theory of single-stage amplifiers is presented in Chapter 8. The reader is referred to this chapter for the theory connected with this experiment.

Equipment
1 transistor socket
assorted $\frac{1}{2}$-watt resistors
2 15-volt batteries
1 signal generator
assorted coupling capacitors
a-c vacuum tube voltmeter
semilog paper
1 transistor, N-P-N or P-N-P

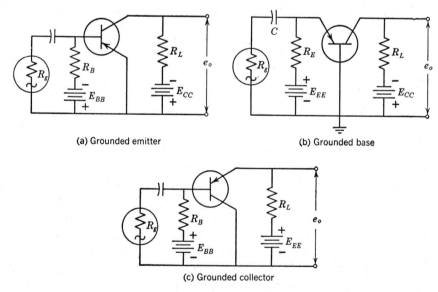

(a) Grounded emitter   (b) Grounded base

(c) Grounded collector

Fig. 15-5. Transistor amplifiers.

Procedure. Design and construct single-stage, grounded-emitter, grounded-base, and grounded-collector amplifiers similar to those shown in Figure 15-5.

Of the many ways of characterizing gain, the easiest to measure is transducer gain, which is

$$\text{transducer gain} = \frac{e_o^2/R_L}{e_g^2/4R_g} \tag{3}$$

where e_o = rms output alternating voltage,
  R_L = load resistance,
  e_g = open-circuit generator voltage,
  R_g = generator internal impedance, as shown in Figure 15-5.

Measure the transducer gain for each circuit over a wide frequency range. Remember that the generator open-circuit voltage will probably vary with frequency.

The variation of input resistance with load resistance may also be determined from these circuits. Vary the load resistance an order of magnitude either side of your design value and measure e_o and e_{in} with a generator frequency of 1 kc.

From Figure 15-6 it can be determined that the input resistance is

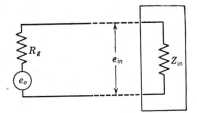

Fig. 15-6. Equivalent circuit used for calculation of Z_{in}.

$$R_i = \frac{e_{in}}{(e_o - e_{in})/R_g} = \frac{R_g e_{in}}{e_o - e_{in}} \tag{4}$$

Problem. Compare the transducer gain at mid-frequency with that which you calculated from the design equations in Chapter 8.

Plot on semilog paper the transducer gain converted to decibels versus frequency for the three amplifiers tested. Check the measured R_i against that calculated from the design equations. Also check the measured mid-frequency gain against the calculated value.

Experiment 4. Cascaded Grounded-Emitter Amplifier. In Chapter 10 the subject of cascaded transistor amplifiers is discussed. It is shown that it is impractical to cascade grounded-base or grounded-collector circuits except in combination or where transformer coupling is used. Therefore this experiment on cascaded amplifiers will be restricted to the grounded-emitter configuration.

The theory of cascaded transistor amplifiers is covered in Chapter 10, and the student is referred to this for review.

Equipment
   3 transistors
   3 transistor sockets
   assorted $\frac{1}{2}$-watt resistors
   assorted capacitors
   1 15,000 ohm potentiometer
   1 audio signal generator
   1 a-c vacuum tube voltmeter
   1 27-volt battery

Procedure. Using the theory and equations of Chapter 10, design a two-stage grounded-emitter transistor amplifier or use the three-stage *RC* coupled amplifier design set forth in Chapter 10. Measure the open-circuit generator voltage and the output voltage of the amplifier. These measurements should be obtained at a frequency in the mid-band range.

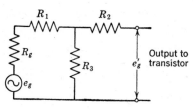

Fig. 15-7. Voltage-dividing network.

From these measurements the transducer gain may be calculated from Equation (3) of Experiment 2.

Check the frequency response by performing the above measurements at various frequencies from below the lower cutoff frequency to a frequency above the upper cutoff point.

It may be necessary to use a voltage-dividing network to reduce the output of the generator to a level suitable to apply to the input of the transistor. Such a network is shown in Figure 15-7.

This network is obtained in the following way. The sum of resistors R_2 and R_3 is set equal to the desired source resistance R_g' or

$$R_g' = R_2 + R_3 \tag{5}$$

Let us say that the output voltage of the generator must be reduced by a factor N, or in other words,

$$\frac{(e_g)_{\text{open-circuit}}}{(e_g')_{\text{open-circuit}}} = N \tag{6}$$

Then the ratio of R_1 to R_3 is

$$\frac{R_1}{R_3} = N \tag{7}$$

if N is much larger than 1 and R_g is small with respect to R_1.

The open-circuit voltage c_g' necessary to calculate the transducer gain may be obtained by measuring the open-circuit voltage e_g of the generator, and dividing it by N. The source impedance used in the transducer gain equation is the sum of $R_2 + R_3$, or R_g'.

Problem. Check the mid-frequency transducer gain obtained experimentally with that calculated for the design.

Check the frequency response curve obtained by plotting the transducer gain converted to db versus frequency against the calculated upper and lower half-power points obtained from the design calculations. The frequency response curve is best plotted on semilog paper.

Experiment 5. Power Amplifiers. In Chapter 9 the theory and design methods for power amplifiers are discussed. This experiment will deal with two of the various types of power amplifiers; namely, a single transistor Class A circuit and a dual transistor Class B circuit. For the theory the student is referred to Chapter 9 for review.

Equipment
    transistor socket
    power transistor
    assorted resistors
    assorted capacitors
    a-c vacuum tube voltmeter
    milliameter or d-c voltmeter
    oscilloscope
    9 volt battery
    transformer

Procedure.
Class A: Design your own circuit or use the design set forth in Chapter 9 for a single transistor grounded-base power amplifier. If you design your own circuit a grounded-emitter configuration may be used.

The power gain is not necessarily the most important design feature of a power amplifier; often the collector efficiency is of primary importance. Therefore we will deal at length with a method of obtaining this efficiency.

In order to obtain the efficiency we must obtain the power drain from the battery. This may be accomplished by inserting a milliameter in the battery lead. If a milliameter is not available a resistor may be placed in the battery lead and the voltage checked across it. This voltage divided by the value of the resistance will give the d-c battery drain. A capacitor should be placed across this resistor to ground as shown in Figure 15-7. This capacitor should be large enough to reduce the a-c impedance of the RC network so that it is much smaller than R_L, the load impedance.

The battery power may be calculated from the following equation:

$$P_{\text{battery}} = E_{CC} I_{CQ} \qquad (8)$$

and the collector efficiency is

$$\text{collector eff.} = \frac{(E_C^2/R_L)\,100}{I_{CQ}\,E_{CC}} \tag{9}$$

where E_C = collector output alternating voltage when driven to maximum range.

To show that the power from the battery does not vary with signal level, change the input level from zero to maximum and watch the battery current. It will not change until distortion occurs. The distortion may be checked by monitoring the output with a scope.

Also, check the transducer gain as outlined in previous experiments.

Class B: Using the circuit of Chapter 9 or your own design, repeat the checks indicated under Class A amplifiers. These are battery drain, collector efficiency, and transducer gain. Remember that the battery drain measured in this section is for both transistors and that it will vary with the amount of input signals and therefore should be measured at various power levels.

Problem. Check the results of your measurements on the Class A circuit against the design.

Check the results of your measurements on the Class B circuit with the design and plot the power output and collector dissipation versus input signal. This plot should appear similar to that given in Figure 9-14.

Experiment 6. Feedback in Transistor Circuits. The theory and application of feedback for transistor circuits is presented in Chapter 12. It is pointed out in this chapter that feedback may be used to reduce distortion, extend the frequency response, change the impedance levels, and stabilize the gain of transistor amplifiers.

In this experiment we will investigate the effect of feedback upon single-stage transistor amplifiers.

Equipment
    1 transistor socket
    assorted $\frac{1}{2}$-watt resistors
    2 15-volt batteries
    1 signal generator
    assorted coupling capacitors
    a-c vacuum tube voltmeter
    semilog paper
    1 transistor, N-P-N or P-N-P

Procedure. Use the circuit designed in Experiment 3 and place a 100 ohm resistor between emitter and ground. Measure the transducer gain over a wide range of frequencies.

Remove the emitter resistor and place a 100,000 ohm resistor in series with a 1 μf capacitor from collector to base. Again measure the transducer gain over a wide range of frequencies.

To determine the effect of feedback on gain stabilization, measure the gain of the circuit, using several different circuits. Measure the gain again with first shunt and then series feedback for the same group of transistors.

The use of feedback to compensate for temperature changes may be determined by measuring the gain with and without feedback as the

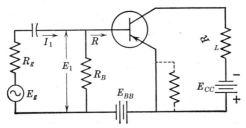

Fig. 15-8. Input resistance measuring circuit.

temperature of the transistor is varied over a wide range. The temperature oven is discussed in Experiment 2.

The change in impedance level may be checked by measuring R_i without and with feedback. To measure the input resistance, we must measure the quantities E_1 and E_g shown in Figure 15-8.

From this circuit we may write

$$R_i = \frac{E_1}{I_1 - E_1/R_B}$$

where E_1 = input alternating voltage to transistor,
   R_B = bias resistor,

$$I_1 = \frac{E_g - E_1}{R_g},$$

   R_g = generator a-c impedance,
   E_g = open-circuit generator voltage.

Problems. Plot the frequency response curves for both shunt and series feedback and compare the results with those obtained without feedback from Experiment 2.

Was the variation in gain of the circuit greater with or without feedback for various transistors and with change in operating temperature? Does this check with theory?

From the results obtained on the impedance level checks with and without feedback, which type of feedback reduces the input resistance and which increases it? Does this check with theory?

Experiment 7. Simple Transistor Circuits. To give the student experience with operating transistor circuitry, a group of simple transistor devices will be constructed and checked for correct operation in this experiment.

These circuits consist of a broadcast receiver, an audio amplifier, a relay control, an audio oscillator, and a radio frequency oscillator.

Equipment
> ferri-loop stick
> 350 $\mu\mu$f capacitor
> 1N64 diode or equivalent
> 0.05 μf capacitor
> 330,000 ohm resistor
> 3 volt battery
> ear phones
> 22,000 ohm resistor
> 1 henry choke
> 2500 ohm, 20 volt relay
> reset switch
> 0.02 μf capacitor
> 1 henry choke, center-tapped
> 0.01 μf capacitor
> 25 μf capacitor
> 100,000 ohm resistor
> 1000 $\mu\mu$f capacitor
> 45-380 $\mu\mu$f variable air capacitor
> radio frequency choke
> CK722 transistor or equivalent

Connect the circuit shown in Figure 15-9 for a transistor radio. A long length of wire will serve as an antenna if it is connected to the

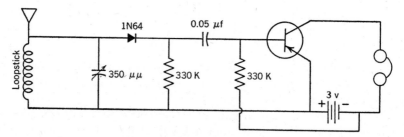

Fig. 15-9. Broadcast receiver.

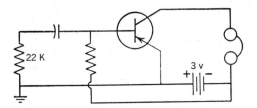

Fig. 15-10. Audio amplifier.

upper end of the tank circuit composed of the ferri-loop stick and the 350 μμf variable capacitor. The antenna may not be needed if there is a strong broadcasting station in the vicinity.

If there is insufficient gain in the transistor stage to give good reception, a second stage of audio amplification may be used. This is shown in Figure 15-10. This stage may be used by replacing the ear phones in Figure 15-9 by the 22,000 ohm resistor of Figure 15-10. The same battery may be used for both stages.

The circuit of Figure 15-10 may be used for any audio amplification application. A microphone or phonograph pickup may be used in place of the 22,000 ohm resistor if desired.

The circuit of Figure 15-11 is a relay control device that may be used in applications such as automatic garage door openers. The signal applied to the base is rectified by the base-to-emitter junction applying a d-c signal to the base. This is in turn amplified through the transistor, resulting in a direct current which activates the relay. When the relay closes the external circuit it removes the ground from the connection between the 22,000 ohm resistor and 1 henry choke. This applies a direct current to the base which keeps the relay closed until the reset button is depressed returning the circuit to its original condition.

This circuit in a garage door opener application could use a microphone as the signal source. The horn on a car could thus be used to activate the circuit. The relay would then control the driving motor

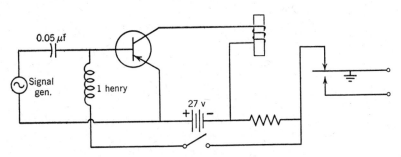

Fig. 15-11. Relay control with hold feature.

used to open the garage door or any other mechanism used for this purpose.

The signal to activate the circuit must remain on long enough to cause the relay to operate. Once the relay operates, it is self-holding.

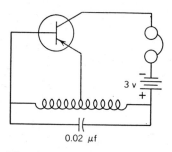

Fig. 15-12. Audio oscillator; 1-henry center-tapped toroid.

0.02 μf

In order to check this circuit an audio signal generator may be used as the input. Check the time it requires for the relay to operate after the signal is turned on and also the magnitude of signal necessary to cause the relay to operate.

In Figure 15-12 is shown an audio oscillator. This is a unique device. The amount of battery power necessary to drive this device is very small. If a coin is wrapped in a saliva-saturated paper and a contact is made with an alligator clip to the outside of this combination and another contact is made to the coin and this is used as the battery, the audio oscillator should work. However, to insure that the circuit is operating, use a conventional battery to check out the circuit.

The circuit of Figure 15-13 may be used as a phone oscillator or as a

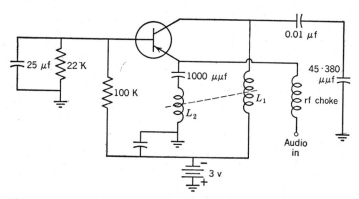

Fig. 15-13. *RF* oscillator and modulator: L_1, ferri loop stick; L_2, several turns on ferri loop stick.

wireless microphone. The circuit will oscillate in the low end of the broadcast band and the signal may be picked up on a conventional receiver.

A phonograph or microphone may be used as the audio input. Greater sensitivity may be obtained by using the audio amplifier circuit of Figure 15-10 to increase the audio signal to the desired level for modulation.

Appendix I:

Determinants

Much of the electric circuit analysis consists of solving simultaneous equations. Such equations result when either the mesh or the nodal analysis is used. Hence, in electronic circuits, simultaneous equations appear whenever the equivalent circuit concept is used. Chapter 8 was much concerned with simultaneous equations.

There are two general ways to solve such simultaneous equations: (1) the method of elimination, and (2) the method of determinants. The two methods are related, but they differ in procedure. Essentially, "determinants" represents an organized, consistent procedure, whereas "elimination" is less organized and more flexible.

In this text the method of determinants was used throughout. The reason for this is because it allowed a consistent portrayal for each case. We will present the method of elimination first, however, since it is probably more intuitive. Since we usually encountered two simultaneous equations, the methods will be illustrated by the use of two equations. It should be remembered that in simultaneous equations there are as many equations required as there are unknowns.

Two general simultaneous equations can be written

$$a_1 x + b_1 y = c_1, \qquad a_2 x + b_2 y = c_2 \qquad (1)$$

By convention, the first letters of the alphabet (a, b, c, etc.) represent the constants of the system, and such letters as x, y, etc., represent the unknowns. The parameters of the system being considered determine the constants, whereas the unknowns are those variables which are sought. For example, in transistors the constants will be given by the h parameters, and the unknowns will be the currents or

377

the voltages. Note that if currents are the unknowns, the known voltages will be the c's of Equation (1), and vice versa.

The method of elimination consists generally of combining the two equations in such a manner as to eliminate one variable. The value of this variable is then found; following this, the known variable is substituted back into either of the original equations and the remaining unknown is evaluated.

To illustrate this procedure, we eliminate the y variable from Equations (1). To accomplish this, we multiply the first equation by b_2 and the second equation by b_1. The result is

$$a_1 b_2 x + b_1 b_2 y = c_1 b_2, \qquad a_2 b_1 x + b_1 b_2 y = c_2 b_1 \tag{2}$$

If we now subtract one equation from the other, it is seen that the y variable is eliminated since its coefficient is zero. Hence we have an equation for x:

$$(a_1 b_2 - a_2 b_1) x = c_1 b_2 - c_2 b_1, \qquad x = \frac{c_1 b_2 - c_2 b_1}{a_1 b_2 - a_2 b_1} \tag{3}$$

If we now substitute this value of x into *either* equation of (1) we obtain

$$y = \frac{a_1 c_2 - a_2 c_1}{a_1 b_2 - a_2 b_1} \tag{4}$$

Note that this process could have been reversed; the x variable could have been eliminated first and the y found by substitution. To do this, the first equation is multiplied by a_2 and the second equation by a_1. In this case, the unknown y is found first. The result, of course, would be identical to that above.

As illustrated above, then, the method of elimination consists of removing one variable by combining the equations. The remaining variable is then found by substituting the evaluated variable back into an original equation.

This method, illustrated for two equations here, can be extended to any number of simultaneous equations. The procedure is to take two equations at a time, and eliminate one variable between them. Pairs of equations must be thus treated, and the resulting equations combined until one variable remains. Then one begins working in reverse to evaluate the other variables. The elimination method quickly becomes very tedious when more than three equations are involved.

As mentioned, the determinants method essentially consists of *organizing* the above procedure into a compact form. Also, it is possible to generalize the determinants method for large numbers of equations with relative simplicity.

The essential idea in the determinants method is to arrange the *constants* of the simultaneous equations in <u>arrays</u> (called a determinant), and then to evaluate these arrays. The variable, it can be shown, is equal to the ratio of two such determinants.

If we have two simultaneous equations, they can be written as before:

$$a_1x + b_1y = c_1 \qquad\qquad (5)$$
$$a_2x + b_2y = c_2$$

Then it can be shown that the unknowns x and y can be written as the ratio of two determinants:

$$x = \frac{\begin{vmatrix} c_1 & b_1 \\ c_2 & b_2 \end{vmatrix}}{\begin{vmatrix} a_1 & b_1 \\ a_2 & b_2 \end{vmatrix}}, \qquad y = \frac{\begin{vmatrix} a_1 & c_1 \\ a_2 & c_2 \end{vmatrix}}{\begin{vmatrix} a_1 & b_1 \\ a_2 & b_2 \end{vmatrix}} \qquad (6)$$

This is, of course, only a symbolic representation of the solution. We have now to see how the arrays that form the determinants are achieved, and how to evaluate the determinants.

First, we note that the denominator determinant is the same for both variables. This denominator is formed by arranging the *coefficients of the unknowns* in the same positions as they occur in the equation. This assumes, of course, that the original equations are arranged as in (5) above, with the unknowns appearing in a vertical line. For the numerator determinant in the x solution, we first *replace the x coefficients by the constants of the right side (c's)*. Then the resulting coefficients are formed into an array. Likewise for the y numerator; the coefficients of y are replaced by the c's. The resulting array of constants forms the numerator of y. .

To evaluate a determinant, one multiplies the elements along a diagonal, including both downward and upward diagonals. The downward diagonals are positive, and the upward diagonals are preceded by a negative sign. The value of the determinant is consequently formed by subtracting the upward diagonal value (product of the elements in the diagonal) from the downward diagonal value. This procedure can be illustrated by a representation:

$$\begin{vmatrix} d & \ \diagdown\nearrow & u \end{vmatrix} = \text{value of } d - \text{value of } u \qquad (7)$$

If this is applied to both numerator and denominator determinants of Equation (6), we find

$$x = \frac{\begin{vmatrix} c_1 & b_1 \\ c_2 & b_2 \end{vmatrix}}{\begin{vmatrix} a_1 & b_1 \\ a_2 & b_2 \end{vmatrix}} = \frac{c_1 b_2 - c_2 b_1}{a_1 b_2 - a_2 b_1}$$

and

$$y = \frac{\begin{vmatrix} a_1 & c_1 \\ a_2 & c_2 \end{vmatrix}}{\begin{vmatrix} a_1 & b_1 \\ a_2 & b_2 \end{vmatrix}} = \frac{a_1 c_2 - a_2 c_1}{a_1 b_2 - a_2 b_1}$$

(8)

As seen, these results are identical to those of Equations (3) and (4), where the method of elimination was used.

We can now summarize the steps:

1. Arrange the equations so that like unknown variables appear in a vertical line.

2. Form the denominator determinant (for either unknown) by putting the coefficients of the variables in an array.

3. Form the numerator determinant by substituting the right-side constants for the coefficients of the sought unknown, using the same relative positions and again forming the array.

4. Evaluate the determinants by taking products along the diagonal; subtract the upward diagonal product from the downward diagonal product.

Thus the use of determinants results in an orderly, consistent procedure for solving simultaneous equations.

The above procedure can be generalized, with some caution, to the cases of more than two equations. For any number of simultaneous equations, the unknown can be written as a ratio of two determinants:

$$x_1 = \frac{N_1}{D}, \quad x_2 = \frac{N_2}{D}, \quad x_3 = \frac{N_3}{D}, \quad \ldots$$

(9)

where x_1, x_2, etc. are the unknown variables.

The determinants in these ratios are formed exactly as illustrated for the two-equation case. There is a difference in evaluating the determinants, however. *Only two- and three-equation sets can be evaluated by the "diagonal" method.* If the determinant is greater than a three-by-three, a procedure involving co-factors must be used. The reader is referred to any standard mathematics textbook for this latter procedure.

The diagonal method of evaluation for the case of three equations is similar to that of the two-equation case and is depicted below. The main difference is that now all possible diagonals are used; this is most easily accomplished by repeating the first two columns as shown.

$$\begin{vmatrix} a_1 & b_1 & c_1 \\ a_2 & b_2 & c_2 \\ a_3 & b_3 & c_3 \end{vmatrix} = \begin{matrix} a_1 & b_1 & c_1 & a_1 & b_1 \\ a_2 & b_2 & c_2 & a_2 & b_2 \\ a_3 & b_3 & c_3 & a_3 & b_3 \end{matrix}$$

$$= a_1 b_2 c_3 + b_1 c_2 a_3 + c_1 a_2 b_3 - a_3 b_2 c_1 - b_3 c_2 a_1 - c_3 a_2 b_1$$

To re-emphasize, if a determinant is larger than three-by-three, the diagonal method can no longer be used for evaluating the determinant.

Appendix II:

Parameter Conversions

For a two-terminal pair device, such as the transistor, there are a number of forms in which the parameters can be specified. Based on the black-box concept (see Chapter 6), different sets of parameters may be specified depending on which currents and voltages are assumed known and which ones are unknown. Also, parameters may be specified according to a given equivalent circuit. If the parameters are based on the black-box concept, they are often called *matrix* parameters, since they lend themselves to matrix manipulations. Parameters based on an equivalent circuit may or may not be of the matrix type, depending on the equivalent circuit.

When transistors first appeared, it was the practice to specify the *T-equivalent circuit* parameters (see Chapter 7). The parameters specified for this circuit are r_e, r_b, r_c, and α or r_m, which consist of three resistance values and a current gain or resistance, respectively. Because of the particular impedance values in a transistor, the parameters are most easily *measured* in terms of the h matrix parameters. For this reason most manufacturers in the past few years have been specifying the transistor h parameters. These are the parameters used in this text.

Nevertheless, many times, parameters other than the h parameters are given. It is the purpose here to show the relationship between the parameters.

Consider the transistor in terms of a black box (see Fig. A-1), i.e., in terms of input and output voltages and currents. If we regard the input current and the output voltage as the unknowns, the equations

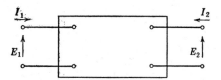

Fig. A-1. The transistor as a black-box.

for the transistor appear as

$$E_1 = h_{11}I_1 + h_{12}E_2$$
$$I_2 = h_{21}I_1 + h_{22}E_2$$

h parameters (1)

This is the basic set of equations used in this book. Other possible forms are the following:

$$E_1 = z_{11}I_1 + z_{12}I_2$$
$$E_2 = z_{21}I_1 + z_{22}I_2$$

z parameters

where I_1 and I_2 are the unknowns.

$$I_1 = y_{11}E_1 + y_{12}E_2$$
$$I_2 = y_{21}E_1 + y_{22}E_2$$

y parameters (2)

where E_1 and E_2 are the unknowns.

$$I_1 = g_{11}E_1 + g_{12}I_2$$
$$E_2 = g_{21}E_1 + g_{22}I_2$$

g parameters

where E_1 and I_2 are the unknowns.

It should be stressed that, for a single circuit, each of the above representations is equally valid. If circuits are to be combined, however, one form is preferred over the others, based on the manner in which the circuits are connected. As stated previously, the h parameters are usually given for the transistor. Each of the parameter types listed above is of the matrix type.

Given any one set of parameters, we can find any of the other sets. Table 1 shows the relationship between each of the various matrix parameters. This table is to be read in the horizontal direction. Although we are interested mainly in the first row, showing how to obtain the h parameters from the other matrix quantities, the other relations are included for completeness. Row 2 shows how to obtain the z parameters, etc. The quantity Δ in this table means,

TABLE 1

Given	$\to h$		$\to z$		$\to y$		$\to g$	
To find:								
$\to h$	h_{11}	h_{12}	$\dfrac{\Delta^z}{z_{22}}$	$\dfrac{z_{12}}{z_{22}}$	$\dfrac{1}{y_{11}}$	$\dfrac{-y_{12}}{y_{11}}$	$\dfrac{g_{22}}{\Delta^g}$	$\dfrac{-g_{12}}{\Delta^g}$
	h_{21}	h_{22}	$\dfrac{-z_{21}}{z_{22}}$	$\dfrac{1}{z_{22}}$	$\dfrac{y_{21}}{y_{11}}$	$\dfrac{\Delta^y}{y_{11}}$	$\dfrac{-g_{21}}{\Delta^g}$	$\dfrac{g_{11}}{\Delta^g}$
$\to z$	$\dfrac{\Delta^h}{h_{22}}$	$\dfrac{h_{12}}{h_{22}}$	z_{11}	z_{12}	$\dfrac{y_{22}}{\Delta^y}$	$\dfrac{-y_{12}}{\Delta^y}$	$\dfrac{1}{g_{11}}$	$\dfrac{-g_{12}}{g_{11}}$
	$\dfrac{-h_{21}}{h_{22}}$	$\dfrac{1}{h_{22}}$	z_{21}	z_{22}	$\dfrac{-y_{21}}{\Delta^y}$	$\dfrac{y_{11}}{\Delta^y}$	$\dfrac{g_{21}}{g_{11}}$	$\dfrac{\Delta^g}{g_{11}}$
$\to y$	$\dfrac{1}{h_{11}}$	$\dfrac{-h_{12}}{h_{11}}$	$\dfrac{z_{22}}{\Delta^z}$	$\dfrac{-z_{12}}{\Delta^z}$	y_{11}	y_{12}	$\dfrac{\Delta^g}{g_{22}}$	$\dfrac{g_{12}}{g_{22}}$
	$\dfrac{h_{21}}{h_{11}}$	$\dfrac{\Delta^h}{h_{11}}$	$\dfrac{-z_{21}}{\Delta^z}$	$\dfrac{z_{11}}{\Delta^z}$	y_{21}	y_{22}	$\dfrac{-g_{21}}{g_{22}}$	$\dfrac{1}{g_{22}}$
$\to g$	$\dfrac{h_{22}}{\Delta^h}$	$\dfrac{-h_{12}}{\Delta^h}$	$\dfrac{1}{z_{11}}$	$\dfrac{-z_{12}}{z_{11}}$	$\dfrac{\Delta^y}{y_{22}}$	$\dfrac{y_{12}}{y_{22}}$	g_{11}	g_{12}
	$\dfrac{-h_{21}}{\Delta^h}$	$\dfrac{h_{11}}{\Delta^h}$	$\dfrac{z_{21}}{z_{11}}$	$\dfrac{\Delta^z}{z_{11}}$	$\dfrac{-y_{21}}{y_{22}}$	$\dfrac{1}{y_{22}}$	g_{21}	g_{22}

in each case, the determinant value of the parameters. The table is used by simply equating the desired parameter to the quantity in the corresponding position of the other parameters. For example,

$$h_{11} = \frac{\Delta z}{z_{22}}; \quad h_{22} = \frac{1}{z_{22}}; \quad z_{12} = \frac{-y_{12}}{\Delta y}; \quad \text{etc.} \tag{3}$$

Although this table suffices for all the matrix-type parameters,

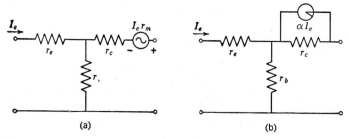

Fig. A-2. T-equivalent circuits for transistors. (a) T-equivalent circuit with voltage generator. (b) T-circuit with current generator.

there still remain the T-equivalent circuit parameters. For the reader's convenience, the T-circuit is repeated in Fig. A-2.

These parameters are most closely related to the z parameters. The relations are

$$z_{11} = r_e + r_b, \qquad z_{21} = r_b + r_m$$
$$z_{12} = r_b, \qquad\qquad z_{22} = r_b + r_c \tag{4}$$

$$\alpha = \frac{r_b + r_m}{r_b + r_c} \approx \frac{r_m}{r_c}$$

To find the h parameters from the T-parameters we have the relation

$$h_{11} = r_e + r_b \left(1 - \frac{r_b + r_m}{r_b + r_c} \right) = r_e + r_b(1 - \alpha)$$

$$h_{12} = \frac{r_b}{r_b + r_c}$$

$$h_{21} = -\left(\frac{r_b + r_m}{r_b + r_c} \right) = -\alpha \approx -\frac{r_m}{r_c} \tag{5}$$

$$h_{22} = \frac{1}{r_b + r_c} \approx \frac{1}{r_c}$$

Table 1 and the above relations allow the conversion of any set of parameters to the h type, so that the results found within the text can be applied consistently, no matter what parameters are specified.

Appendix III:

Transistor Parameters

The following is a selected sample of transistor characteristics. These characteristics are included for two reasons; to give an indication of the parameters of available transistors and to serve as a source for parameters of commercial transistors for use in solving the problems included in this text.

CBS 2N180-2N181 P-N-P GENERAL-PURPOSE TRANSISTORS

CBS types 2N180 and 2N181 are P-N-P alloy-junction germanium transistors which are recommended for low-to-medium power, high-gain applications.

These transistors are for general-purpose low-frequency use. They also have a wide variety of possible applications, because of the collector dissipation of 150 mw for the 2N180 and 250 mw for the 2N181.

Suggested applications are: Class-A amplifier, P-P Class-B output stage, driver for P-P Class-B stage, microphone or phono preamplifier, and low-frequency flip-flop circuit. An additional feature is the ability to maintain high amplification at high current levels, thus lending themselves to medium power applications such as the output stage of a portable radio receiver.

Mechanical Data

	2N180	2N181
Case material...................................	Metal	Metal
Maximum case length.............................	0.375	$\frac{3}{8}$ in.
Maximum case diameter...........................	0.25	$\frac{5}{16}$ in.
Maximum clamp length............................		$1\frac{3}{16}$ in.
Lead diameter..................................	0.017	0.017 in.
Minimum lead length............................	1.25	1.25 in.

Transistor Basing Diagram
Count from the red dot
  1. Collector.
  2. Base.
  3. Emitter.

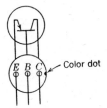

Electrical Data

RATINGS, ABSOLUTE MAXIMUM, AT 25°C:

	2N180	2N181
Collector to base voltage, d-c........................	−30	−30 v
Dissipation, total in free air..........................	150	250 mw
Derating per °C ambient temp. increase..............	3	5 mw
Operating temperature, junction......................	−50 to +75°C	
Storage temperature.................................	−50 to +85°C	

TYPICAL CHARACTERISTICS AT 25°C:

	2N180	2N181
Collector peak reverse voltage, emitter open............	−40	−40 v
Collector current, emitter open at −30 v..............	−10	−10 μa
Collector current, base open at −10 v................	−0.3	−0.3 ma
Emitter peak reverse voltage, collector open...........	−30	−30 v
Emitter reverse current, collector open at −20 v.......	−8	−8 μa

387

Low-Frequency Small-Signal Parameters:

Collector voltage, V_{cb}	-6	-6 v
Emitter current, I_e	1.0	1.0 ma
Frequency	270	270 cycles
Base-collector current amplification, β	60	60
Emitter-collector current amplification, α or h_{fb}	0.985	0.985
Alpha cut-off frequency, $F_{\alpha co}$	600	600 kc
Emitter input resistance, output shorted, h_{ib}	32	32 ohms
Collector output conductance, input open, h_{ob}	0.5	0.5 μmho
Collector-emitter feedback voltage ratio, h_{rb}	4×10^4	4×10^4
Collector capacitance, at 500 kc	25	25 $\mu\mu$f
Noise figure	12	12 db

Large-Signal Low-Frequency Parameters:

Base-collector current amplification, $B = I_c/I_b$		
$I_b = 0.1$ ma, $V_c = -1$ v	70	70
$I_b = 1.0$ ma, $V_c = -1$ v	50	50
Base input resistance, $R_i = V_b/I_b$		
$I_b = 0.1$ ma, $V_c = -1$ v	2000	2000 ohms
$I_b = 1.0$ ma, $V_c = -1$ v	500	500 ohms
Saturation resistance, R_s	2.5	2.5 ohms

TYPICAL OPERATIONS AT 25°C

Class-A Low-Level Audio Amplifier (Common emitter connected)

Collector supply voltage	-6	-6 v
Collector current, d-c	-1	-1 ma
Current amplification	60	60
Load resistance, dynamic	20	20 K
Input resistance, dynamic	1500	1500 ohms
Power gain	43	43 db

Class-A Medium-Power Amplifier (Common emitter connected):

Collector supply voltage	-9	-12 v
Collector current, d-c	-15	-20 ma
Base current, d-c	-250	-300 μa
Dissipation, max	135	250 mw
Current amplification	50	50
Stabilizing resistance in emitter circuit,		
bypassed with 200 μf capacitor	10	10 ohms
Base-emitter circuit d-c resistance, max	1000	500 ohms
Input resistance, dynamic	250	250 ohms
Load resistance, dynamic	560	110 ohms
Power output, max	65	110 mw
Power gain	37	34 db

Push-Pull Class-B Amplifier (Common emitter connected):[2]

Collector supply voltage	-9	-12 v
Collector current, max. signal	-25	-38 ma
Collector current, zero signal	-5	-7 ma
Peak collector current, max. signal	-75	-110 ma
Base current, max. signal	-500	-800 μa
Base current, zero signal	-60	-80 μa

Dissipation per unit, max. signal	100	200 mw
Dissipation per unit, zero signal	40	80 mw
Stabilizing resistance in emitter circuit, not bypassed	10	10 ohms
Base-emitter circuit d-c resistance, max.	1000	500 ohms
Input resistance, dynamic	800	700 ohms
Load resistance, dynamic	110	100 ohms
Power output, total max.[1]	300	600 mw
Power input, total max.[1]	1.0	2.0 mw
Power gain	25	25 db

NOTES:

[1] Values for both units.
[2] Information on matched pair specification available on request.

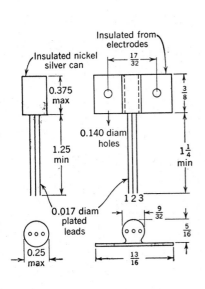

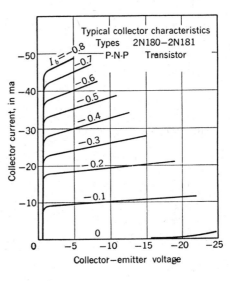

GENERAL ELECTRIC 2N43 P-N-P JUNCTION TRANSISTOR

The General Electric type 2N43 germanium fused junction transistor triode is a P-N-P unit particularly recommended for high-gain, low-to-medium power applications. A hermetic enclosure is provided by use of glass-to-metal seals and resistance-welded seams. This transistor is capable of dissipating 150 mw in 25°C free air.

Specifications

ABSOLUTE MAXIMUM RATINGS:

Collector voltage (referred to base), V_e .... −45 volts
Collector current, I_c .... −50 ma
Emitter current, I_e .... 50 ma
[1]Junction temperature, T_j .... 100°C

AVERAGE CHARACTERISTICS (Common base, $T_j = 30°C$, $f = 270$ cycles):

	Design Center	Typical Production Spread Max.	Min.	
Collector voltage....................	−5.0			volts
Emitter current....................	1.0			ma
Output admittance (input open circuit), h_{22}.....................	1.0	2.0	0.5	μmhos
Current amplification (output short circuit), h_{21}.....................	−0.98	−1.0	−0.97	
Input impedance (output short circuit), h_{11}.....................	40	50	30	ohms
Voltage feedback ratio (input open circuit), h_{12}.....................	4×10^{-4}	6×10^{-4}	2×10^{-4}	
Collector Cutoff Current, I_{co}.........	10	15	1.0	μa
Output Capacitance, C_c.............	40	50	30	mmf
Noise figure ($V_c = -1.5$ v; $I_e = 0.5$ ma; $f = 1$ kc; BW $= 1 \sim$); NF........	22	33	11	db
Maximum power gain (common emitter)	40	44	37	db
[2]Frequency cutoff, f_{co}................	1.0	2.5	0.5	mc
Temp. rise/unit collector dissipation (in free air).....................	0.5			°C/mw
[3]Temp. rise/unit collector dissipation (infinite heat sink)................	0.2			°C/mw

TYPICAL OPERATION (Small Signal Amplifier) ($T_j = 30°C$, $f = 1$ kc):

	Common Base	Common Emitter	Common Collector	
Collector voltage....................	−5	−5	−5	volts
Emitter current....................	1.0	1.0	1.0	ma
Input impedance....................	60	1,000	30,000	ohms
Source impedance....................	100	600	30,000	ohms
Load impedance....................	50,000	30,000	600	ohms
Power gain (PG)....................	28	39	15	db

Typical Operation (Medium Power Amplifier, Class A) ($T_j = 75°C, f = 1$ kc):

	Common Base	Common Emitter	Common Collector	
Collector voltage....................	−20	−20	−20	volts
Emitter current.....................	5	5	5	ma
Input impedance....................	10	500	200,000	ohms
Source impedance..................	50	500	200,000	ohms
Load impedance....................	4,500	4,500	4,500	ohms
Power output (5% distortion)........	45	40	42	mw
Power gain........................	25	37	17	db

Notes:

[1] Junction temperature may be determined by the method outlined in curve number 6. As an alternative method, a small thermocouple may be attached to the transistor shell (allowing 0.2°C/mw temperature drop between junction and shell). Rating may not be exceeded when soldering into circuit or during operation.

[2] Frequency at which the magnitude of h_{21} is 3 db down from its 270 cps value.

[3] Temperature rise with transistor clamped to metallic heat sink.

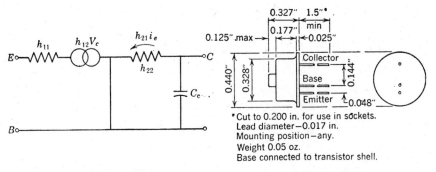

EQUIVALENT CIRCUIT

OUTLINE DRAWING

* Cut to 0.200 in. for use in sockets.
Lead diameter—0.017 in.
Mounting position—any.
Weight 0.05 oz.
Base connected to transistor shell.

Approximate Conversion Formulas: h to r Parameters (Assume $r_b \ll r_c$)

$$r_e = h_{11} - \frac{h_{12}}{h_{22}} (1 = h_{21}) \qquad r_c = \frac{1}{h_{22}}$$

$$r_b = \frac{h_{12}}{h_{22}} \qquad \alpha = -h_{21}$$

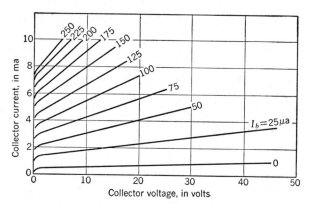

COMMON EMITTER CONNECTION

$$T_j = 30°C$$

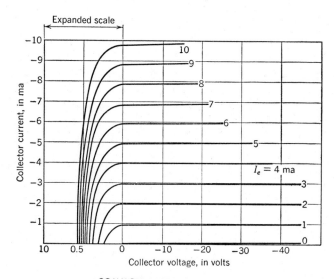

COMMON BASE CONNECTION

$$T_j = 30°C$$

HONEYWELL H4 POWER TRANSISTOR

General Information

Type: Germanium, P-N-P, alloyed junction, hermetically sealed power transistor.

Nominal Output Rating: 2 watts.

Supply Voltage Rating: 28 volts.

Dimensions and Connections:

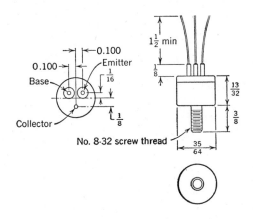

Maximum Ratings

Maximum Collector Voltage:

- −60 v common base. (Mounting base must be below 100°F unless the circuit is stabilized.)
- −60 v common emitter. (Circuit must be stabilized at all temperatures, or, without stabilization, −30 v may be applied if the mounting base temperature is below 100°F.)

Maximum Emitter Reverse Voltage: −30 v.

Maximum Base Current (Mounting base temperature 70°F): −0.25 amp.

Maximum Power Output (Mounting base temperature 70°F):

Class A, single unit. . . . . 2 w
Class B, push-pull, two units. . . . . 6 w
Switching capability, single unit. . . . . 16 w

Maximum Transistor Dissipation (As a function of temperature): Allowable dissipation is determined by the mounting base temperature. Attachment of the transistor to a chassis or to some other heat dissipating medium is necessary. The maximum total dissipation shown is considered to be the instantaneous peak power dissipation of the cycle. For purposes of thermal design the temperature at the end of the mounting stud can be substituted for the mounting base temperature.

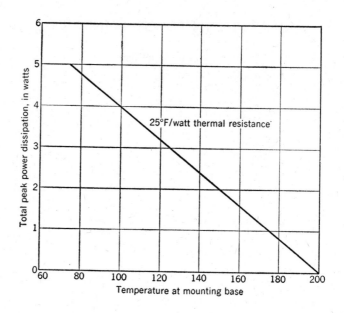

Typical Operating Conditions

(Common emitter, transformer output, 28-v supply,
mounting base temperature 70°F.)

Peak Collector Current (amperes)	Class A Single Unit			Class B P-P Two Units		
	Output (watts)	Gain (db)	R_L (ohms)	Output (watts)	Gain (db)	R_L (ohms)
−0.1	0.6	30	560	1.25	27	280
−0.2	1.25	25	280	2.5	22	140
−0.3	1.9	21	187	3.75	18	93
−0.4				5.00	16	70
−0.5				6.25	14	56

Reducing the supply voltage to 14 v will reduce the power output and power gain by approximately 3 db when current is brought to above values by reducing the load resistance.

Collector Characteristics

COMMON EMITTER CHARACTERISTICS (Mounting base temperature 70°F, 60 cycle oscilliscope pattern):

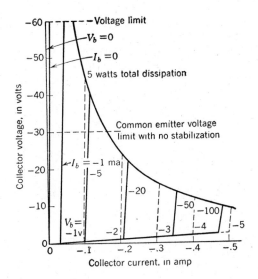

COMMON BASE CHARACTERISTICS (Mounting base temperature 70°F, 60 cycle oscilliscope pattern):

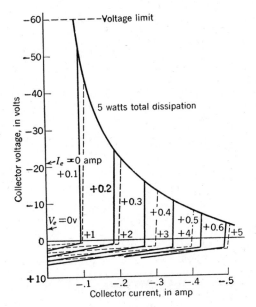

PHILCO SB-100 SURFACE BARRIER TRANSISTOR

Applications

The Philco type SB-100 is a hermetically sealed surface barrier transistor designed for use as a general purpose i-f and r-f oscillator or amplifier at frequencies up to 30 mc, as a wide band video amplifier, and as a switching transistor at switching frequencies as high as 1.5 mc. The polarities of the emitter and collector voltages are similar to those of P-N-P junction transistors. The tinned flexible leads may be soldered or welded directly into the circuit or they may be clipped and used with standard plug-in sockets.

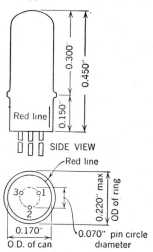

SIDE VIEW

BOTTOM VIEW

Electrical Data

MAXIMUM RATINGS[1]

Collector voltage (common emitter)[2]...........................	−4.5 v
Collector current...	−5 ma
Collector dissipation (at 40°C)................................	10 mw

TYPICAL CHARACTERISTICS (AT 25°C)[3]

Collector voltage, V_c..	−3.0 v
Collector current, I_c..	−0.5 ma
Common emitter current amplification, h_{fe}...................	20
Common base output impedance, $1/h_{ob}$........................	400,000 ohms
Common base input impedance, h_{ib}...........................	70 ohms
Extrinsic base resistance-collector capacitance product, $r_b'C_c$.....................................	800 μμsec. (1500 μμsec. max.)
Common base output capacitance (shell grounded), C_o...........	3.5 μμfd
Collector cutoff current (measured at $V_c = -3.0$ v), I_{co}..............	0.5 μamp
Maximum frequency of oscillation, f_{max}.....................	45 mc (30 mc min.)

Alpha cutoff frequency, $f_{\alpha b}$, can be calculated using the equation:

$$f_{\alpha b} = \frac{30 r_b'C_c (f_{max})^2}{\alpha}$$

where f_{ab} is in megacycles, f_{max} in megacycles, $r_b'C_c$ in $\mu\mu$sec, and α is the low frequency common base current amplification factor.

Mechanical Data

Base: 0.016 in. tinned flexible leads. Emitter lead length 1.45 in. min. Collector and base lead length 1.50 in. min. on a 0.070 in. diameter circle.

Terminal connections (red line adjacent to lead #1):

Lead 1: Collector.
Lead 2: Base.
Lead 3: Emitter.

Mounting position: Any.

NOTES:

[1] Maximum ratings indicate limiting values above which transistor life and/or performance may be impaired. Connection of the transistor to a suitable heat sink will insure best performance when operating at maximum power ratings.

[2] Voltage at which the common emitter output impedance with open base is $\frac{1}{2}$ of the typical value measured at $V_c = -3$ v and $I_c = -0.5$ ma.

[3] Accidental application of large voltage surges to transistors may alter their characteristics. Such surges may be derived from soldering irons and test equipment operating from 110-v a-c lines. As a precaution against this, test equipment should be carefully grounded and gun type soldering irons are recommended. The use of isolation transformers is also a satisfactory safeguard.

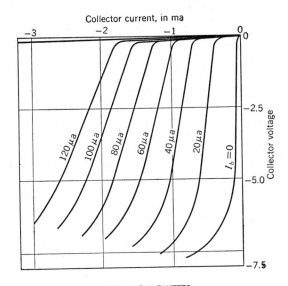

COMMON EMITTER

Collector Characteristics

RAYTHEON 2N106 P-N-P JUNCTION TRANSISTOR

The 2N106 is a hermetically sealed P-N-P junction transistor intended for use in low-level audio applications where low noise factor is of prime importance. The tinned flexible leads may be soldered or welded directly to the terminals of circuit components without the use of sockets. Standard inline subminiature sockets may be used by cutting the leads to a suitable length.

Mechanical Data

Case: Plastic and glass.

Base: None. (0.016 in. tinned flexible leads. Length: 1.5 in. min. Spacing: 0.08 in. center-to-center.)

Terminal connections (red dot is adjacent to lead 1):

Lead 1: Collector.
Lead 2: Base.
Lead 3: Emitter.

Weight: 0.025 oz.

Mounting position: Any.

Electrical Data

RATINGS—ABSOLUTE MAXIMUM VALUES:

Collector voltage......................	−6 v
Collector current......................	−10 ma
[1]Collector dissipation..................	
Emitter current.......................	10 ma
Ambient temperature.................	85°C

CHARACTERISTICS (AT 27°C):

Collector voltage......................	−1.5 v
Collector current......................	−0.5 ma
Current amplification factor (min.)......	25
Collector resistance (min.).............	1.0 meg
[2]Collector cutoff current (max.)..........	12 μa
[3,4]Noise factor (max.)...................	6 db

AVERAGE CHARACTERISTICS—COMMON EMITTER CIRCUIT (AT 27°C):

Collector voltage...	−1.5 v
Collector current...	−0.5 ma
Generator resistance...	1000 ohms
Load resistance..	20,000 ohms
Gain..	36 db
[3]Noise factor...	4.5 db

AVERAGE CHARACTERISTICS—COMMON BASE CIRCUIT (AT 27°C):

Collector voltage...	−1.5 v
Collector current...	−0.5 ma
Generator resistance...	100 ohms
Load resistance..	0.2 meg
Gain..	28 db
[3]Noise factor...	4.5 db

AVERAGE CHARACTERISTICS—COMMON COLLECTOR CIRCUIT (AT 27°C):

Collector voltage..	−1.5 v
Collector current..	−0.5 ma
Generator resistance..	0.1 meg
Load resistance...	10,000 ohms
Gain..	14 db
[3]Noise factor...	12 db

NOTES:

[1] This is a function of maximum ambient temperature (T_A) expected. It is approximately equal to $1.7(85°C - T_A)$ mw.

[2] With zero emitter current in grounded base connection.

[3] In a one-cycle bandwidth at 1000 cycles.

[4] Measured under conditions described under "Common Emitter Circuit."

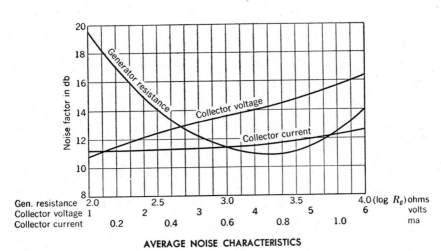

AVERAGE NOISE CHARACTERISTICS

Common Emitter

Conditions

Collector voltage (V_c)............	$R_g = $ 1 K
	$I_c = -0.5$ ma
Collector current (I_c).............	$R_g = $ 1 K
	$V_c = -1.5$ v
Generator resistance (R_g).........	$V_c = -1.5$ v
	$I_c = -0.5$ ma
Load resistance = 20 K	

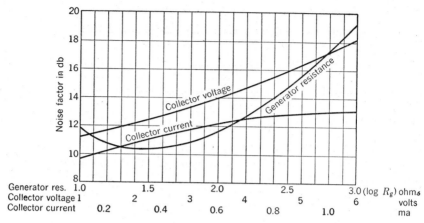

AVERAGE NOISE CHARACTERISTICS

Common Base

Conditions

Collector voltage (V_c) . . . . $R_g =$ 100 ohms
                                         $I_c = -0.5$ ma
Collector current (I_c) . . . . $R_g =$ 100 ohms
                                           $V_c = -1.5$ v
Generator resistance (R_g) . . . . $V_c = -1.5$ v
                                           $I_c = -0.5$ ma

Load resistance = 200 K

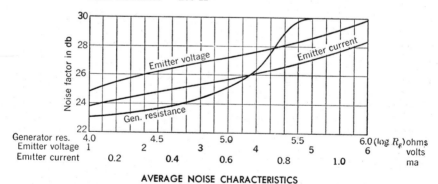

AVERAGE NOISE CHARACTERISTICS

Common Collector

Conditions

Emitter voltage (V_e) . . . . $R_g =$ 100 K
                                           $I_c = -0.5$ ma
Emitter current (I_c) . . . . $R_g =$ 100 K
                                           $V_c = -1.5$ v
Generator resistance (R_g) . . . . $V_c = -1.5$ v
                                           $I_c = -0.5$ ma

Load resistance = 10 K

RAYTHEON 2N130 P-N-P JUNCTION TRANSISTOR

The 2N130 is a P-N-P junction transistor intended primarily for use in audio or low radio frequency applications. The tinned flexible leads may be soldered or welded directly to the terminals of circuit components without the use of sockets. Standard inline subminiature sockets may be used by cutting the leads to a suitable length.

Mechanical Data

Case: Metal with insulating coating.
Base: None. (0.014 in. tinned flexible leads. Length: 1.5 in. min. Spacing: 0.04 in. center-to-center.)
Terminal connections (red dot is adjacent to lead 1):
Lead 1: Collector.
Lead 2: Base.
Lead 3: Emitter.
Mounting position: Any.

Electrical Data

RATINGS—ABSOLUTE MAXIMUM VALUES:

Collector voltage (V_c)...................	−22 v
[1,2]Peak collector voltage (V_d)..............	−44 v
Collector current......................	−10 ma
[3]Collector dissipation....................	
Emitter current.......................	10 ma
[4]Ambient temperature...................	85°C

AVERAGE CHARACTERISTICS (AT 27°C):

Collector voltage......................	−6 v
Emitter current.......................	1.0 ma
Collector resistance...................	2.0 meg
Base resistance........................	350 ohms
Emitter resistance....................	25 ohms
Base current amplification factor..........	22
Cutoff current (approx.)................	6 μa
[5]Noise factor (max.)....................	25 db

AVERAGE CHARACTERISTICS—COMMON EMITTER (AT 27°C):

Collector voltage....................................	−1.5	−6 v
Emitter current.....................................	0.5	1.0 ma
Input resistance....................................	1400	800 ohms
Load resistance.....................................	20,000	20,000 ohms
Power gain (matched input)...........................	37	39 db

AVERAGE CHARACTERISTICS—COMMON COLLECTOR (AT 27°C):

Collector voltage......................................	−6 v
Emitter current.......................................	1.0 ma
[6]Input resistance.......................................	0.35 meg
Load resistance.......................................	20,000 ohms
Power gain (matched input).............................	13 db

AVERAGE CHARACTERISTICS—COMMON BASE (AT 27°C):

Collector voltage... −6 v
Emitter current... 1.0 ma
Input resistance.. 50 ohms
Load resistance.. 20,000 ohms
Power gain (matched input).................................... 32 db

NOTES:

[1] Collector voltage V_{ce} at which I cycle rises to 2 ma in common emitter circuit with base lead connected directly to emitter lead. Ambient temperature = 25°C.

[2] In circuits stabilized for I_c or I_e and which do not have critical distortion requirements, absolute maximum peak voltage is 75 v.

[3] This is a function of maximum ambient temperature (T_A) expected. It is approximately equal to 1.4(85°C − T_A) mw in free air and to 3(85°C − T_A) when the case is clipped to the chassis.

[4] This is the maximum operating or storage temperature recommended.

[5] Measured under conditions for grounded emitter operation at V_{cb} = −2.5 volts for a 1-cycle bandwidth at 1000 cycles.

[6] Higher input impedances, without appreciable loss in gain, can be achieved by operating at lowered collector current.

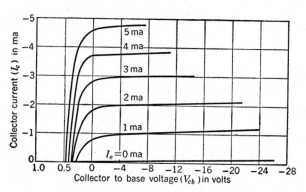

GROUNDED BASE

Typical Collector Characteristics

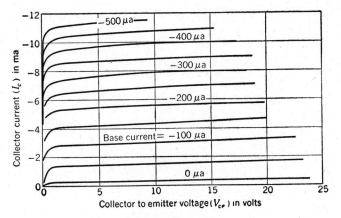

GROUNDED EMITTER

Typical Collector Characteristics*

* This family is a function of $1 - \alpha$ and thus changes appreciably with small changes in α.

RAYTHEON CK790 P-N-P JUNCTION TRANSISTOR

The CK790 is a medium gain, silicon fused alloy P-N-P junction transistor intended primarily for use in high temperature audio applications and in circuits where low reverse saturation current is of paramount importance. The combination of low saturation voltage and high reverse voltage rating on both emitter and collector make the CK790 ideal for high temperature audio switching applications.

Mechanical Data

Case: Metal and glass.
Base: None. (0.016 in. tinned flexible leads. Length: 1.5 in. minimum. Spacing: Leads
    1–4 are 0.144 in. center-to-center. Other leads 0.048 in. center-to-center.)
Terminal connections:
  Lead 1: Collector.
  Lead 4: Base.
  Lead 5: Emitter.

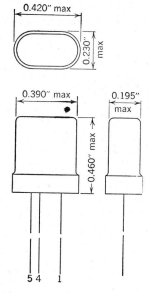

Electrical Data

RATINGS—ABSOLUTE MAXIMUM VALUES:

	25°C	125°C	
Collector voltage	−45	−30	v
Emitter voltage	−22	−12	v
Collector current	−50	−50	ma
Emitter current	50	50	ma
Collector dissipation	200	50	mw
Ambient temperature	−55 to +135°C		

TYPICAL CHARACTERISTICS—GROUNDED BASE[1]

Parameter	Symbol	Conditions	25°C Min.	25°C Av.	25°C Max.	125°C Min.	125°C Av.	125°C Max.	Units
Collector cutoff current	I_{co}	$V_c = -20$ v	...	0.1	0.2	...	30	50	μa
Emitter cutoff current	I_{eo}	$V_e = -20$ v	...	0.1	0.2	...	30	50	μa
Base resistance	r_b		...	1200	...	...	2200	...	ohms
[2]Current transfer ratio	α_{cb}		9	14	18	...	24	...	
Collector resistance	r_c		...	0.50	...	...	0.55	...	meg
Input impedance	h_{11}		50	100	200	...	110	...	ohms
Feedback pot. ratio	h_{12}		0.5	2.4	...	...	4.0	...	$\times 10^{-3}$
Current transfer ratio	$1 + h_{21}$		0.05	0.066	0.10	...	0.04	...	
Output admittance	h_{22}		...	2.0	...	...	1.8	...	$\mu mhos$
[2,3]Noise factor	N.F.		...	15	30	...	18	...	db
Cutoff frequency	$F_{\alpha co}$		200	400	...	...	300	...	kc
Collector Capacitance	C_c	$f = 2$ mc	...	30	40	...	...	...	$\mu\mu f$
[3]Power gain	P_g		30	32	...	...	32	...	db

NOTES:

[1] $V_c = -6$ v, $F = 1000$ cycles, $I_E = 1$ ma except as noted.
[2] Grounded emitter. [3] $R_g = 1000$ ohms, $R_L = 20,000$ ohms.

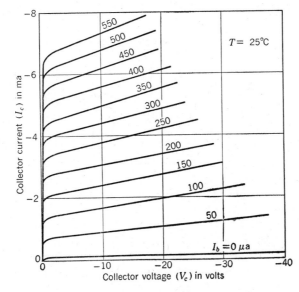

GROUNDED EMITTER

Collector Characteristics ($T = 25°C$)

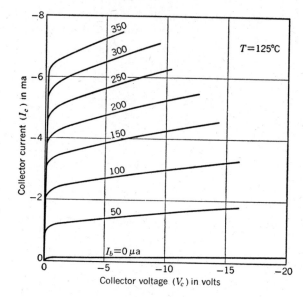

GROUNDED EMITTER

Collector Characteristics ($T = 125°C$)

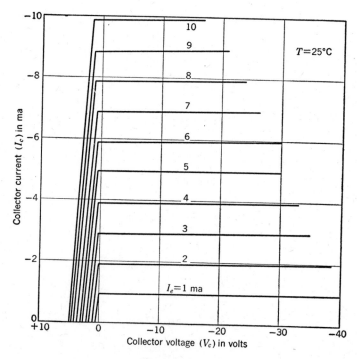

GROUNDED BASE

Collector Characteristics ($T = 25°C$)

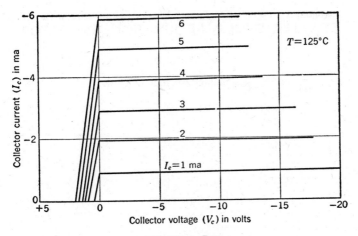

GROUNDED BASE

Collector Characteristics ($T = 125°C$)

SYLVANIA 2N68 P-N-P JUNCTION TRANSISTOR

Mechanical Data

[2]Ambient temperature: 25°C maximum dissipation of 2.5 w.
Mounting position: Any.
Cooling structure: At collector potential.

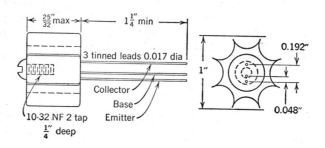

Electrical Data

RATINGS—ABSOLUTE VALUES (25°C Ambient):

Collector voltage	−25 v max.
Collector current	−1.5 amp max.
[2]Total dissipation	
Heat sink	4.0 w max.
Free air	2.5 w max.
[3]External base to emitter resistance	200 ohms max.

CHARACTERISTICS (Typical Small-Signal, Low Frequency Parameters $V_c = -6$ v,
$I_e = +50$ ma):

Alpha	0.975
Base to emitter current gain	40
Emitter resistance	1 ohm
Base resistance	30 ohms
Collector resistance	100,000 ohms
I_{co} (10 v)	100 μa
Collector capacitance	300 $\mu\mu$f
Alpha cutoff frequency	400 kc

TYPICAL OPERATION[4] (25°C Ambient):

Class A Amplifier, Common Emitter Connection:

Collector supply voltage	−12 v
Collector current	−150 ma
Base current	−5.0 ma
Generator resistance	50 ohms
[5]Input resistance	75 ohms
Load resistance	100 ohms
Power output	600 mw
Gain	23 db

Push-Pull Class B[6] Amplifier,[4] Common-Emitter Connection[1]:

Collector supply voltage..............................	−12 v
Collector current (maximum signal)........................	−550 ma
(zero signal)[6]...........................	−1.0 ma
Generator resistance..................................	50 ohms
Input resistance[5]...................................	50 ohms
Load resistance (per collector)......................	12 ohms
Power output..	5 w
Gain..	15 db

Push-Pull Class B[6] Amplifier,[4] Common Collector Connection[1]:

Collector supply voltage..............................	−12 v
Collector current (maximum signal)........................	−550 ma
(zero signal)[6]...........................	−1.0 ma
Generator resistance..................................	100 ohms
Input resistance......................................	250 ohms
Load resistance (per collector)......................	12 ohms
Power output..	5 w
Gain..	10 db

Push-Pull Class B[6] Amplifier,[4] Common Base Connection[1]:

Collector supply voltage..............................	−24 v
Collector current (maximum signal)......................	−950 ma
(zero signal)............................	−1 ma
Generator resistance..................................	2 ohms
Input resistance......................................	2 ohms
Load resistance (noninductive).......................	24 ohms
Power output..	10 w
Power gain..	10 db

Switching Applications (Common Emitter):

Collector supply voltage..............................	−12 v
Collector load resistance.............................	12 ohms
Switching power gain.................................	17 db
Switching power output...............................	12 w

NOTES:

[1] For two units.

[2] Air cooling derate 50 mw/°C. With heat sink, derate 100 mw per °C based on aluminum chassis $\frac{1}{16}$ in. thick, 25 sq in. or equivalent for each transistor.

[3] Common emitter or common collector.

[4] Stabilization of d-c operating points is strongly recommended in all applications to minimize the possibility of collector current "runaway."

[5] The values of input impedances given may be somewhat greater if the emitter stabilization resistance is not well by-passed.

[6] "Cross-over" distortion may be reduced or eliminated by Class AB operation. Zero signal collector current of 15–30 ma per unit is sufficient.

Application Data

The Sylvania Type 2N68 is designed for high current, low voltage operation from 6 to 24 volt power supplies. Power output to 750 mw in Class A and to 10 w in Class B(1) may be obtained. It is especially useful in the driver and output stages of audio systems and in power switching applications.

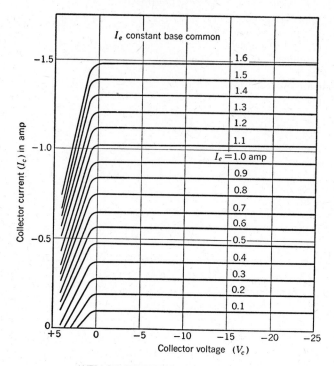

AVERAGE COLLECTOR CHARACTERISTICS

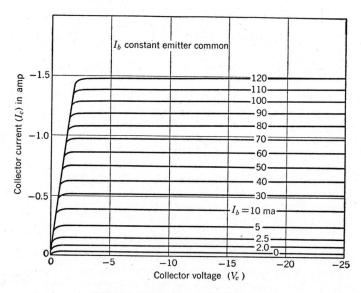

AVERAGE COLLECTOR CHARACTERISTICS

TEXAS INSTRUMENTS 2N243 N-P-N GROWN JUNCTION SILICON TRANSISTOR

Texas Instruments Type 2N243 N-P-N grown junction *silicon* transistor is especially designed for use in audio or servo amplifier stages requiring medium power output. Beta is limited to a 3 to 1 spread, permitting closer control in circuit design. The large energy gap of silicon permits operation at ambient temperatures up to 150°C. Each unit is thoroughly temperature cycled. This process consists of four temperature shock cycles from −55°C to +150°C and four cycles at 95% relative humidity from −55°C to +75°C. In addition, the hermetic seal is checked by vacuum testing. Every unit is completely tested for design characteristics and undergoes a rigorous tumble test to check for mechanical reliability.

Mechanical Data

Metal case with glass-to-metal hermetic seal between case and leads. Approximate weight is 2 grams.

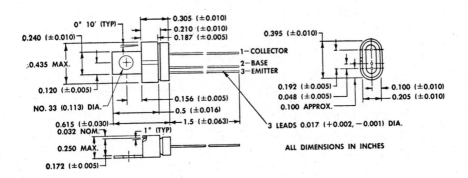

Electrical Data

ABSOLUTE MAXIMUM RATINGS AT 25°C (except where advanced temperatures are indicated):

Collector voltage referred to base.	60 v
Collector current.	60 ma
Collector dissipation.	750 mw
at 100°C.	300 mw
at 125°C.	150 mw

JUNCTION TEMPERATURE:

Maximum range.	−55°C to +150°C

Typical Design Characteristics at $T_j = 25°C$:

		Test Conditions		Min.	Design Center	Max.	Unit
BV_{co}	Collector breakdown voltage	$I_c = 50 \mu a$	$I_e = 0$	60	—	—	volt
I_{co}	Collector cutoff current	$V_{cb} = 30 v$	$I_e = 0$	—	—	1	μa
V_{be}	Bias voltage	$I_b = 3 ma$	$I_c = 20 ma$	—	—	1	volt
R_{cs}	Collector saturation resistance	$I_b = 3 ma$	$I_c = 20 ma$	—	—	350	ohm
h_{ib}	Input impedance	$V_{cb} = 10 v$	$I_e = -5 ma$	—	12	30	ohm
h_{rb}	Reverse voltage transfer ratio	$V_{cb} = 10 v$	$I_e = -5 ma$	—	60	300	$\times 10^{-6}$
h_{fb}	Forward current transfer ratio	$V_{cb} = 10 v$	$I_e = -5 ma$	-0.9	-0.94	-0.968	—
PG_e	Power gain *	$V_{cb} = 28 v$	$I_c = 20 ma$	30	—	—	db

* As measured in the circuit shown below.

Test Circuit

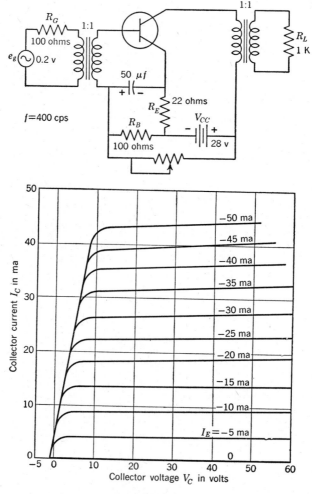

COMMON BASE

Output Characteristics

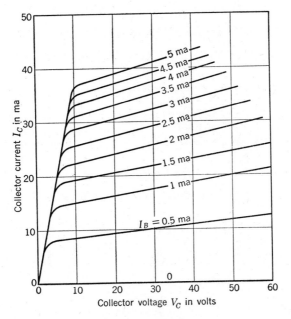

COMMON EMITTER

Output Characteristics

TEXAS INSTRUMENTS TYPE 300 P-N-P
ALLOYED JUNCTION TRANSISTOR

Type 300 germanium P-N-P transistor is especially designed for general purpose applications and features narrow beta spread and *close parameter control*. To assure maximum reliability, stability and long life, all units are cycled from −55°C and room humidity to +75°C and 95% relative humidity for four complete cycles over a 24-hour period. In addition, the hermetic seal is checked by vacuum testing. All units are thoroughly tested for design characteristics.

Mechanical Data

Metal case with glass-to-metal hermetic seal between case and leads. Unit weight is 1 gram.

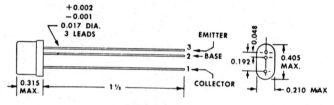

ALL DIMENSIONS IN INCHES

Electrical Data

ABSOLUTE MAXIMUM RATINGS AT 25°C AMBIENT:

Collector voltage referred to base.................................. −30 v
Emitter voltage referred to base................................... −10 v
Collector current... −50 ma
Emitter current... 50 ma
Device dissipation (free air)...................................... 100 mw
Junction temp. rise per milliwatt (free air)....................... 0.5°C/mw
Device dissipation (infinite heat sink)............................ 150 mw
Junction temp. rise per milliwatt (infinite heat sink)............. 0.33°C/mw
Storage temperature... −55°C to +75°C

COMMON BASE DESIGN CHARACTERISTICS AT T_j = 25°C:

				Min.	Design Center	Max.	Units
I_{co}	Collector cutoff current	$V_c = -30$ v	$I_e = 0$	—	8	30	μa
I_{co}	Collector cutoff current	$V_c = -5$ v	$I_e = 0$	—	5	10	μa
h_{11}	Input impedance	$V_c = -5$ v	$I_e = 1$ ma	25	34	50	ohms
h_{22}	Output admittance	$V_c = -5$ v	$I_e = 1$ ma	0.30	0.89	2	μmhos
h_{12}	Feedback voltage ratio	$V_c = -5$ v	$I_e = 1$ ma	150	350	750	$\times 10^{-6}$
h_{21}	Current transfer ratio	$V_c = -5$ v	$I_e = 1$ ma	0.900	0.937	0.950	—
β	Beta, common emitter	$V_c = -5$ v	$I_e = 1$ ma	9	15	19	—
NF	Noise figure,* common emitter	$V_c = -2.5$ v	$I_e = 0.5$ ma	—	25	40	db
F_{co}	Frequency cutoff	$V_c = -5$ v	$I_e = 1$ ma	0.30	0.7	—	mc
C_{ob}	Output capacitance	$f = 10$ kc		—	33	50	μμfd

* Conventional noise, compared to 1000-ohm resistor, 1000 cycles and 1-cycle bandwidth.

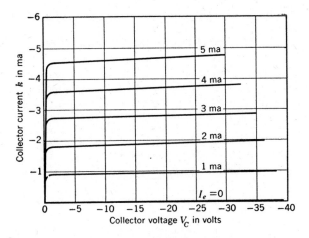

COMMON BASE

Output Characteristics

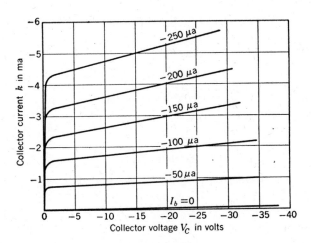

COMMON EMITTER

Output Characteristics

TEXAS INSTRUMENTS TYPE 905 N-P-N
GROWN JUNCTION TRANSISTOR

Texas Instruments Type 905 N-P-N grown junction *silicon* transistor is especially designed for high gain, low level applications where maximum reliability at *high ambient temperature* is of prime importance. Featuring *close parameter control*, all units are thoroughly heat cycled from −55°C to +150°C. This test consists of eight cycles, including four at 95% relative humidity (from −55°C to +75°C). In addition, the hermetic seal is checked by vacuum testing. All units are completely tested for design characteristics and undergo a rigorous tumble test to check for mechanical reliability.

Mechanical Data

Metal case with glass-to-metal hermetic seal between case and leads. Unit weight is 1 gram.

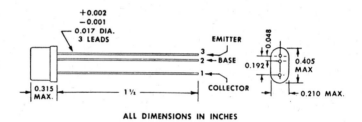

ALL DIMENSIONS IN INCHES

Electrical Data

ABSOLUTE MAXIMUM RATINGS AT 25°C AMBIENT (except where advanced temperatures are indicated):

Collector voltage referred to base.	30 v
Emitter voltage referred to base.	1 v
Collector current.	25 ma
Emitter current.	−25 ma
Collector dissipation.	150 mw
at 100°C.	100 mw
at 150°C.	50 mw

JUNCTION TEMPERATURE:

Maximum range.	−55°C to +175°C

COMMON BASE DESIGN CHARACTERISTICS AT $T_j = 25°C$ (except where advanced temperatures are indicated):

Proposed IRE-AIEE Standards	Existing Standards				Min.	Design Center	Max.	Units
I_{co}	I_{co}	Collector cutoff current	$V_c = 30$ v	$I_e = 0$	—	0.1	10	μa
I_{co}	I_{co}	Collector cutoff current	$V_c = 5$ v	$I_e = 0$	—	—	1	μa
		at 100°C	$V_c = 5$ v	$I_e = 0$	—	—	10	μa
		at 150°C	$V_c = 5$ v	$I_e = 0$	—	—	50	μa
h_{ib}	h_{11}	Input impedance	$V_c = 5$ v	$I_e = -1$ ma	30	42	90	ohms
h_{ob}	h_{22}	Output admittance	$V_e = 5$ v	$I_e = -1$ ma	0.1	0.4	1.5	μmhos
h_{rb}	h_{12}	Feedback voltage ratio	$V_c = 5$ v	$I_e = -1$ ma	50	400	1500	× 10⁻⁶
h_{fb}	h_{21}	Current transfer ratio	$V_c = 5$ v	$I_e = -1$ ma	−0.975	−0.980	−1	—
A_p	P_g	Power gain, * common emitter	$V_c = 5$ v	$I_e = -1$ ma	—	36.5	—	db
NF	NF	Noise figure, † common emitter	$V_c = 5$ v	$I_e = -1$ ma	—	25	—	db
f_{hb}	F_{co}	Frequency cutoff	$V_c = 5$ v	$I_e = -1$ ma	—	6	—	mc
C_{ob}	C_{ob}	Output capacitance	$f = 1$ mc		—	7	—	μμfd
	R_{cs}	Saturation resistance	$I_b = 2.2$ ma	$I_c = 5$ ma	—	140	300	ohms

* $R_g = 1$ K; $R_L = 20$ K.
† Conventional noise, compared to 1000-ohm resistor, 1000 cycles and 1 cycle bandwidth.

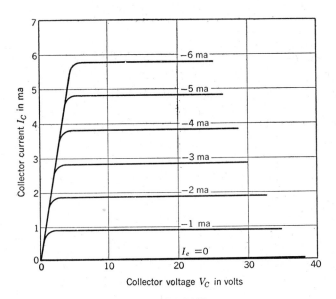

COMMON BASE

Output Characteristics

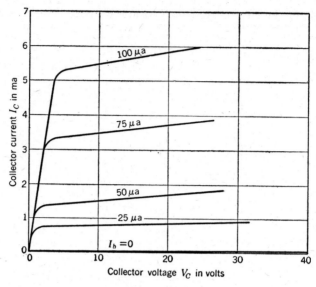

COMMON EMITTER

Output Characteristics

Index